W9-BUE-573

Crossing in the Rain

By Martha Lou Perritti

Copyright 1996 Martha Lou Perritti

This book is a work of fact and fiction. It is inspired by a true story. Segments of this story, dates, names, places, events have never been documented. They are perceptions of the author as told to her by her father and others. The characters, names, incidents, dialogue, and plot are the product of the authors imagination or used fictitiously. Names have been changed to protect individuals privacy.

ISBN # 1-884707-37-8

Published in the U.S.A. by
Lifestyles Press
P.O. Box 1140
Tavares, FL 32778
(352) 742-2155

Cover design by Nicki Forde

ACKNOWLEDGMENTS

Poems:

"Guess Who? I Will Give You A Clue, Inez Ready, 1983
"The Drunkard's Boy," as printed author unknown
"Sheridan's Ride" (October 19, 1864), Thomas Buchanan Read
"Dewey's Stand In Manilla Bay," as printed author unknown

DEDICATION

This book is dedicated to the past, present and future generations of my family and to my father who passed on to me a legacy of Pride, Courage and Patriotism.

PREFACE

I am the youngest daughter of Reuben Oliver Kincaide and was 50 years old when he died in 1989. When I buried my dad, I was disturbed by my feelings toward him. Like other members of the family, I felt he was a stranger to me. All my life I believed my relationship with Dad was one of closeness and understanding. This is why these feelings I had were so perplexing.

The best way for me to understand my thinking about my dad's life was to sit down and write about it. In the beginning I didn't really know why this endeavor was so important to me. I could only hope that the study of Reuben's one-hundred-one years of life would reveal to me why I was searching, just what I was looking for and what would provide an understanding of this man from Tallapoosa, Georgia.

In talking with my brothers and sisters, I quickly found out who would help me gather information, which ones were interested in my writing and those who were not. I learned that since my dad's death, my two older sisters had been to Tallapoosa, Georgia, and had collected many documents. These two sisters were eager to help in any way they could. After we joined forces, the three of us took trips, spent hours pouring over census records, searching library shelves, demanding records from courthouses and funeral homes. We wrote numerous letters to government agencies. We walked graveyards and sought the living out to speak the truth.

Rather quickly our search began to reveal the mysterious, hidden life of our dad. We discovered records of his marriage other than the one with our mother, a child, mistresses, other children and because of his involvement with criminal activity we knew him ultimately as a man on the run. My sisters and I vowed to keep an open mind. We would not be hurt by any of our findings.

Our first trip took us to the door of a half-sister in Atlanta, Georgia. We did not know her, and she did not know us. In preparation for the visit, phone calls had been made and letters written. This meeting revealed tangible clues to our dad's life.

There were two gold-faced lockets: a small one Reuben had given to his first-born child when she was a year old and a larger one he had given to his first wife.

We looked at a crystal dish and a sewing cradle that had belonged to our grandmother. We were shown a beautiful porcelain shaving mug and were told it belonged to our dad. He left it the day he disappeared from Tallapoosa in 1915.

In a room of our half-sister's home, there was a handmade wooden chest. She said to us, "My daddy made this chest for his mother to put her quilts in." When I entered the bedroom of my half-sister's home, my two sisters and my half-sister had been discussing a photo they had laid on the foot of the bed. The picture was of a young man wearing a suit and tie, seated in a high back wicker chair. He wore wire-framed glasses.

All doubt faded from my mind. The proof of connection had been accomplished. My eyes filled with tears and my voice quivered when I said, "That's my dad."

Upon leaving the house, I noticed a pocket watch sitting in a small glass dome. I looked at it closely and exclaimed that I had my dad's old pocket watch and it looked just like that one. My half-sister said the watch there belonged to her husband. She said her husband and our dad probably got the pocket watches at the same place and at the same time.

I could see physical traits of my dad in my half-sister. She was small like him, she had sparkling blue eyes, often sat with her hands folded, twiddling her thumbs like I had seen my dad do many times.

She was a beautiful lady, a debutante raised in high society. My newfound half-sister felt the pain when she raised her hands to her chest and said, "Why didn't he come to see me?" There were many doubts, questions and fears, but the sisters, deciding they could not change the past, parted as friends.

Subsequent trips would lead us to the grave of another half-sister we never knew about. We were told this half-sister lived her entire life in Tallapoosa, Georgia. She was a wonderful person, pretty, with dark hair, and she had worked in the dime store in town. In my search for the truth, I knew that around every corner I turned, I ran the risk of being hurt by new evidence of my dad's indiscretions. When I stood in a graveyard where my grandmother and uncles laid in unmarked graves, I cried because I knew my Dad had abandoned his family.

I met a cousin in Tallapoosa who said, "Yes, I knew Reuben. He used to come down here to see his brother Frank. He came in a big black car and he and Frank played cards using corn kernels for money. I always fixed him coffee and put out two saucers for his cup. Frank had some chickens and Reuben loved the chickens."

Many visits with this cousin helped me establish the story of the family that Dad had been born into. She took me down into the plush green hollow where my Uncle Frank's log house had stood. She told me that Reuben's mother had come to live with Frank and that late in the evenings my grandmother could be seen strolling along the flowing stream picking watercress. It had bothered Frank that he had no way of contacting Reuben when his mother died.

Hearing the truth about my grandmother, I felt a deep loneliness and wondered if I would ever be able to understand why my dad had left her there and could not be found when she died. The only thing I could do to right the wrong was put a marker at my grandmother's grave. With the help of my two sisters, the family graves would be marked and these people would not be forgotten.

In my travels and research, I crossed the Atlantic Ocean, the St. John's River, the Tennessee River, the Ohio River, and the Tallapoosa River. I sat on the banks of the Tallapoosa River and listened to the roar of the water as it flowed through the Southland of Georgia. I walked the streams of my ancestors' farmland, took pictures of the old barn still standing there, and I revisited the family graveyard sitting on a hill surrounded by trees.

My family's Indian heritage was explored and studies were made of the Argonne Forest in Europe and the Bankhead National Forest in northern Alabama. Time spent in Tallapoosa, Georgia; Sanford, Florida; Decatur, Alabama; Jeffersonville, Indiana; Louisville, Kentucky; Jacksonville, Florida; Birmingham, Alabama; and Orlando, Florida led to uncovering the multiple, separate, secret lives of my dad. During my writing, I encountered mystical forces. I had dreams of my grandmother near a stream of water and could describe the surroundings perfectly before I had the knowledge of such a place existing. I wrote an episode of a stabbing done with an old rusty knife before I found out that my son actually has the old rusty knife in his possession.

Perhaps the most amazing thing happened when a friend brought a woman to my home one day, and before entering the house, the stranger said to me, "I know a song that has your name in it." Then she began to sing in a beautiful soprano voice. The song contained words that described my grandmother and assured me that she did not die lonely.

Much of the information I gathered came from the memories of my two older sisters. The miracles came when we found proof of their memories.

By the end of my research, I had gathered a monumental amount of material. I organized the facts, used the memories, unraveled the truths from the lies, and listened to my inner self using my mystical experiences. I glued my story together with history and historical events of the United States from the year 1888 to 1989.

Using my imagination of fiction, I was intrigued with how everything seemed to fall into place. I was truly amazed at how Reuben, my dad, had survived 101 years of a uniquely crossing of life.

Today I sit in my writing room surrounded by photographs and stacks of research material. The last hat my dad wore is placed in a chair; on my desk, close to me, my dad's pocket watch still ticks.

If you ask me how I feel about my dad, my answer is, "See this Elgin pocket watch, it belonged to my dad. The sound of its tick is like the beat of his heart. When I listen to the watch I feel that in my heart my dad still lives."

During the many days of writing about my dad's life, I could feel his presence. Often times as my pen met paper, I had no control over the words written there. I came to terms with the realization that my dad lied to me and died with secrets locked in his heart, however I believe that all of his actions were motivated by the love he had for four women and especially the love he had for all of his children.

While writing, I began to understand what happened and why. My hope is that through me, the door to my dad's heart has been unlocked and I have set him free. I do know that after finishing my story, my dad, this man from Tallapoosa, Georgia, is no longer a stranger to me. I still love him very much. The only truth that matters is that he loved me.

PROLOGUE

From the start you must know that this book is about a man who lived over one hundred years. He was born in the deep South of the United States. He experienced travel from the horse and buggy days of the 1800s to the first automobiles, air flight through the dawn of the space age, putting a man on the moon and beyond. His life can be related to a train. It consisted of four or more major cars, and this man was the locomotive, the driving force. During his lifetime, the cars were never uncoupled, but the baggage each carried was never mixed. When he died, the train stopped, the baggage was taken out of each car and sorted.

With the opening of each bag a part of his life was revealed. He had two wives, two mistresses and thirteen children. He experienced World War I, the Great Depression, escapes from the law, the deaths of his two wives and both of his mistresses as well as the deaths of three of his children, and a favored grandson. This man tried to share his life with all the people he loved, but ultimately he went down the track alone.

Although he tried to live in denial, this man's past was as much a part of him as his future. To tell the story of one-hundred-one years lived by a man called Reuben Oliver Kincaide, one must understand the history of the times in which he lived. Life began for Reuben in a town nestled deep in the South, called Tallapoosa.

CHAPTER ONE

*I*t seems to me that we are as much a part of our past as we are of our present and future. When one tells the story of another's life, it is important to understand the times in which he lived.

I would like to tell you the story of one-hundred-one years lived by a man called Reuben Oliver Kincaide. Life began for Reuben in Tallapoosa, a small town nestled deep in the South. Long before the first European came to North America, the land was inhabited by various Indian tribes — the Tulsa, Moskoquia, Alibamons, Seminoles, Creeks, and Cherokee. Eventually, in the 1700s, the area was founded by English colonists and named Georgia after King George II of England. Today, Georgia is the largest state east of the Mississippi River, and one of the most beautiful. Lofty pine forests grow across the state, and magnolia trees and flowers flourish in the sunny climate. Running through the land is a winding, forceful river named the Tallapoosa. Even after European settlement, Indian tribes lived along the shores of this river. One of the tribes, the Creek Nation, established their village in the shade of seven chestnut trees along the Tallapoosa. Then, after forcing the Creeks to retreat with the Indian Springs Treaty of February 12, 1825, American settlers founded "Old Possum Snout," the town that is now called Tallapoosa.

In the early 1800s, the town, with the Tallapoosa River to nurture farming and trade, attracted settlers. In 1810, a pioneer from North Carolina, Robert G. Kincaide, moved his family to this riverside community. He arrived before the Indian Springs Treaty, and struggled to build a farm for his family out of the Georgia wilderness. Robert's claim was five hundred acres of fertile, untouched land. The woods were thick with underbrush, which he cleared to build a house in the shade — protection from the hot Southern sun. There were meadow fields for growing crops and a perfect spot for the garden.

There was pasture land for the horses, cows, and any farm animal that Robert and his family could wish to raise, such as the family pet billy goat. A stream ran through the pasture, providing fresh water for the animals and a restful place to wet one's feet and wipe one's brow after a long day's work in the fields and tending to the animals.

The house was built of wood with a stone-stacked chimney for the fireplace and a porch across the front. A large hallway ran through the middle of the house. The kitchen and parlor were on one side and bedrooms on the other. The hall was like a tunnel, creating a breeze, where the women would set up their quilting frames in the summer to make quilts, where one could cool off and the old dog was always asleep on the floor. The outhouse was about seventy-five feet from the back door. The barn was down the hill from the house with a road leading to it from the house and continuing on toward town.

There was a particularly serene place on this land, an area sitting on top of a hill. It was surrounded by trees, and around the edges it dropped off into the trees and underbrush. It was the highest spot on the land and seemed to hang up there in the middle of the trees. When standing in this vacant spot, one could hear the wind. The feel of the air changed with the seasons, but the presence of peace remained the same. This is where the cemetery would be. The family members would rest here and wait to be visited by generations to come.

In 1850, Robert was fifty-six years old and his real estate was worth $3,000.00. He would raise twenty-one children on his farm, and his claim would be known for years to come as the Kincaide farm.

Francis Marion was one of the Kincaide children. Francis was raised on the farm and grew up to see many changes and to face many hardships. He was born in 1830 and his early years were spent on the Kincaide farm. He did not have the privilege of attending school, even though in 1818 the Georgia legislature passed the Poor School Fund Act, which provided for the education of poor children in the state. The schools in Haralson County, in which the Kincaide farm was located, did not benefit from this fund because county residents were too proud to declare themselves paupers, a requirement in order to receive aid from the Poor School Fund. Progress was made in Georgia's public school system until 1860 when the outbreak of the Civil War postponed all planned improvements.

The Civil War years, 1861-1865, brought poverty and confusion to the families of the South. The issues of states rights and slavery meant very little to the Kincaide family, who were struggling to survive. Only the large plantation owners profited from slavery. The cost of the war was staggering. Not only did 600,000 Americans die, but much of the countryside was destroyed by the fighting. The grand "march to the sea" by Union General William T. Sherman after the capture of Atlanta in 1864 meant only grief and pain to this little riverside community. The people of Tallapoosa, fifty miles west of Atlanta, wanted only to be left alone, farming their lands, fishing the wonderful Tallapoosa River and hunting along its shores.

They wanted a secure place to raise their children with dignity and pride. During this period, the future of the Kincaide family was gloomy indeed, but the war ended in 1865 and the country was busy adopting the Thirteenth Amendment to abolish slavery in the United States. Other changes to the Constitution took place such as in 1868 the Fourteenth Amendment granted citizenship to all former slaves and in 1870 the Fifteenth Amendment prohibited all states from denying a person the vote because of his race.

The war-torn country was busy with uniting and repairing, but for the rural area of Tallapoosa, there was little change. The farmers mustered their strength and toiled their soil, providing the necessities. In 1880, the business people rechartered the city of Tallapoosa. They encouraged a railroad survey which would connect them with Atlanta. The railroad tracks ran through the middle of Tallapoosa, and it quickly became the town's lifeline. The railroad, called the Georgia Pacific, was completed in 1884 and connected Atlanta, Georgia, and Birmingham, Alabama. The one-hundred-forty-one miles of railroad track meandered through the countryside of the deep South and quickly became an integral part of the lives of people who lived in this riverside community.

The railroad was a way to bring progress, supplies, and people into Tallapoosa, but, as the Kincaide family was to experience, it would also become a way out for future generations. The late 1800s was a period of

3

recovery for the Kincaide family farm and for the city of Tallapoosa. Gold was discovered north of the town, and as a result, between 1883 and 1886 Tallapoosa grew by leaps and bounds. Many people from the North moved to Tallapoosa, and the city became knows as "the northern city under the southern sun." Fourteen new businesses opened with a capital investment of $120,500,000. Blueprints of the city included seven miles of boulevards, parks, horticultural gardens, lakes, and drives on lands west of the railroad depot. Tales of diamond mines richer than those of South Africa circulated, and it was said that the First National Bank of Atlanta was founded with gold taken from the Holland and Camille mines of Tallapoosa.

The boom was on! Newspapers in the North and West carried colorful articles about this new boom town. Excursion trains ran, connecting Tallapoosa with New York, St. Louis, Kansas City, and many other cities. People from all over the United States were coming to Tallapoosa.

It was during this time that Francis Marion Kincaide married Mary Ann "Nannie" Adams. After Francis Marion's first wife had died, he had taken up with his brother's daughter, Nancy. Even though Nancy was his niece, he had shared her bed and they had a son named Frank. But it was Mary Ann, Nancy's daughter from a previous relationship, whom Francis Marion would marry. Mary Ann had long beautiful red hair that seemed to flow around her shoulders. Her eyes were sparkling blue, expressing her gleeful spirit and loving heart. Francis Marion was sixty years old when he married Mary Ann, who was twenty-nine, on April 11, 1887. In 1888 they had a son and called him Reuben Oliver Kincaide.

Reuben was a healthy baby; a blessing, especially because his mother and father were related. However, in generations to come, this impure bloodline would cause Reuben and his family a great deal of pain and suffering. Reuben spent his childhood on the Kincaide farm playing around the wraparound porch of his grandfather's house, skipping along the dirt road leading to the barn, following along behind his father in the fields, tossing rocks as they were turned over by the horse's plow. He often helped his mother with her chores — working in the garden, baking bread, and stitching seams. But his favorite thing to do was feed the chickens. When he was a toddler, he would chase the chickens around the yard and turn over their water jars. The water jars were made with a fruit jar and a pan. The jar was filled with water and turned upside down in the pan. As the chickens drank the water, the seepage from the jar kept the pan filled.

As Reuben grew older he thought of the chickens as pets and happily cared for them. He would gather eggs from the henhouse, but when his mother picked a hen out for Sunday dinner, Reuben headed for the woods. All of his life, Reuben never ate chicken. He was truly a happy, gentle soul.

Late in the evening, the children often played in the yard; one of their favorite games was "snap the whip." Reuben didn't care for this game, but his brother Frank always insisted he play. To play the game, the boys would hold hands and sling each other like a rope whipping. The strongest boy stood steadfast on one end while the other thrashed about. The one on the end would always get slung off, and, naturally, it was always Reuben who was first to get catapulted off. He was such a small boy. The children would all laugh as he went flying in the air and rolling on the ground. But no matter how much Reuben was hurt, pride or otherwise, he would never show it. He was a good sport. After the game he would join the others tumbling on the grass.

As Reuben grew older, he always carried a slingshot in the back pocket of his denim overalls as he rambled the woods on the farm. Unlike most boys his age, he never went near the river.

Reuben was seldom taken into town, which was in the middle of a boom at this time. It was during these years — 1890 – 1892 — that the Lithia Springs Hotel was built by the Tallapoosa Real Estate and Industrial Company. It was financed by a Chattanooga firm for one million dollars. Four floors contained one-hundred-seventy-five rooms, not including a card room, a banquet hall, billiard parlor, ballroom and a spacious lobby complete with an elevator. Furnishings were valued at $75,000. It was the largest wooden building east of the Mississippi and it was the showplace of the South. Famous people, such as George Vanderbilt, signed the hotel register.

It was during these years that a streetcar line was laid out by the Tallapoosa Street Railway Company. It made a circle from the railroad depot to the Lithia Hotel and back. Taking a ride on this streetcar was Reuben's favorite thing to do when Papa took him to town.

Tallapoosa was also recognized as the largest wine center east of the Rocky Mountains in 1893. At one time, 10,000 acres were planted with grapes. Grapes were shipped to the northern states in refrigerator cars, but soon so many grapes were being produced that there were not enough refrigerator cars to handle the demand for shipping. This brought a new industry to Tallapoosa — wine making.

The Kincaide family enjoyed drinking the wine more than growing grapes, and did not prosper from this industry. But even though his family didn't take part in this industry, Reuben would always remember the wonderful fields of grapes.

The Kincaide family suffered great losses when typhoid fever hit Tallapoosa in 1893. Many family members died. Gatherings at the family cemetery were frequent. Enough of the family survived to continue tending the farm, and Reuben's Uncle Grier, who owned a feed store in Tallapoosa, would walk all the way to the Kincaide farm each morning to fix the plow and hitch the mules for the children to work through the day. Uncle Grier did whatever he could do to help. The Kincaides were a loving family and shared the responsibility for keeping the farm going.

When the typhoid epidemic had ended, Reuben and his mother and father survived, although Reuben's eyesight was affected by the fever. The local doctor did all he could to help him keep his eyesight, and it was successful. By the time Reuben was five years old, he was ready to start school in the fall.

Before the boom years in Tallapoosa, almost everyone in the county was poor. Families could not provide supplies and clothes for their children to attend school, let alone the money necessary to supplement the state education fund. Because the people of the county were so poor, in 1888 Tallapoosa established the first entirely free public school system in the state of Georgia. In December 1888, by special act of the General Assembly of Georgia, Tallapoosa was authorized to establish a system of public schools and to provide for the maintenance and support of those schools.

Many of the teachers were people from the North who came to the South to teach school during the winter. The Buchanan High School was opened on July 1, 1889, and its first graduating class was held in 1894. This was the same year Reuben started school. He was a bright little boy and was very excited about starting school. He was eager to get dressed every morning, wearing his pants with suspenders and a long sleeve shirt, although he was often barefoot. He had one pair of shoes, but they had to last, so he would go without them when he could.

6

His travel to school was on foot and it was his older brother's duty to see that he arrived there safely. Frank should have been in school himself, but he didn't think it was that important. Frank was a great prankster. One day he took a billy goat to school, slipping him out of the barn while saying to Reuben, "Never, never tell or Papa will skin you alive!" Frank put a rope around the goat's neck and lead him through the underbrush to the school yard with Reuben trailing behind.

Reuben went into the school house, but Frank hid himself and the goat in the bushes nearby. Frank knew that if you wave a red flag in front of a billy goat, the goat would charge. The scene was set, and Frank intended to leave the goat in the bushes untied while he went into the schoolhouse. When class was over and the children came out, Frank was going to wave the red flag at the goat to get it to charge the children.

When the recess bell rang, the door to the schoolhouse opened and out walked Mr. M. D. West, the dean of the school. Frank had already waved his flag, and the billy goat was on the move. With his head bent, sharp horns facing forward, the goat hit the dean squarely on the backside, sending him into the air yelling. The dean's dignity was injured far more than his backside, and the children's gales of laughter didn't help the situation.

Frank took off into the woods and hid for days — as long as he thought it would take for the dust to settle. The dean was horrified and demanded that there be no more recess until the one responsible for the prank was punished. Of course the goat was caught and identified as belonging to the Kincaides. Reuben was called into Miss Lizzie Anthony's office. She was the dean's assistant. "Reuben," she said, "what have you got to say about this incident?"

Reuben stood in front of her, small, barefoot, and scared with his head hung low and tears on his cheeks. He took a moment, then he held his head up and said, "Miss Lizzie, Frank took the goat from the barn, I followed them to school, Frank hid in the bush, and Papa's going to skin me alive."

Francis Marion was notified and in due time Frank was punished. Reuben received a lecture about why the trick was wrong and a stern warning about taking part in Frank's pranks. But Reuben adored his big brother and would again and again witness his mischievous behavior. He didn't follow Frank's lead though — he was more interested in books and learning.

7

Typhoid and constant reading left his eyes weak, and his parents were afraid he would lose his sight. They found out about a doctor in Atlanta who could help Reuben, so his Papa decided to take him there. Uncle Grier gave Francis Marion the money for the trip and the doctor's visit. He thought Reuben was a special little boy and wanted to help him.

Reuben was so excited about the trip that he stood on one leg then another while he watched his mother pack. He said, "Mother, please come with us. I want you to sit next to me on the train. I want you to keep the new doctor from hurting me."

His mother pulled him into her arms, kissed the top of his head, and said, "You are my big boy now, and very brave. Papa will take care of you. Atlanta is not a safe place for a woman right now, but Papa said he can slip you in and out without any trouble. Don't you worry, the new doctor is going to be good to you. He will make it so you can read all those books you love so much. Now you run along and take your bag out to Papa. It's almost 2:00."

Papa and Reuben boarded the 2:00 p.m. train for Atlanta, and as he snuggled close to his Papa and looked out the window, he couldn't quite believe he was actually on a train. He had watched it go through town so often and dreamed about what it would be like to ride on it. "The trees go by so fast Papa, it makes me dizzy," he said. "Lean back on the seat and close your eyes. We'll be there soon," Papa replied.

They arrived in Atlanta before dark. Reuben noticed there seemed to be a lot of men hurrying around, yelling. The railroad depot was noisy and crowded, so they got their bags and walked down the street to a tall building where Papa said they would spend the night. The room was small but clean, and it was three stories up. Reuben liked climbing the stairs. He had never seen so many steps. They washed up and went down to a big dining room for supper. Only adults were there and it was a little scary for Reuben. He just watched everything, not saying much. He didn't eat much, either. It wasn't his mother's cooking and he was nervous about his visit to the doctor's the next day. After dinner, they went back upstairs to their room, and Reuben was glad to crawl between the nice clean sheets and go to sleep.

The next morning Papa woke him up early so they could dress, eat breakfast, and have plenty of time to get to the doctor's office. The trip across town was amazing to Reuben. They had to walk and the streets were rough. Wagons came barreling along and the horses just about ran them over. The buildings were tall, the people were loud, and nobody seemed very friendly. Finally they reached the doctor's office, and a nice lady told them to have a seat and that the doctor would be there soon.

Well, soon turned into an hour and Papa paced the floor. He had some coins in his pockets and he jingled them impatiently. He looked at Reuben and could see how scared he was. Everything was so strange to him. He handed Reuben some coins and said, "Here Reuben, put these in your pocket."

Reuben said, "Thanks, Papa." Then the doctor came in. He was a fat, jolly looking man who wore glasses. He talked the entire time he was examining Reuben, and when he finished, he assured them that Reuben's eyes would be fine. He would need to wear glasses for the rest of his life, though, and he would need to replace them once a year. Papa thanked the doctor and they walked out of the office and down the street with Reuben wearing his new glasses, jingling the coins in his pocket.

They went back to the hotel to spend the night before catching the train for home in the morning. They had a quiet supper and, strangely, no noise like the night before. Reuben was sound asleep when he heard Papa say, "Son, wake up. Be very quiet and get dressed quickly!"

"What's wrong, Papa?" Reuben asked in a drowsy voice. Then he looked out the window and saw hundreds of little lights moving up and down the street. "What is it, Papa?" he asked again.

"There is going to be a riot, son. If we are going to get to that train station, we best get there now, before daybreak," his father replied. They hurriedly packed their bags and slipped down the stairs to the street. Reuben's papa warned him to stay close. There were men all over the place, carrying things. Now Reuben could see what the lights were. They were torches, and many of the men had knives and clubs.

Just before they reached the station, it seemed as though these torch carrying crusaders went mad. They began yelling, grabbing, cutting, and burning anything in their way. The noise and smells were terrible. It was like a horrible nightmare, and Reuben thought he was going to die at any minute. Papa kept pushing them nearer to the station, and finally they were inside the depot. A man told them to get on the train; that it would be leaving early. Reuben and his father didn't hesitate. As it was pulling out of the station, day was breaking. Papa said, "Don't look out the window,

9

Reuben."

But Reuben just had to. He saw the most horrifying sight imaginable: smoke and fire everywhere, men running around shouting in a frenzy and carrying long sticks, like spikes, with bloodied human heads on them. Reuben screamed and Papa held him close. "Papa, what are those heads, tell me, Papa, what are they?" he cried.

"Son, close your eyes and ears. You must forget this. In times like these, men do strange and terrible things. When you are older we'll talk about this, but not now," soothed his father.

As the train raced down the track toward Tallapoosa, Reuben and his father thought about the slave man they had buried in the Kincaide family cemetery. The Civil War was over, but the fighting was not. Slavery would be a thorn in the side of the South for years to come.

As Reuben grew older he became an avid reader. He had a wonderful memory and, with the encouragement of his teacher, Effie Cox, he memorized several poems. Miss Cox was so impressed with his abilities she had him recite his poems in a school recital contest. He would travel from school to school reciting his poetry. His father took him to the different schools and sat in the back row as his son stood proudly in front. Reuben made such a stately little figure, so erect and confident, only his twinkling blue eyes hinted that he was truly just a gleeful little farm boy. Reuben's favorite poems were "The Drunkard's Boy" and "Sheridan's Ride." Both poems reflected the prevalent political and social attitudes of the time, although Reuben wasn't aware of this. He just loved the rhythm of the words and the stories they told.

THE DRUNKARD'S BOY

You ask what makes my heart so light
My home so glad and gay
I'll tell you all things has been right
Since one glad happy day.

I was not always kept so well
Sometimes I wanted a bed
And often times I and sister Nell

10

Wished that we were dead

Oh, Mother she did all she could
To teach us what was right
She made us say our prayers
She would for Father every night
And the only time she struck me, Sir
Was when I wouldn't say
God bless dear Father in my prayers
Or when I did not pray

She said it was the dreadful drink
That made our Father mad
And but for that he would never think
Of treating us so bad

So I said I would give it a whirl
If I could shut up all the liquor shops
And Sir I mean to try

I wore a band of hope
And wore it ever bright
I learned a lot of tempered songs
And sang with all my might

You guess I was there and sister, too
They give us all the tea and some to spare
And sitting reading after tea
I scarcely raised my eyes
When I saw my teacher beacon me
Here Willy, here is your prize
For didn't the ladies shout
And wave their handkerchief about
They said that I must make a speech
And I felt that I would cry
So I says thank you and sat down

Then I caught my Father's eye
Yes, there he sat and Mother, too
He walked up to the platform
As I trembled with a fright
Then turning to the crowd, he said
You see this crippled boy
Poor little chap
I want to make his life one dream of joy
So I will, so I can
I'll sign and be a sober man
I'll sign the pledge tonight
He took the pen and signed his name
Oh, didn't the youngsters yell
And then my gentle mother came
And wrote her name as well

You guessed, I said my prayers at night
And prayed for Father, too
I don't think he would have kept it right
If we hadn't prayed to you

So that's what makes my heart so light
Father has kept his word
And he is making my poor life
As gay as any bird.

Before Reuben reached the end of the poem, Francis Marion, who sat quietly in the back row, sobbed aloud because he know the poem was not taken from text. It was a gift from his son. That night Reuben had recited "The Drunkard's Boy" first because he wanted to make sure his papa heard it before he slipped out of the room for a fresh chew of tobacco, as he usually did. Not tonight though, Papa stayed in his seat for the entire recital. When he finished reciting his first poem, Reuben waited for the applause to stop, then he continued with his next poem.

SHERIDAN'S RIDE
Thomas Buchanan Read

(October 19, 1864)

Up from the South at break of day,
Bringing to Winchester fresh dismay,
The affrighted air with a shudder bore,
Like a herald in haste to the chieftain's door,
The terrible grumble, and rumble, and roar,
Telling the battle was on once more.
And Sheridan twenty miles away.

And wider still those billows of war
Thundered along the horizon's bar;
And louder yet into Winchester rolled
The roar of that red sea uncontrolled,
Making the blood of the listener cold,
As he thought of the stake in that fiery fray
With Sheridan twenty miles away.

But there is a road from Winchester town,
A good, broad highway leading down;
And there, through the flush of the morning light,
A steed as black as the steeds of night
Was seen to pass, as with eagle flight;
As if he know the terrible need,
He stretched away with his utmost speed.
Hills rose and fell, but his heart was gay,
With Sheridan fifteen miles away.

Still sprang from those swift hoofs, thundering South,
The dust like smoke from the cannon's mouth,
Of the trail of a comet, sweeping faster and faster,
Foreboding to traitors the doom of disaster.
The heart of the steed and the heart of the master
Were beating like prisoners assaulting their walls,
Impatient to be where the battlefield calls;
Every nerve of the charges was strained to full play,
With Sheridan only ten miles away.

Under his spurning feet the road
Like an arrow Alpine river flowed,
And the landscape sped away behind
Like an ocean flying before the wind;
And the steed, like a bark fed with furnace ire,
Swept on, with his wild eye full of fire;
But, lo! he is nearing his heart's desire;
He is snuffing the smoke of the roaring fray,
With Sheridan only five miles away.

The first that the general saw were the groups
of stragglers, and then the retreating troops;
What was done? What to do? a glance told him both.
Then striking his spurs with a terrible oath,
He dashed down the line, 'mid a storm of hussas,
And the wave of retreat checked its course there, because
The sight of the master compelled it to pause.
With foam and with dust the black charger was gray;
By the flash of his eye and the red nostril's play
He seemed to the whole great army to say:
"I have brought you Sheridan all the way
From Winchester down to save the day."

Hurrah! Hurrah for Sheridan!
Hurrah! Hurrah for horse and man!
And when their statues are placed on high
Under the dome of Union sky,
The American soldier's Temple of Fame,
There, with the glorious general's name,
Be it said, in letter both bold and bright:
"Here is the steed that saved the day
By carrying Sheridan into the fight,
From Winchester — twenty miles away!"

The Civil War had ended in 1865, but when Reuben was a little boy, there were many men around who remembered details of the battles. Reuben learned Sheridan's Ride — a poem about one of those battles —

14

felt great patriotism and pride in General Sheridan's strength, and he was intrigued by the bravery of the general's horse.

During the Civil War, on September 19, 1864, Confederates attacked Union troops led by general Philip Henry Sheridan at Winchester, Pennsylvania. The general and his troops won that battle, and the general felt that the Confederates had been severely punished during the battle. He took that information to Washington on an official visit, leaving his men strongly posted on Cedar Creek. On the morning of October 19, 1864, Confederates attacked the troops from the front, flank, and rear. Sheridan, who was returning from Washington, had slept at Winchester the night of October 18, 1864, and early the next morning he heard the sounds of the battle. He mounted his horse and started for the field. He reached the battlefield just in time to rally his retreating troops. He turned a defeat into a decisive victory and drove the Confederates back to Virginia.

Reuben was ten years old in 1898 during the Spanish-American War and he learned a poem in school about this war.

DEWEY'S STAND IN MANILA BAY

Upon Manila Bay
The Spanish corsair lay
In the shelter of the ports upon the shore
And they dared to hoist the sail
Through the crushing iron hail
Which from deck and billowment would pour
Lower little squadron sails
It is flameless and alone
Allies they have none
But our fearless sailors sing a lonely song
Where ten thousand miles away from home
Ocean waves and layers of foam
Shelter us form that land we love so far away
But we will bury their heads and minds
And we will face the blazing lines
Yes, we'll bury the ships sitting
In their own bay
Oh, God, it was a sight

Until the smoke is black as night
It devoured our ships from light of day
And when it lifted from the tide
Smitten low in Spanish pride
Dewey and his gallant fleet
Was master of the bay.

The Spanish-American War (February 15, 1898 — August 12, 1898) didn't last long, but it was significant in the history of the United States. The U.S. battleship *Maine* was sunk in the harbor of Havana, Cuba. The U.S. blamed the Spanish, but their guilt was never proven. The U.S. demanded that the Spanish leave Cuba, and, when they refused, Congress declared war. The war was brief. Admiral George Dewey destroyed a Spanish fleet in Manila Harbor in the Philippines, a Spanish colony in the Pacific Ocean. Theodore Roosevelt lead the "Rough Riders" into Cuba and forced the Spanish to surrender. Cuba won its independence, but the U.S. military controlled the island until 1902.

The U.S. took over the Philippines, Puerto Rico, and the Pacific island of Guam, and, as a result, became a world power.

Reuben would remember these poems all of his life, and at the age of ninety-five he would recite them for his children.

Frank was proud of his little brother. He would say to Reuben, "Brother, don't every forget our times together. The day I put wine in a bucket beside the pig trough. The pigs got drunk and staggered all over the pig pen. And the day me and some boys tied gourds to the black boy's feet and threw him in the river. We could depend on you to run and get Papa to rescue him. You were always around, like the day I got arrested for spitting on the sidewalk, and all the times I was arrested for being drunk. Little brother, don't be like me. You're smart, so put your traveling shoes on and be somebody."

Frank never left Tallapoosa, and he never learned to read or write. Francis Marion was determined that his son Reuben would become "somebody." Rural children usually finished their education by the time they were thirteen years old. To attend high school, you had to pay tuition and board unless you lived close enough to walk to and from school each day. The Georgia state legislature passed the McMichael Law in 1900, which allowed counties and local school districts to tax property within a five-mile radius of an elementary school to support the schools, but this law did not include a provision for high schools. Since Reuben had finished elementary school and was ready for high school in 1901, it was up to Francis Marion to see that his son traveled that road to school each day on foot.

There was a deep-seated prejudice against local taxes to support schools, and it was not until that subsided in 1912 that the Stoval Amendment made it possible for public high school systems to receive tax support. Reuben never minded the walk to school. He walked with speed and an eagerness to get somewhere, a determination to get the job done. After all, he was preparing himself for his future. Reuben was graduated in 1905, and Mary Ann and Francis Marion were proud parents. They had done well by their son, but what was Reuben to do there on the farm. For the next four years it was days of working with Papa and hanging out with the local boys.

During the period of the early 1890s, the population of Tallapoosa was 1,699, although it was said that about 5,000 people lived in the vicinity. Over 5,000 pounds of mail passed through the post office daily.

The appearance of the railroad track through the middle of town created a symbol of the social classes in Tallapoosa. The Kincaides, being a farm family, established themselves as members of the lower class living on the "wrong side of the tracks." The Kincaide farm had been settled by Robert G. Kincaide, who had twenty-one children. When he died, he left his son Archie, Sr. in charge of the farm. In 1893, Archie, Sr. died from typhoid fever, and at that time the estate was divided. Children by Robert G.'s first wife received money; children by his second wife received the property. Francis Marion was Robert G.'s first wife's child, so he should have received money from the estate, but the family was angry with him about his marriage to his brother's granddaughter, so they punished him by not giving him anything. It was Reuben's cousin, Felix, who ended up with the farm.

Felix had been like a brother to Reuben. He was only two years older than Reuben, and they had played together all throughout their childhood. Felix told Reuben that when he died, he would see to it that Reuben's children got the Kincaide farm because of the injustice done to his papa.

Reuben and Papa worked hard over the years on the farm and in other jobs. They heard that you could get a good buy on a place in town because

17

a lot of people were moving back north. So they bought a place on Head Street in Tallapoosa. They were crossing the railroad tracks to the upper class. Reuben was now twenty-one years old, and he finally would have his chance to be somebody.

Francis Marion put the title of the house in Reuben's name. Mary Ann, Francis Marion, and Reuben were living in style on Head Street. Reuben took a job as a clerk in his Uncle Grier's feed store. Uncle Grier was an important person in Reuben's life. He was someone Reuben could depend on, look up to, and trust. Uncle Grier had helped out on the farm when the children were little, and it was Uncle Grier who had paid for Reuben's trip to Atlanta to get eyeglasses. Now Reuben was twenty-one, and his uncle was still helping him. Reuben would never forget his Uncle Greer.

Tallapoosa had experienced an economic boom with the gold rush and the wine making industry, but it was not a lasting economic surge. Tallapoosa's businesses did not perfect their exports, and business began to slow down. In 1907, the State Prohibition Act was passed prohibiting the sale of intoxicating beverages. This put an end to wine making in Tallapoosa. Businesses closed up and people moved back north, leaving their houses and, many times, their possessions. By 1911, the town was back in the hands of the original population. The boom had lasted a little less than twenty-five years.

Uncle Grier's feed store continued to prosper because he provided for the farmers' needs and it was the farmers who survived the economic crash. Reuben spent his days at the feed store and wandering around town conversing with shopkeepers. He was always interested in the arrival of the 2:00 p.m. train. Sometimes he went over to the depot to check out who was coming into town. As the train pulled out, he would look longingly down the tracks. Where are you going? he would wonder. What's out there? Reuben had a rambling soul.

The biggest event in town at this time was the infrequent arrival of the "Tin Lizzie," a nickname for the Model T Ford car. Reuben said that out there in the quiet country you could hear it coming from miles away. The cars would come from Atlanta, about 40 miles away. In the early years of this century, only a few cars were being made and most of these were luxury cars. Henry Ford revolutionized the U.S. automobile industry by making a simple car that many people could afford.

His assembly line method of construction meant that cars could be

18

made cheaper and faster. Between 1909 and 1925, Ford cut the price of the Model T, "Tin Lizzie," from $850.00 to $260.00. He said, "Each time I lower the price by one dollar, I sell another thousand cars." The workers on the assembly line remained loyal because their wages were so good. In 1914, The average wage was $2.40 per day. Ford paid $5.00 per day, minimum. By 1926, he was paying his workers $10.00 per day, and thus the automobile industry grew beyond his dream.

Reuben woke up one morning and looked in the mirror. It was 1912 and he was twenty-four years old. He couldn't complain about his life. He had a good job in Uncle Grier's feed store. His life in the house with Mother and Papa was pleasant. Papa spent some days down on the Kincaide farm with family members, and Mother was always caring and kind. But what about the future? He shaved and got dressed for work. He wore a pressed shirt with a collar and the top button was always fastened. His dress pants were held up with a belt; he no longer used the boyhood suspenders. His shoes were shined and he wore gaiters to hold up his socks. And, of course, Reuben always wore a hat.

Reuben was in Bailey's Dry Goods Store in Tallapoosa the day the first shipment of Stetson hats arrived. That was the day he purchased his first hat. John B. Stetson (1830–1906) created many different kinds of hats. The one that Reuben wore was made of felt, with a narrow brim and a medium high, soft crown. It came in black, brown, and dark blue. Reuben preferred the brown color. Reuben's hat was a statement of his "Americanism," and it became a part of his character description. To Reuben, this hat was more than just a cover to shield his head from the sun, he wore it as a revolutionary statement. Usually, styles were based on European fashion, but this hat was purely American. His hat was the first outward sign of Reuben's deep seated patriotism. He wore a Stetson hat for the rest of his life.

Reuben walked to work through town and across the railroad tracks to the feed store. At the end of the day, he was in no hurry to get home because supper wouldn't be ready until nearly dark after Papa came in from the farm. He thought he would stop by and see Mary. Reuben had several girlfriends, but none like Mary.

She was a high-spirited little blond. Her hair hung in ringlets around her face, and her darting blue eyes reflected her energetic spirit. She was cute, witty, and smart. She was always bright and gay, and with Reuben

19

she sparkled. Everyone in town knew she was after Reuben. No one could blame her, though — he was a dashing young man, polite, educated, employed, and he was attentive to Mary. Or, maybe, he just accepted the attention she paid him. Either way, Reuben thought Mary was a delight to be with; he always thoroughly enjoyed her company. One hot summer afternoon, Reuben started his walk home. He planned to walk past Mary's house two streets over from his own home. He would get a glass of lemonade and let her dance around, giggle, and please him for a spell.

As he neared her house, he noticed a large wagon. Furniture and other household items were being moved into the house next door to Mary. This house had been vacant for some time since the rich financier had moved back north. He had heard that a new doctor was coming to town, and wondered if these could be his things.

The house was a lovely southern home. It had two stories with large white columns and a balcony above the front porch. An ornate railing surrounded the balcony with the columns extending to the roof. Reuben had always admired this place and dreamed of one day owning a home like it, but on this day his admiration would fall on another object. As he glanced up to the balcony, he saw a girl standing near the railing, leaning slightly on a column.

Her clothes seemed to be all white, fine like silk, and they caught the breeze as it came across the balcony. She pressed her hand on her skirt to hold it down and her other hand went to her forehead to wipe her hair from her brow. Her hair glistened in the evening sun. The dark curls fell around her shoulders like soft rose petals. Reuben stumbled over a pebble in the road, then he stood still to stare, but being a stately little man, he quickly gained his composure and, as he was sure she was watching him, he tipped his hat.

Reuben stood there bent with hat in hand for what seemed to him like hours, but was in fact only seconds, then he placed his hat firmly on his head and quickly walked to the house next door.

He no sooner reached the yard when Mary can bounding out the front door saying, "Reuben, Reuben why not come on in here out of that hot sun and let Mary fix you a glass of cold lemonade? Just lay that hat right there on the table and sit on the sofa so we can sit close together after I get your lemonade. No one is home, you know. Daddy won't be home until after dark, and Mama is visiting Aunt Mae in Albany. So I guess that just leaves little old me, unprotected, if you know what I mean."

She gave a cute little giggle as she bounced off toward the kitchen. Reuben knew what she meant. He knew what Mary always meant, but he wasn't interested this afternoon. When Mary returned to the room, she handed Reuben his drink, then she settled herself, snuggling close to him. Reuben moved away slightly and said, "It's a little warm to sit so close, just let me cool off a bit." Mary was a little hurt, but she still sat close enough to reach her hand to the back of his neck and caress him slightly with her fingers.

Finally, after a few sips of lemonade, Reuben asked, "So, Mary, who is moving in next door?"

Mary wasn't in the mood for conversation, so she answered curtly, "Oh, that new doctor man. He has a wife, a couple of kids. One girl about my age. Mama says to be nice to her. I met her already. She thinks she's smart, but she's dumb. She thinks she's bright, but she's dull, and I hate her!" All this was just Mary's way of saying that the girl next door was beautiful, and Mary was jealous.

Reuben didn't mention that he had seen the girl on the balcony. He just replied to Mary, "Now my sweet, do like your mama says and be nice." Mary was getting impatient and wanted to carry this afternoon encounter with Reuben a little further, but Reuben was tired and he used that as his excuse. Plus, he had some chores to get done when he got home. So, as gingerly as possible, he released himself from Mary and made it out the front door with his hat. Mary stood at the door as he walked quickly down the front walk, "I'll see you later, Reuben Kincaide!"

That night when Reuben's head lay on the pillow, it was not Mary's beaming little face and sparkling blue eyes he was visualizing; instead, it was the figure he had seen on the balcony of the house he dreamed about owning someday.

It was April, the beginning of spring. The fields on the farm were resplendent with the colors of wild flowers in bloom. Trees were sporting fresh green coats, and the grass was soft to the touch. Reuben loved going out to the farm on Sundays to be with his cousin Felix. They would talk and roam the woods together. Reuben could tell Felix anything, and these days he had only one thing on his mind.

One Sunday, as he and Felix were walking, he said, "There is something terribly wrong with me. I feel sad and happy at the same time.

I can't keep my mind on my work. Why, the other day, I let old man Parker get away from the store without paying for his entire summer supply of feed, and Uncle Grier was really mad at me. He said, 'Well there, now we won't see him 'til fall. No money coming from that feed. I oughta take it out of your wages young man.' Mother says she is going to quit cooking for me, 'cause I hardly eat anything anymore."

Felix stood in front of Reuben and placed a hand on each shoulder. "Tell me, brother, have you been seeing any girls lately?"

"Just Mary, and once in a while I get a glimpse of that girl who lives next door to her. She sure is a pretty thing. The other day I saw her down at the depot with her papa. He was going to Atlanta to a medical convention. He is a doctor, you know. She didn't go with him, and she seemed sad to see him leave. She sure had on a pretty dress, and then I saw her in Green's Drug Store with her mother. Now that mother of hers has the air of a queen. They say she came from high society in Atlanta, and that now she is trying to establish a woman's club there at the Lithia Hotel. Guess she is one for Tallapoosa to reckon with. That girl never seems very happy when she is with her. Now that girl..."

Reuben was about to continue, but Felix interrupted with "Whoa, listen, do you hear anything? Reuben looked bewildered. "I think I hear the voice of a man in love! Can't you see man, this girl has you in a spin. I think it is about time you meet her — what is her name anyway?" asked Felix.

"Why I don't know," Reuben said.

"Well, there you go, you don't even know her name and she already has you spinning," Felix joked.

"Well, what am I supposed to do, Felix? When I go by Mary's house I see her sitting on the porch, sorta cradled in a white wicker chair, kinda mystic like. I tip my hat, but she doesn't seem to see me. Of course, Mary would never introduce me, she's jealous you know."

"Reuben, we gotta make a plan," declared Felix. Reuben and Felix stayed in the woods all that Sunday afternoon coming up with possible meeting sights and possible conversations. Reuben finally went home about dark hoping that one of these plans would work because he couldn't get that girl out of his mind.

It was not one of Reuben and Felix's well-laid plans, but his mother who ended up bringing the two young people together. The following

Sunday Mary Ann insisted that Reuben accompany her and Papa to church. They attended the Methodist church in town. Mary Ann was very religious and would have liked Reuben to go to church more often than he did. Perhaps this Sunday she wanted him to go because she knew he had been troubled. Did she know about the girl? They entered the church and Mother lead them close to the front where they entered a pew and sat down.

Reuben leaned forward to get a hymnal from the holder on the back of the pew in front of him. As he did, he smelled gardenia flowers like Mother had planted at the edge of the house. He looked up, searching for the source of the fragrance. He saw dark, soft curls of hair resting on small shoulders covered with snow-white material. About that time her head turned and their faces were inches apart. She smiled, and it brought a warm, wonderful glow to her face. Reuben hiccuped and said "Excuse me," and quickly sat straight back in his seat. What was he to do? It was her, the girl! The sermon began and Reuben was boxed in. He went through all the motions of the service in a trance. When the last song had been sung and the last prayer had been said, the service was finally dismissed.

The doctor, his wife, and their daughter turned to greet the people behind. "Hello, I am Dr. Sherwood, and this is my wife. This is my daughter, Victoria."

As they shook hands, Papa replied, "I am Francis Kincaide, my wife Mary Ann, and our son, Reuben."

There was a brief greeting, but Reuben couldn't say a word. It was her, the girl, and her name was Victoria. Reuben retrieved his hat from the rack at the door and placed it on his head as he walked down the front steps. Standing at the bottom of the steps, as though waiting for him, was Victoria. In a very pleasant, regal way, she said to him, "Reuben, now that we have been introduced, maybe when you pass my house you will stop by the porch for a glass of lemonade or a cup of tea."

Reuben replied, "Thank you," trying his best not to do something stupid. He walked away from her, turned and tipped his hat, knowing that she had seen him do this many times before.

Reuben walked from church straight out to the farm to see Felix. He felt great. The sad feeling was gone. His heart sang. He had met the girl and her name was Victoria! Although Victoria was the only thing he could think about these days, it took Reuben several days and several visits to the farm to talk to Felix before he could muster up the courage to walk by her house. Did she mean what she said? If he walked that way, would she be there? He ran the scene through his mind over and over again. It took Felix to put an end to the agony. "Listen to me, Reuben," he said, "don't you come back out to this farm 'til you go see that girl. I don't want to hear another word about it. Face her, brother, it's not your papa's whip you know."

The next day at work, Uncle Grier noticed Reuben working later than usual. "Go on home, Reuben, tomorrow is another day!" he said. Reuben washed up at the basin in the storage room. He had brought an extra clean shirt from home. He put that on, combed his hair, and walked across the railroad tracks toward home. Today, he would take the street past Mary's house, only today it was not Mary who was on his mind.

As he approached the house with the large white columns, he could see her sitting on the porch. Was she waiting for him? Should he keep walking? Turn around? What? Then he saw her hand go up and give a graceful wave into the air. That boyhood transformation came over him. He threw his shoulders back and walked across the yard to the porch with dignity. After all, he was a man now and she was just a young girl.

The young girl sat next to a small table with a lacy white cloth and a bouquet of fresh flowers. As Reuben stepped up onto the porch, removing his hat, she remained seated with a gentle composure. She wore a pale yellow vest with a white linen skirt. It was a dress to stave off the summer heat. Her hands rested softly in her lap, and her beautiful long black curls tossed as she lifted her face and said, "Hello, Reuben. Summer seems to be early this year. I don't think I could face the afternoons if it weren't for this porch."

Holding his hat in his hands, Reuben seemed calm and relaxed as he replied, "Yes, it does get warm this time of day, but you seem to have found a cool shade out here on the porch. I guess you can just sit here and watch life's parade." Victoria didn't know quite what he meant by that, but she asked him to put his hat down on the table and rest in the wicker chair across from her. As he came near her to take his seat, he smelled the same scent as he had in church. Next to her on the table he noticed a small dish with water and a flower in it. "That flower is a gardenia, right?" he asked to make conversation.

Victoria touched its petals and said, "Yes, I often wear it as a corsage, then I like to float the whole blossom in a bowl so I can enjoy its fragrance for as long as possible. Do you like it?"

"Yes, very much." said Reuben. Victoria stood and offered him a cold drink or tea. "No thanks," Reuben replied, "I have to get on home, it has been a long day. Maybe next time." He got up and walked to the steps, and then turned to her. The late afternoon sunshine peeked around the posts and glistened in her hair. "I'll stop by again tomorrow if that is okay with you."

Without hesitation, Victoria said, "Oh, yes, I would like that very much!"

As Reuben hurried home, he said to himself, "She was waiting for me. Yes, Victoria, I'll be back tomorrow and for many days to come." It was a brief encounter, but neither of them would ever forget that summer day, and in years to come they would often yearn to return to those first moments together.

All through the long, hot summer, Reuben often stopped by to visit with Victoria after work. They walked in the gardens or just laughed and talked on the porch. Victoria's parents didn't like the idea of Reuben Kincaide spending time with their daughter, but she assured them he was just a friend. They pointed out his age and questionable family background, and told her she was never to see him privately. After all, Victoria was only sixteen. She would be seventeen in May, and she would "come out" as a debutante at an inaugural ball in June.

CHAPTER TWO

*V*ictoria Dawn Sherwood, daughter of Dr. and Mrs. William Sherwood of Tallapoosa, Georgia, was to be formally introduced into society. The event was to be held in the garden of the Lithia Springs Hotel. Preparations had been underway for days. Reuben heard that they needed people to work at the hotel for the occasion and he could certainly use the extra money. So he worked late afternoons and weekends. He had not seen Victoria for the past few days because she was busy preparing for her social events. Reuben didn't put much thought into all this. He just thought her "introduction into society" was a passing thing. He began to plan a future with her.

Victoria was calm about her coming out celebration; her mother was excited enough for both of them. Her father would be her escort to all of the events, and even though she would have many young men standing in line for a dance with her or a chance for conversation, she didn't care about their attention. Her thoughts and dreams were of someone more mature; someone with a twinkle in his eyes and delightful manners, a man who liked the smell of gardenias and who when he saw her, always tipped his hat.

The girls arrived at the debutante ball looking like a flock of graceful white birds, and their occasional giggles only diminished their dignity slightly. The Lithia Springs Hotel was the perfect place for such an elegant occasion. It was a grand old building with wonderful gardens. It was easy to see why it had been an oasis of Southern comfort for years. On this day, twenty-six young ladies gathered in the upstairs parlor. Then they made their way slowly down a grand wooden staircase that spiraled its way to the hotel foyer. There they paused to reassemble and to find their fathers, who escorted them onto the verandah. Each girl gently held her father's arm as they passed through an archway that was covered with fern and roses. As each couple took their place in the garden below, the fathers stepped aside to present their daughters. The girls were radiant in their elegant white cotton voile dress with silk ribbon sashes and roses in their arms.

In the evening light, Victoria stood looking out over the sprawling hotel gardens. She could still see the flamboyant blooms of the magnolia trees and the array of hedges surrounded by a wall of greenery. Gazing through the slightly moist air into the distance, she noticed a majestic oak tree covered in a carpet of green ivy. Underneath stood a man. He wore glasses and held himself proudly erect with his hat in his hand.

The ceremonies ended with a prayer for each young lady's reputation for excellence to continue to grow as they entered into womanhood. The quiet turned to laughter and talking as friends and family who had witnessed the occasion greeted each other. It was a day to remember and one Mary had experienced a year before.

She had attended this year's ceremonies, and never once took her eyes off the girl who lived next door to her. Knowing Victoria was occupied with her society friends, Mary went in search of Reuben. Not finding him in the garden, she meandered her way through the crowd to the outside gate. When she spotted him, she walked over to him slowly, her hips swaying slightly.

"Hey, Reuben, you wanna walk me home?" she asked softly. She looked adorable in a peach and coral silk taffeta dress and a white chiffon sash. Her golden hair was in ringlets about her face. She was a fetching sight, just what Reuben needed to lift his spirits and take him out of his wretched mood. He couldn't be with Victoria, so why not enjoy Mary's company? She was just a friend, after all. The summer was long and hot in that Georgia town. Reuben spent his days working at the feed store and evenings trying to be with Victoria, but Victoria always seemed to be busy with her parents.

She spent many evenings at the summer concerts held at the Lithia Springs Hotel. The concerts were society occasions where ladies would arrive in opulent gowns and men wore the "Abe Lincoln" small-brim, high-crown hats. Reuben would walk by Victoria's house every evening hoping to see her. He would never forget the time on a late evening when he glanced toward her back yard and saw her perched on a lower branch of an oak tree. She sat poised like a butterfly as the breeze billowed the soft folds of her chiffon dress and the color of the sunset sky gently framed her face.

Reuben approached the gate and she beckoned him to come near her. "You could help a lady down," she said in her soft voice. He laid his hat on the swing nearby and walked over to the tree. He gently caressed her tiny waist and lifted her effortlessly, his first time to touch her so. It seemed like forever that he held her in the air. This was the beginning of a love affair that would last all their lives.

The remainder of summer and beginning of fall found their romance in full bloom. They could be seen together about town, in church, and on Sunday afternoons in the park. On their walks, Victoria always wore a hat. The hat was usually made of fine woven straw, steam shaped to achieve the upswept, eye-flattering contour. She would wear a large ribbon around the base of the crown to match her dress or she would place flowers along the brim. Was the hat to shield her delicate skin from the sun or was she trying to make a statement as Reuben did? To Reuben, her hat conveyed a spirit of whimsy and it often heightened the playfulness between them.

The Sherwoods had wanted their daughter to go on to finishing school in Atlanta, but Victoria would not leave Reuben. Over the winter months, they gave up all hope of changing her mind and finally reconciled themselves to the fact that Victoria was going to marry Reuben.

The wedding date was set. It would take place on the third of March. Victoria insisted that she handle every detail. Every invitation would be hand written. A dressmaker from Atlanta would come to prepare her wedding ensemble. Her excitement was boundless as she gathered her family and friends and negotiated every aspect of the ceremony. She wanted to make this day memorable to everyone in Tallapoosa. Victoria insisted that pictures be taken.

Since the dawn of photography in 1839, the finishing of photographs had improved and became a good business. Several men in Tallapoosa had photo shops. Victoria made an appointment with her chosen photographer. Reuben put on the suit he would wear for his wedding day. The single-breasted, black suit was made of a finely textured wool. Reuben was a small, wiry man, and the suit was tailored to fit him perfectly. He wore a white, long-sleeved shirt and a light colored tie.

One of the photographs taken was of Reuben seated alone in a high backed wicker chair. He held his back ramrod straight, and placed his right hand on the arm of the chair with his fingers slightly curved over the edge and he rested his left hand loosely on his left leg. On the smallest finger of his left hand, he wore a ring. A pendant of a picture of Victoria was pinned to the left lapel of his jacket. His dark hair was cut short and combed with a part on the left side. He wore his wire-framed glasses. Without a smile on his face, he looked straight into the eye of the camera. The camera shutter clicked. Eighty years later, Reuben's youngest daughter would be shown this photograph for the first time, and with tears in her eyes would say, "Yes, that is my Daddy."

Reuben agreed to Victoria's every wish. He wanted this girl more than anything he had ever wanted in his life. His parents were pleased that he was marrying into such a fine society family. They felt that they had prepared him for this. Other members of the family were not so sure that Reuben was doing the right thing. Frank came to visit his brother on the eve of the wedding. "Brother," he said, "You know I am just a poor farm boy and dumb at that, but I came here to say my piece. You sure did pick you out a pretty filly, but you done gone in the wrong pasture to do your picking. You are who you are, and you will never be able to please that girl. I know you moved into town, got yourself educated, got yourself a job in a store, and you look good all gussied up in them fine clothes, but I'm telling you today that you will never be able to make enough to keep her satisfied. I don't want to embarrass you, so I won't be coming to the wedding. You know I want what is best for you, and I'll be out on the farm if you ever need me."

Frank hugged his brother, and as they parted the words "never be able to make enough" lingered in Reuben's mind. The wedding day was here and the atmosphere around the church was cheerful as friends and family gathered for the event. When all were seated and Reuben stood in his position before the altar, the piano began to play.

Everyone stood as Victoria appeared in the aisle. It was a dream-like moment. All eyes were on this beautiful princess — time seemed to stop as they gazed at her. Her gown was white silk with a sweetheart neckline. The bodice was embroidered with a rose pattern in front and had satin-covered buttons down the back. The skirt was gathered into petal like

29

folds, and tiny beads shimmered like butterfly wings as they mingled with the fabric. The sleeves were a very deep flounce of antique lace. Her veil was a circlet of rose blossoms with a delicate lace train. Her black curls were pulled away from her face and hung gracefully to her shoulders. She walked as a cloud floats, softly carrying her bouquet of roses, ribbon, and lace. She was the very essence of romance.

After the vows were exchanged and the bride and groom left the church, the fragrance of fresh cut blossoms lingered in the air. The wedding reception was held in the backyard of the Sherwood home. It had been elaborately decorated and, fortunately, the weather was beautiful. There was gaiety in the air, and for these few hours the two families seemed to enjoy each other's company. Everything was going just as Victoria had planned. Reuben had rented a room at the Lithia Springs Hotel for their honeymoon night. This was the best he could do since he had also rented and furnished a house on Freeman Street.

Uncle Grier had given him the money for his wedding suit and Papa had bought him a new hat. It had been a long, wonderful day when Reuben closed the door to the honeymoon suite. Victoria was still wearing her lovely wedding gown. As she looked down at the billowing skirt, her voice was low and soft, "Oh, Reuben, I just want to wear it forever. I want to feel like this for the rest of my life. I am afraid it is like magic and when I take it off, everything will disappear."

Reuben took her in his arms and kissed her gently on the cheek. "I promise you the magic will not go away and I will love you forever."

He unfastened all the satin covered buttons down the back of the dress and she disappeared into the adjacent bathroom. Reuben had not been nervous all day, but he began to shake as he took off his coat and tie. He had been with girls out on the farm and there had been Mary, but this was not the same. He didn't have any idea of how he was going to deal with this situation. He was beginning to feel like running out that door and never looking back when the bathroom door opened and all his fears faded as he looked at Victoria.

She stood almost transparent with the light behind her. She wore a robin's egg blue gown. It clung to her as she crossed the room and turned out the light. She had tied her hair back with a ribbon. When Reuben touched one end of the ribbon, the entire bow fell loose and her hair flowed around her bare shoulders. He caressed her gently. His kisses were tender, his hands caring. She pulled him close and encouraged his every move. This was the man she loved, and she gave herself to him completely. She was as delicate as a flower unfolding, and he felt a sense of comfort in her arms. They felt the joy of love, the ecstasy of lovemaking. The dawn was near when their bodies rested in the sheets that smelled as though they had been washed in gardenias.

The bright morning sun came dancing around the shade over the window, and Reuben woke up to see Victoria sleeping next to him. He did not want to disturb her, so he eased out of bed, dressed, and went downstairs to the coffee shop. He sat with his coffee, reading the morning paper. After awhile, he decided he should go up and wake Victoria because they would need to check out of the hotel before noon. As he approached the foyer, he saw her descending the stairway.

First he noticed her long, pink-tinged, silk-satin skirt; she had a white crochet shawl draped across her breasts and over her shoulders. When she saw Reuben coming toward her, she stood still on the steps with one hand resting at her neckline, the other gracefully at her side. Her hair was pulled up in back off her neck. She was poised, but there was a slight flush in her cheeks. As Reuben took her hand from the banister, they both remembered their passion the night before. "Would you like to have some breakfast?" were the only words Reuben could think of with his body tingling all over.

"Perhaps a cup of tea," Victoria managed to reply. They enjoyed a quiet breakfast on the garden patio and then prepared to leave. Reuben was taking his flower home. She was the girl he had first seen on the balcony. Her name was Victoria and she was his wife now. Reuben and Victoria set up housekeeping in their rented house just one block from his parents' place on Head Street.

Reuben's parents still depended on him for many things. Papa was eighty-one years old and insisted on going out to the Kincaide farm every day to help out. Reuben would work at the feed store five days a week, go with Papa out to the farm on Saturday, and he would spend Sunday with Victoria. Many afternoons he would stop by and help his mother out with chores. It was a busy life for Reuben, but he was happy and everything seemed to be pleasing Victoria.

Only one month had passed when Felix brought the word to Reuben at the feed store. Papa had died working out in the field down on the farm. Reuben went to his mother. She was home cooking supper. When he

31

opened the back door and walked into the kitchen, she looked at him and said, "Your papa is dead, isn't be?"

"Yes," he replied as he took her in his arms. "Don't worry Mama, I'll take care of you."

They shared their grief and together with family and friends mourned the passing of someone they all loved very much. Reuben would always remember that day in April 1913, when they buried his papa. There was a light chill in the air as the morning mist settled over the Kincaide family cemetery. This was a place where everything seemed to come together — the past, the present, and the future. Today Reuben would see Papa placed here to become a part of his past. As the black buggy approached the cemetery, Reuben, Felix, and Frank stood beside the grave site. The buggy was pulled up close to the grave and several friends helped to lower the pine coffin into the grave.

All the Kincaide women wore black and surrounded each other, crying in their grief. The only brightness on the hilltop was the slight shimmering of new spring growth on the trees, and wild flowers blooming where the earth sloped down to surround the cemetery. Spring flowers grew along the base of the trees. They were a sign of new life where one life had passed on to join others resting here. The service was brief, and as Reuben started to walk away, his brother Frank touched his arm. "Brother, would you help me put a stone at Papa's grave?" he asked.

Together they searched the woods and found a small, rectangular stone. Frank got out his pocket knife and with Reuben's help carved into the stone: F.M. Kincaide, D. 1913. They placed it at the head of Papa's grave. It was a poor man's grave, only a few of the graves in this cemetery had a marble stone as a marker. Reuben stood there looking at the stone, hands in his pocket, jingling his change. "Papa, someday you will have a marble stone, I promise I will put it here." It was sixty-five years before Reuben kept his promise.

Reuben's marriage one month before had been so happy — the beginning of a hopeful new life together. This day in April would be the beginning of a life filled with loss and heartbreak. Victoria helped Reuben cope with the loss of his father, and they both took care of his mother in her time of need. Reuben not only stopped by her house after work, but each morning before he went to the feed store he would check to make sure his mother was okay. The house on Head Street was in Reuben's name, but things remained the same; his mother continued to live there.

Reuben and Victoria were a very happy couple. Three months after their marriage Victoria became pregnant and this only increased their love and joy for each other. But the summer months were dreadfully hot in Tallapoosa. Victoria became weak and was having problems with the pregnancy. Reuben moved her into the house on Head Street with his mother so she could look after her during the day. Victoria's mother was busy with her social life, and her father only tolerated Reuben at family gatherings despite Reuben's continuous efforts to show the Sherwoods that he could provide for their daughter.

Reuben worked hard, but it seemed like there was no pleasing Victoria. She would spend days in bed, blame Reuben for everything. She hated losing her girlish figure, she was sick most of the time, and she didn't want Reuben to touch her. She accused him of not loving her in her condition. His mother tolerated Victoria's outbursts and tried to reassure Reuben that his wife was just going through a difficult time of adjustment. She was young and having her first baby. She would say, "Be patient son, the next time will be a lot easier."

Reuben had not visited the farm much since his Papa died. He was always busy with his job, his wife, and his mother. But this Sunday morning he needed to walk down to the farm. He needed to talk with Felix. Things were not going very well in his life, and he knew that somehow Felix would help him sort things out. When he arrived at the house, he was told that Felix was down at the barn getting a horse and wagon ready for a trip into town to see Uncle Grier. He walked down to see Felix before he left. "Hey, there brother!" Felix always greeted Reuben like this even though they were cousins.

"Going into town on a Sunday?" Reuben asked.

"Thought I would visit Uncle Grier for a spell and I need to pick up some gear he is letting me borrow. Come on, jump in and go with me," Felix called out to Reuben as he pulled the horse and wagon out from the barn ready to go.

Reuben took his hat off and scratched his head a bit. Then putting his hat back on, he replied, "No, Felix, I got some thinking to do, so I think I'll stay out on the farm for a while."

"Okay brother, you do your thinking and when I get back we'll go over it together. I'd ask you to stay for supper, but I know that "filly" of yours don't let you stay out past dark. I'll see you later, you best get your thinking done."

Felix drove the horse and wagon on down the little dirt road toward town and Reuben headed across the field toward the river. While growing up on the farm, Reuben had stayed away from the river. He did not like the water. When he was with the other boys, he would go with them to the river banks, but he never felt safe there. For some reason, today was different. It was the middle of October and trees along the river edge were ablaze with autumn color. Leaves fell like rain and Reuben walked along kicking up the ones that had settled on the ground.

He finally came to a small clearing on the river bank. Standing looking across the water to the other side, he heard a rustling in the leaves behind him. Turning around he saw a small figure with a red coat on. He recognized the blonde hair and the merry little face with sparkling blue eyes.

Mary hurried toward him, reached up and snatched his hat off his head. "Why Reuben, don't you know to take your hat off when you see a lady comin'?" she teased.

"Lady, who, where?" asked Reuben.

"What I want to know, Mr. Reuben Oliver Kincaide, is have you forgotten me altogether? Did you intend never to see little ole me again?" Mary asked, pretending to pout.

Putting both arms around her to retrieve the hat she was holding behind her, Reuben replied, "My darling little girl, I could never forget you." Still holding her in his arms, he questioned, "Just what do you think you're doing out here in these woods? Are you alone? Did you know I was here?"

Her head tilted up at him, she said, "I came out here to see you. I saw Felix at your Uncle Grier's in town and he told me you were out at the farm. Said you didn't look too good. Looked like you needed something. I often come out here to the river, and had the feeling that what I had been dreaming about might be out here today."

Reuben lightly pushed her away. "You know I am a married man now. By the way, you didn't come to my wedding."

"Wasn't asked," she replied, "wouldn't have come anyway." Reuben sat down on a bed of leaves and Mary snuggled close to him. "I been missing you like crazy, Reuben. I been wantin' to see you so bad. Don't you love me at all any more?"

He put his arm around her shoulders as she shivered a little. "Now, Mary I just told you I am married and..."

She wouldn't let him finish. She put her little finger to his lips, "I don't care about that. I just know what we are to each other. You say you are married, but your eyes look lonely. You don't look happy and alive. Don't you remember how happy I used to make you?" She began to place soft kisses on his face and her little hands slipped around his neck. "Reuben," she whispered, "I want to make you happy again, that's all, just once again."

Reuben pulled her close to him and cradled her in his arms as he lay her down. Their bodies sank into the softness of the leaves and the chilly autumn air tossed the leaves about them. Their hunger for each other was intense and they had not forgotten what they once meant to each other. She had ways to please him and he fulfilled her need like no other. In her arms, coupled with her wild little body, he released his love for her and, at the same time, months of frustration.

They clung to each other in their ecstasy till the sun went down. When darkness approached, they roused themselves, holding onto each other as they walked away from the river bank, through the woods, across the farm field toward town. They didn't talk much. No words were needed. They both knew it couldn't last forever. It could never happen again. As they parted in front of Mary's house, she released his hand and said "I love you, Reuben Oliver Kincaide."

His reply was, "I love you too, Mary."

On this day, Reuben hadn't talked with Felix, but Felix had helped him out just as he always did. The next morning Reuben sat at the breakfast table reading his paper and drinking his coffee. His mother had been up early and had prepared the coffee. Victoria came into the room and said softly, "Looks like someone overslept, no wonder since you got in so late last night."

Reuben got up and pulled out a chair for his wife. Without hesitating, he began to discuss the news of the day. "I see where Japan has given President Taft and the American people some cherry trees to plant in Washington, D.C. I wonder if they will grow there."

Victoria replied, "I'm sure they will. Maybe one day we can go there to see them in bloom."

35

"Yea, right," Reuben remarked, "Maybe if I live to be 100. Looks like now I will spend the rest of my days right here in Tallapoosa working at the damn feed store." With that he got his hat and went out the back door.

As the time for their baby to be born grew closer, Reuben and Victoria became loving and caring toward each other again. It was like in the beginning. Victoria was so excited about the baby, she prepared a wicker bassinet, lined on the inside with snow-white muslin. Soft linen ruffles edged the sides and extended along the hood, which had a covering of handmade lace. A tiny satin pillow was placed inside. Altogether it had a light, airy, delicate look. The christening dress was white silk and embroidered lace with a handmade lace bonnet.

The hand sewing was done by Reuben's mother, but Victoria chose the designs. Just as for her wedding, everything for this birth was prepared and perfect. Reuben's first child arrived in January. He and Victoria were extremely happy. After such a long and hard pregnancy, everything was fine. They were blessed with a baby girl. As he cradled the baby in his arms, he said to her, "Vanessa, I will love you and your mother always."

Victoria and Mary Ann took good care of the baby, and Victoria's parents doted on their grandchild. They showered the baby with gifts and attention. Reuben settled back into a routine of work and taking care of his family. The winter months in Tallapoosa, Georgia, were cold and rainy. January weather, especially, was not very pleasant. Reuben had to walk to work and often arrived soaking wet. He kept a suit of clean clothes at the store for these times. It was early one morning when he was changing into his dry clothes that a young boy of about seventeen approached him in the back room.

"Hi there, Jessie," Reuben said. Reuben had known Jessie since his family moved into town when he was ten years old.

"Mornin' Reuben, came to give you a message," Jessie replied, standing there with a straw hanging out of his mouth.

"What's up, boy?" Reuben asked offhandedly.

"Mary's mother says for you to come by her place today after you get off work. Said she would be waitin'. If you don't show up, she will come over to your place. Don't think you would want that. Sounded real mad about something. Reuben, what have you gone and got yourself into now?" Jessie asked, hoping Reuben would give him a clue as to what this was all about.

But Reuben snapped at him, "Okay, okay. I got your message. Now get out of here, so I can get a day's work done."

The day seemed long as every so often Reuben would be reminded of the message Jessie had brought that morning. As soon as the doors to the feed store were locked, Reuben headed home. He walked across the railroad tracks and he took the old familiar street that went past the house with large white columns with the balcony where he had first seen his lovely Victoria. As he passed by he glanced up somehow hoping that time had stood still and she would be there. Not today, though, the balcony was empty.

When he got to Mary's house, he paused in the yard. The front door did not swing open with Mary's little figure darting out to greet him. Instead it was cold and lonely in the front yard, and Reuben was afraid of what waited for him inside the house. He knocked on the door and without hesitation Mary's mother opened the door.

"Good evening, Mrs. Nicholson, you sent a message that you wanted to see me." Reuben said as he removed his hat.

"Yes, Reuben, come on in," replied Mary's mother.

When Reuben entered the living room, he saw Mary sitting on the sofa. At first glance she looked adorable cuddled in the corner of the sofa, wearing a colorful plaid dress that reached high around her neck to touch her golden curls in the back. But as he got closer and could see into her eyes, he saw that she was sad, tired from crying. He knelt down in front of her, and taking her little hand in his, he said, "What is it, Mary? What's wrong?"

Mary did not answer, but from across the room, her mother said, "I'll tell you what's wrong, young man, she is pregnant. Say's it belongs to you. Now what do you plan to do about it?"

"Is this true?" Reuben questioned Mary. She didn't answer out loud, just nodded her head to say yes. "The night on the river bank?" Reuben asked as he moved to sit next to her on the sofa. Again Mary just nodded her head to say yes.

He put his arms around her and she lay her head on his shoulder. "I'm sorry, Reuben, I'm sorry," she repeated in between her soft cries.

Reuben pushed back the curls from her forehead and kissed her there. "Don't say that, it's my fault too. Come on now, don't cry anymore. We will work this thing out. We will work it out together."

"You got that right, Reuben Kincaide." Mrs. Nicholson was showing no sympathy. Reuben stood up to face Mary's mother. It was almost like the time in his young school years when he had faced Miss Lizzie about the Kincaide billy goat butting the principal. Only this time it was not his brother Frank's fault. But, using the same courage, he answered Mrs. Nicholson.

"First of all, let's get this straight. I will take care of this. I know I am a married man, but that doesn't stop me from having feelings toward Mary. At this moment I don't know just what to do, but you can be sure I will take responsibility. Now, Mrs. Nicholson, you can either help me and your daughter or you can shut up and leave us alone."

Mrs. Nicholson took a seat near the sofa and said, "I didn't intend to be rude. It is just that I don't know what to do either. You see, Reuben, Mary loves you. She has always loved you, and she wants to have this baby of yours..."

"Mama, please," Mary whispered in a soft voice. She reached for Reuben to sit down.

The three of them sat for what seemed like hours sharing tears and "what ifs," but they knew the reality was that Reuben was married and his wife had just had a baby. There was no way he could change that situation now. Mary's mother suggested Mary go to Albany and stay with her Aunt Mae until things could be worked out. Reuben would have to choose which one of these women he wanted to live with: his charming, gleeful little Mary or his gracious, lovely wife, Victoria. He already had a beautiful baby girl whom he adored, but what about Mary's baby? He remembered the autumn day in late October when Mary had come to him. They shared a passionate love and had fulfilled their needs. How could he not love her child, who was a product of that love?

The two women followed Reuben to the door. As he reached for his hat, he said to Mary, "I will give your mother money to send to you in Albany. I will think of you and our baby every day. We will be together some day Mary, I promise you that. I do love you."

He held Mary for a moment and as he let her go, she said, "I love you, Reuben Kincaide." Reuben walked out the door and down the yard. It was now to her mother's arms that Mary returned.

All Mrs. Nicholson could say was, "Let's get ready, you have a train to catch tomorrow."

38

In June, news that Mary had a baby girl came to Reuben. In the little room in back of the feed store, he knelt on his knees and wept. He thought of how wonderful it was the day he held his first baby girl and named her. He would not name this baby. Mary would call her Annie Mae Nicholson. Annie after her mother, Mae after her aunt, and Nicholson because she was born out of wedlock. Mary held no resentment toward Reuben. She understood his situation. She would love and care for the baby and wait for the day Reuben would send for her and they would be together.

In Tallapoosa things were not changing as Mary envisioned. Reuben and Mrs. Nicholson had kept their secret. Reuben sent notes along with money to Mary and his baby, Annie Mae. He made promises without putting much thought into the future. His life with his wife and child was wonderful. Victoria was a loving and giving person. She took care of the baby and Reuben's needs. Also, Reuben's mother was there to help out in every way that she could.

The house was full of happiness on Vanessa's first birthday. Victoria planned a lavish party for their friends and family. Reuben had a surprise for his little girl and her mother — two gold lockets. The smallest locket went to Vanessa. It had her initials inscribed on the front in small script writing and hung from a gold chain. The larger locket was for his wife. On the front were her initials in bold writing and on the back the words, "Mine forever." It was also on a beautiful gold chain.

They both loved their lockets. Victoria knew she had married the most wonderful man in the world, and Vanessa hugged and kissed her daddy's face. Only once did Reuben leave the party to wander off to the edge of the yard and gaze down the road. I wonder how long it takes the train to get to Albany, he thought to himself.

Spring came and everyone in Tallapoosa was busy plowing their fields and sowing their gardens. It was mainly a farming area now that the big business boom was over. People would say, "We just got ordinary folks here now."

All the farming activity kept Reuben and Uncle Grier busy in the feed store. Reuben also helped out on the Kincaide farm. But everything came to a halt one morning in May, when Reuben's Uncle Grier suddenly became ill. The doctor said it was his heart, and soon after he became ill he died. The entire Kincaide family was rocked with sadness. Uncle Grier had been the glue that held the family together. He did everything for everybody. Reuben couldn't remember a time that Uncle Grier wasn't helping him. Felix was devastated. For it was Felix that, as a little boy of seven, after his father died, had tried to work the farm, and it was his Uncle Grier who had hitched the mules to the plow and guided him. It was because of Uncle Grier that the family still had the Kincaide farm.

It was a gloomy day as the family gathered once again at the Kincaide family cemetery. Uncle Grier never had any children. He had always treated all the children of the family as though they were his own. Reuben stood looking at the grave as tears ran down his face. He removed his glasses from his face, and as he wiped them with his handkerchief, he remembered the day Uncle Grier had given Papa the money for their trip to Atlanta to see the doctor and buy his first pair of glasses.

As Felix and Reuben walked away from the cemetery, they wondered what life would be like without their Uncle Grier. Several family members gathered to hear the reading of the will. Uncle Grier willed that his feed store be sold. The money would be divided between his wife and Felix. Felix was to use his share to buy up the shares of the Kincaide property presently owned by his brothers and sisters. Reúben was to inherit all of Uncle Grier's share of the Kincaide farm property. Reuben walked out of the courthouse and started walking down the railroad tracks heading out of town, going nowhere.

He was distraught, angry, and afraid. Talking to himself, he said, "What the hell did he sell the store for? If he thought I was going to work on the damn farm, he was crazy. I'm not a plow boy. God only knows I've worked hard to be somebody. What will I tell Victoria? How will I make enough money to keep her, the baby, and Mother in that house on Head Street? And what about Mary and my baby in Albany? How can I send them money now?"

Reuben walked for miles down that railroad track. He was exhausted and thirsty. He finally turned around and headed back toward town. He knew where he could get a good drink of whiskey. He made one of his rare visits to his brother Frank's house. That night he got drunk and didn't go home. The next morning, Frank sobered him up and sent him home. When he got to the house, Victoria was sitting outside in a swing that he had made and hung from a big oak tree in the back yard.

CHAPTER THREE

*H*e had a sheepish look on his face as he came up to her. He expected her to be angry, but instead she patted the seat next to her and said, "Come sit by me. I heard about Uncle Grier's will. I know you must be upset, and I told your mother you were probably at Frank's house."

Reuben sat down next to her with his hat in his hand. "I'm sorry," he said so she could barely hear him.

"Anyway," she rambled on, "Mr. Bailey saw my daddy yesterday and he told him that you could work in his dry goods store. I told Daddy you would like that. Now, isn't that a blessin'? That Mr. Bailey is a nice man and his son Jessie is your friend and all. Why, it's just perfect for you."

Reuben was silent. Victoria added, "Don't you think so, Reuben?"

"Think what?" he replied half-heartedly.

"That working for Mr. Bailey will be just right for you?"

"That'll be fine, whatever you say," Reuben said and he got up and went into the house.

Reuben took the job at Mr. Bailey's dry goods store. He did the best he could, but his heart was not in it and the days were long and tiring. The most exciting thing that happened while he worked there was the arrival of some men's pocket watches. Reuben bought one of them and Jessie bought the other. They were Elgin watches about the size of a silver dollar. All the pants that Reuben wore had small pockets in front, close to the band, where he could put the watch. There was a jewelry chain attached to the stem of the watch and the hook at the end of the chain closed around his belt loop.

Reuben was proud of his watch. He developed a particular way of bringing it out to check the time. He would pull the watch out of his pocket and rear his head back slightly to observe the time. The purchase of this watch began a lifetime of "clock watching." Reuben was always early or on time, never late, for an appointment.

The summer heat was almost unbearable in Tallapoosa, buried as it was in the middle of Georgia. After putting in long days at the dry goods store, Reuben would join some other men at the local billiard parlor. They would shoot pool and drink some "moonshine" liquor that was passed around in jugs. They talked about everything from their families to politics and current events. This atmosphere created the perfect climate for an action by Reuben that would begin his "life on the run."

In those days, everyone in Georgia was talking about the Leo Frank murder case. Leo Frank had been accused of killing Mary Phagan, a 14-year-old white girl. She was murdered on April 27, 1913 in Atlanta, Georgia. Mary Phagan was a pretty little girl from a poor family. She worked at the pencil factory where Leo Frank was a superintendent. Leo Frank was a part of the elite Jewish community in Atlanta. He was married, but was known to have made unwelcome advances toward Mary Phagan and other women at the factory. He had a reputation as a sexual deviant, with his preferred partners being young women and boys, but his behavior was overlooked because of his wealth and power.

Mary Phagan's body was found in the basement of the factory. She had met a grisly death. Her body was covered with dirt, she had a noose around her neck, and she had deep gashes on her face and body. The news of this horrible death shocked all of Atlanta; the entire state of Georgia mourned for Mary Phagan. The emotions provoked by this murder went beyond mourning. The grief shown by the public took on an almost religious dimension. Approximately ten thousand mourners viewed the body at the morgue and over a thousand attended the funeral. In Marietta, Georgia, a wave of repressed rage from the poor people of the community was unleashed. This murder of a poor little factory girl who made only twelve cents per hour starkly reminded them of the helplessness of their own lives. They were in a frenzy to catch the murderer.

A black night watchman named Newt Lee found the body. He was suspected, but they could find no evidence. Suspicion turned to Leo Frank.

He was at the factory that day, even though it was a Saturday and a holiday. He had given Mary her pay envelope in his office. Once the press released the news, however unreliable, the poor were convinced that the murderer had been caught. Their ready acceptance of his guilt was a reflection of the frustration they felt as a poor, working class community in the South. To them, Leo Frank represented the Yankee capitalism that had taken over their beloved South. He was the boss of the pencil factory. He was the Jewish lord and the women who worked in his factory were exposed to his advances.

Southern men were known for their honor and chivalry. They had a deep concern for protecting women. They remembered the reputation of the European Jews since the 1890s, and they routinely lynched blacks for making sexual advances toward white women.

Reuben had been in Atlanta with his papa and saw the race riot that was caused by rumors that black men had murdered two white women. The reality was that people of certain racial and religious types were not welcome in the South at that time. This atmosphere of emotional prejudice fueled the fire for the press. When they printed a picture of Leo Frank, the people said he was such an odd looking fellow that he must be a pervert. The press reminded the public that even the "perversity" of oral sex was punishable by death in the state of Georgia. The defense lawyers tried to present Leo Frank as a family man and an important member of the community. He was not like the "primitive" black man, according to the defense. But Frank could not provide an account of his whereabouts at the time of the murder, so he was brought to trial.

Hugh Dorsey, who became Georgia's governor in 1916, prosecuted the case. There were many accusations of political manipulation, insufficient evidence, and perjury. Finally, however, a guilty verdict was decided. The poor people of Georgia were jubilant. They felt satisfaction that this rich man, the symbol of those who had been raping their land and women for over a half a century, would now be punished.

However, the verdict was followed by a string of appeals for a retrial and commutation of the death sentence. In June 1915, Governor John M. Slaton decided to commute the death sentence due to the questionable justice of the trial.

This decision provoked widespread outrage in Georgia, and Reuben was just as outraged as all of the other people in Tallapoosa. The poor people of Georgia believed that Leo Frank would escape justice because of his wealth and power. Reuben remembered how rich Northerners had come to Tallapoosa when he was just a boy, and, when they had profited from all that the surrounding country had to offer, they returned to the north with their spoils.

It wasn't surprising that Reuben agreed with "the Knights," a group of men who had sworn to avenge the murder of little Mary Phagan. The Knights were known to be headed by citizens such as a former superior court judge, a former sheriff, and a clergyman. They formed an elite, militaristic group, and on the night of August 16, they attacked the Midgeville Prison Farm where Leo Frank was being held. They dragged Frank from his prison cell, carried him to Marietta where Mary Phagan was buried, and hanged him from a tree. The Knights took it upon themselves to ensure that the people of Georgia would see justice done, something they felt the system had failed to do.

For many years after the hanging, Reuben would talk about how the body had hung from the tree with blood spilling down around its neck and how the people kicked and stamped Leo Frank after he was cut down from the tree. He recalled riding with the boys from Tallapoosa all night to the outskirts of Atlanta, where, arriving at the break of dawn, he witnessed the hanging. While popular opinion in Georgia may have supported the Knights' actions, the rest of the United States was dismayed by the lynching. A grand jury in Georgia investigated the Knights. Many people claimed to know who the Knights were, but no one would testify against them.

It was late afternoon on August 17 when Reuben returned to Tallapoosa. He had missed a day of work at the dry goods store and he had not been home all night. When he started up the steps into the house, he saw his mother in the back yard playing with Vanessa, and he walked back to them. Vanessa held her hands out to him and he picked her up. His mother said, "Son, what is wrong? We were worried about you."

"I'm okay," he replied. "Where is Victoria?"

"She is in the house. She has been crying all day and I know she didn't sleep last night. Please talk to her; she needs you."

Mary Ann took the baby from Reuben's arms and he walked toward the house. He opened the front door and saw Victoria seated near a window in the living room. She was wearing a white muslin dress. Her black hair was pulled away from her neck in back and it fell in ringlets around her shoulders. Her skin was moist from the summer heat, and she held a white handkerchief in her hand.

She stood up and looked at her husband. Her face was pale and her eyes were washed clear. A slight glow surrounded her as she gently reached out her arms. Reuben took a step toward her, paused, gazing into her eyes for a moment, then turned away from her. He walked toward the bedroom, opened the door, walked in and closed it behind him. His wife did not come to him that night.

Several days passed, and life went back to normal for Reuben. After work, he always checked his mailbox at the post office. He had opened this box for privacy after Mary had gone to Albany. He looked forward to Mary's letters. They captured her personality, and she kept him informed about the baby. Annie Mae was over a year old.

Reuben found a letter waiting for him at the post office, and he eagerly tore it open, anxious to read what it contained. Mary wrote, "Reuben, I have decided to return to Tallapoosa. I can't wait for you here in Albany any longer. Annie Mae needs to know her daddy and I miss you. Please understand. I will need some extra money for the trip."

Reuben's hands shook as he folded the letter and put it in his pocket. He walked to the billiard parlor to share a few drinks with the boys. All the talk was of the hanging. Jessie had the latest newspaper from Atlanta. "Says here, the police have a list of people seen at the hanging. Out to get people connected with the Knight gang. Take a look Reuben. You might be interested in this." Jessie laughed and slapped Reuben on the back.

The drinks and conversation couldn't distract Reuben. He put his hat on and walked out the door. Instead of going across the railroad tracks toward home he turned and walked west. He walked down the tracks a good mile out of town, then stopped. With everything in him, he wanted to run, but then he thought of his mother and said to himself, "Not yet, I have something to do first."

The next morning he got up early. He knew his mother always sat on the front porch before dawn every day to meditate. He closed the door gently behind him, then walked over and sat down next to her. "Mother, the other day you asked me what was wrong. Well, I'll tell you, my life is no good here. Since Uncle Grier died I just don't like working at Baileys. I hardly make half what I was making with Uncle Grier. I know Papa always worked on the farm, but I hate that damn farm work. Can't make nothing at it. Besides Victoria is no farm girl. She would never live out there. Seems like Frank was right. I can't please Victoria. Can't make enough money and you know I never did really fit in with her folks."

His mother sat patiently with a look of concern on her face as he continued. "I got a letter from Mary. She is bringing the baby to Tallapoosa. I just can't figure out how to handle that. God knows I love my wife, and Vanessa, she means everything to me. But, there is a part of me that yearns for Mary and the baby. I can't have both Victoria and Mary and I don't know how to choose between them.

"Mama, there are other things." Reuben stopped talking, reached into his pocket to get his handkerchief out. He removed his glasses and wiped them dry. They sat silently for a long time.

Then his mother put her arms around him and said, "Go out to the cemetery and visit your papa's grave and stop by the farm to say goodbye to Felix."

Reuben went to work that day and asked Mr. Bailey if he could take the afternoon off. He walked out to the cemetery and stood by his father's grave. Even on the hottest days of summer, there was always a cool breeze that drifted across this place. Reuben took his hat off and held it in both hands in front of him. His posture was reverent and his thoughts were soul searching, but he found no answers. Reuben walked down the back side of the cemetery, through the trees, and down the lane to the old Kincaide farm house where Felix lived. Felix was working down by the barn, and when he saw Reuben he waved for him to come down.

"What's the matter, boy, don't you know it is a working day?" Felix said to him as he got closer.

"That's just what I came to talk to you about," Reuben replied. "I think my working days around here are just about over."

Felix stopped his work and looked at Reuben, "Sounds serious. You got a plan?"

"Why do you think I am here?" Reuben grinned. "Don't you know I need your help to make out a plan?"

Felix laughed. "Reckon it has always worked that way with us. Well, come on up to the house where we can sit on the porch out of this hot sun. Maybe Alice will give us a glass of that lemonade she makes."

They sat on the porch for several hours while Reuben opened his heart and shared everything with Felix. Felix was understanding and gave his advice when he felt he could. At one point he went into the house, and when he came out he handed Reuben a piece of paper. "Here you go. If you head south, this might be useful to you."

"Thanks," Reuben replied as he stood up getting ready to leave. "Just one favor, Felix. Will you see that Mother is taken care of? Help her get things settled?"

Felix hugged Reuben, then he straightened his hat and said, "You know I'll see that Aunt Mary Ann is taken care of. Now, you go on and get out of here, you city slicker. This poor farm boy's got to git his work done."

Reuben walked down the road, then turned to walk through the open field, a short cut to town. The clouds above were full of moisture drawn up by the hot sun. Most of the grass in the field was dry and brittle, but there were a few hearty wild flowers scattered here and there. By the edge of the road, Reuben noticed a green bush. As he bent close to take a better look at the bloom on it, he smelled a familiar scent. Could it be a gardenia? He touched the bloom and said softly to himself, "I'm sorry Victoria, my sweet, wonderful wife."

Many times he had crossed this field in a maze of sunshine, but this afternoon he was crossing in the rain.

Reuben arrived home in time for supper. After supper he read the newspaper, played with Vanessa before she went to sleep, and then made love to his wife. The next morning he got up and went to work. Everything was routine and normal. Mr. Bailey told him he had to leave the store early that day, and Reuben assured him that it would be no problem for him to lock up the store. Five o'clock came, and Reuben locked the front door of the dry goods store. He counted the money and the day's receipts. He knelt down in front of the safe in Mr. Bailey's office, put the receipts in the safe, and then he counted out the money that he was due for his pay that week. He put the rest of the money in the safe and locked it. He went through the back room and out the back door, locking it behind him.

He walked down the street that ran along the south side of the railroad track through town. Once he got to the edge of town he climbed the small grassy bank to the railroad track and continued walking westward along the railroad tracks. After a few minutes of walking, he noticed a figure standing off to the side of the track about fifty feet in front of him. He could see that it was a woman and she seemed to be holding something in her hands.

As he got closer to her he said, "Mother, I have to do this thing."

She handed him a small bag. "I understand. I always knew that one day you would have to leave Tallapoosa. I told Papa when you were born that you would not spend your life here."

"Just one favor, Mamma, take care of Vanessa and Victoria. I love them you know. Felix will help if you need anything. I will let Felix know where I am. I have to go." Reuben put his arms around his mother and held her for a long while.

She put her hands on his face and said, "Goodbye, son." Then she turned and walked back to town.

Reuben picked up his little bag and walked down the railroad tracks, out of town. The 6:00 p.m. freight train came through Tallapoosa soon afterward and as it pulled out, before it gained much speed, Reuben jumped into one of the open cars. He rode the train to Atlanta, and once he got there paid for a ticket on a passenger train.

He spent the remainder of the night in the train depot in Atlanta. He spoke to no one, just got his ticket and waited for his train. Once aboard the train, he took his seat and placed his bag at his feet. When the conductor came by to collect the tickets, Reuben handed him his. As the conductor punched the ticket he said, "Where you going mister? Oh I see, Sanford, Florida. You have a long ride ahead of you. Hope you'll be comfortable." Reuben didn't respond. He just turned his head toward the window and gazed at the passing trees.

* * *

When Mary Ann got to the edge of town, she turned down a path that led through a thicket of trees. This path came out across the road from her home. It was getting late and the sun was setting over Tallapoosa. Mary Ann walked slowly. Tears were streaming down her face. Her heart felt broken, like Reuben had torn something out and had taken it with him when he left. She had no idea how long it would be until she would see him again. He was a grown man, but he was her only son, and still like a little child to her. She knew his troubles, his weakness, and his pain, and she hurt for him. Before she crossed the road to the house, Mary Ann said to herself, "I must be strong. I have to take care of Reuben's wife and my grandbaby. I must do this for my son." Victoria was standing in the kitchen holding Vanessa when Mary Ann walked in.

"Isn't it late for you to be coming home? I guess you've been out on that farm again. If you like it so much, why don't you just move out there?" Victoria asked curtly.

Mary Ann said nothing as she reached for her apron and went about her chores in the kitchen. The baby started to cry and Victoria slammed the door behind her as she carried her out into the back yard. She walked around the yard comforting her baby in her arms. Vanessa was over a year old, but she was tiny for her age. Even though she was light to carry, Victoria grew tired of walking with her. She sat dawn in the swing that hung from the oak tree and Vanessa laid her head on her mother's shoulder and went to sleep.

It was dark, after 8:00 p.m., and Victoria wondered where Reuben was. He couldn't be working this late at the store, and even though he had not talked to her much lately, he seemed to be content with her and their family life. He had been tender and loving when they had made love last night, and she smiled as she thought about that. She finally took Vanessa inside and put her to bed. Feeling unfriendly toward her mother-in-law, she decided to prepare herself for bed and spend the evening alone in her room reading. The hour was late when Victoria lay down between the sheets and rested her head on the soft pillow.

All through the night, she reached over to gently stroke the pillow next to her. Her husband was not there. Reuben did not come home that night. The following morning the first one to arrive at Bailey's store was Jessie. He unlocked the door and opened the store the same way he usually did for his father. He did notice the time and wondered where Reuben was. Ever since Reuben got his new Elgin pocket watch, he was never late for work.

When Jessie leaned down to open the safe to prepare the cash register for opening, he noticed an envelope lying on the floor. He picked it up and saw that it was addressed to Reuben Oliver Kincaide with a post office box number in Tallapoosa. The return address was Mary Nicholson, with a street address in Albany, Georgia. Jessie put the letter in his pocket just as his father walked into the store.

"Cash register ready?" he asked. Mr. Bailey was short spoken with his son.

"Not yet, just got here." Jessie replied.

"Well, get out of the way, I'll do it myself. Where the hell is Reuben?" Bailey began to count the money and tally the receipts. Jessie knew when to step aside and let his father alone. "What the hell is this?" Bailey shouted. "Where the hell is the rest of the money?"

"What are you talking about?" Jessie asked as he looked in the safe. "Looks like you got it all out, Pop."

Mr. Bailey grew red in the face, "I'm telling you there is money missing. Where the hell is that Reuben? Jessie, you go find him. He'll answer for this. I left him to lock up last night, and don't call me Pops!"

Jessie left the store and walked over to Reuben's house. He knocked on the front door. When Victoria opened the door, Jessie stepped back. For a moment he couldn't say a word. She stood there wearing a long white night robe, her long black hair, even though uncombed, fell gracefully around her shoulders and her face was pale. She was very thin and delicate looking. Jessie thought to himself, God, she is beautiful.

Finally he spoke. "Daddy sent me over to see about Reuben. He didn't get to work yet."

Victoria replied, "I don't know where he is. He didn't come home last night. I am terribly worried about him."

"Oh, don't worry. He is probably just off with them Kincaide boys somewhere. I'll find him. I'm sure everything is all right. Don't you worry now," Jessie repeated as he backed away and turned to leave.

He heard Victoria say, "Thank you, Jessie" as she closed the door.

"That Reuben is crazy," Jessie mumbled to himself. "If I had a woman like that I wouldn't leave her alone, not even one night. She is one fine woman."

Jessie went back to the store to tell his father that Reuben wasn't home and hadn't been there all night. Mr. Bailey cursed and shouted at Jessie to go out to the Kincaide farm and bring Reuben back or he would get the sheriff to go out there to pick him up. "Can I drive the car out to the farm?" Jessie asked.

"No, it won't hurt you to walk, and don't be all day at it," Mr. Bailey snapped. He was an angry man and he never gave Jessie any slack.

Once he got out to the farm, Jessie asked several of the women in the house if they had seen Reuben. They didn't know anything about where he was, so Jessie went out to the field to find Felix. Felix didn't like Jessie much, probably because he was the store owner's son and flaunted his money.

When Jessie asked Felix about Reuben, Felix was short with his answer. "Nope, don't know where Reuben is. He probably up and quit being your Pa's whipping boy. Guess you'll have to do some work now, Jessie. Run along now. You don't want to get any dirt on you out here on this farm. Daddy won't like it." Felix laughed as he tugged at the horse's reins and continued plowing the field.

Jessie couldn't stand Felix; in fact, he didn't like any of the Kincaide people. He didn't even like Reuben, just pretended to be his friend so he would continue to work for his father. Jessie had no intention of working in that dry goods store, ever!

Leaving the farm, Jessie turned off the main road and walked through the trees that bordered the town. He sat down on a tree stump in the cool shade. He took out the envelope he had found earlier in the store. He held it in his hand like a prize. "To Reuben, from Mary," he said aloud, "just what, I wonder, is this all about? Only one way to find out."

He opened the letter and began to read. My darling Reuben... Jessie's eyes grew wider and wider as he read the letter. He read the whole thing through, then he went back and read it aloud. "Reuben, I have decided to return to Tallapoosa. I can't wait for you here in Albany any longer. Annie Mae needs to know her daddy and I miss you. Please understand. I will need sane extra money for the trip."

Jessie grinned as he folded the letter and put it back in the envelope. "Well, well, so that is what happened to that sexy little Mary. My, my, how sweet it is. Jessie, my boy, you done found the prize. Yep, you hold here in your hand a treasure. Now just how to spend it, how to make it work for me? No wonder you flew the coop, Reuben, ole boy. Wonder just who all knows about this thing. Your pretty little wife isn't the only one you been rolling in the hay with."

Jessie laughed and was so pleased with himself. Now he knew what had happened to Reuben. He remembered the day Mary's mother had angrily told him to tell Reuben to come to her house. He had given Reuben the message, but Reuben never said what it was about. They sent Mary off to Albany, and now she was coming back with a baby. "You are running, aren't you, Reuben? You took money from our store and in your haste to get away, you dropped the letter by the safe." Jessie gloated all the way back to the store.

Jessie told his father he had gone out to the Kincaide farm and talked to Felix. He said that Felix had told him that Reuben quit his job at the store and had no intention of coming back. Jessie claimed that Felix said Reuben was in some kind of trouble and had probably left town.

Mr. Bailey was furious. "Damn that boy! Well, good, he took the money owed him for this week's work. He had that coming to him, but he was a coward not to let me know he was quitting. I need help around here. I can't depend on my son to do a damn thing. Well, good riddance, Reuben Kincaide. I only hired you as a favor to my friend Sherwood. His daughter should never have married a low-life Kincaide. Only Kincaide who had any sense was Grier, rest his soul."

Jessie wandered out the front door leaving his father to talk to himself. He was thinking about the letter. His father had mentioned Sherwood. Jessie wondered if Dr. Sherwood knew about this Mary-Reuben affair, wondered what he would pay to find out about it.

"Think I will make a call on Doc Sherwood," Jessie said to himself as he walked to the doctor's office. Jessie caught the doctor just as he was leaving for the day.

"Hello there, Jessie," Dr. Sherwood said. He was very friendly toward Jessie. "Did you need to see me? I was just leaving. It has been a long day, but if you need something, we can go inside."

"No, Doc, no need to go inside. I just have a little something I need to talk over with you," Jessie said as he patted his pocket.

"Well, get in the car. We will go to the house and get something cold to drink." Dr. Sherwood motioned for Jessie to sit in the passenger seat of his new Ford "Tin Lizzie."

"That will be fine. I think your wife will be interested in what I have to say," Jessie said. The doctor gave him a puzzled look.

When they got to the house, Dr. Sherwood's wife made them comfortable in the living room. Jessie was nervous, and he began to make small talk to cover his discomfort. They chatted for several minutes. Finally Jessie pulled the envelope out of his pocket and handed it to Dr. Sherwood. "I guess the best way to tell you the real purpose of my visit is to let you read this. I found it this morning by the safe in my dad's store. When I couldn't find Reuben all day, I decided to read it hoping for a clue

52

as to where he was. Anyway, it isn't any of my business, but I thought I should give it to you, since you are his wife's parents. I saw Victoria this morning, and she was so worried about Reuben that I didn't want to give it to her," he said.

Dr. Sherwood opened the letter and sat down in a chair. His wife leaned over his shoulder as they both read it in silence. "Oh, dear God," Mrs. Sherwood cried as she snatched the letter from her husband's hands. "Who knows about this? What will people say? Our name will be ruined! I knew that Reuben was no good. How could he do this to us?"

Dr. Sherwood just sat in the chair and with tears rolling down his face, he said, "Victoria, Victoria, Victoria."

Jessie didn't know what to do. He had started toward the door when Mrs. Sherwood said, "Where are you going young man? Have you told anyone about this? Come back in here and sit down!" Jessie did as she said.

Dr. Sherwood got up, put his arms around his wife and said, "Calm down, dear. Jessie hasn't done anything wrong. There, there, just relax, we will work this out. First of all, we have to find out if Victoria knows about this." Mrs. Sherwood left the room. She was crying and talking to herself. Dr. Sherwood said to Jessie, "Son, I hope I can trust you not to say anything about this to anyone. I know how you feel about my daughter, and Victoria has often mentioned how much she likes you. She will need a friend like you, and I know you don't want to hurt her."

Dr. Sherwood was a smart man. He knew how to play on Jessie's vulnerabilities. He guessed about Jessie's feelings for Victoria. After all, he had a beautiful daughter and who wouldn't be in love with her. Dr. Sherwood's instincts about Jessie couldn't have been more accurate. Jessie left the house feeling sorry for Victoria and determined not to do anything to hurt her. He would help the Sherwoods do whatever was needed to protect Victoria.

The Sherwoods didn't get any sleep that night. They decided that in the morning Mrs. Sherwood would go over and have a talk with Mrs. Nicholson, Mary's mother, and Dr. Sherwood would go to his daughter. Mrs. Sherwood was relentless in her attack on Mrs. Nicholson. She blamed her, she blamed Mary, she blamed Reuben, she blamed everyone for bringing shame on the Sherwood family name. When she finally wound down, Mrs. Nicholson assured her that no one knew that Reuben was the father of Mary's baby. She told her that Reuben had known from the beginning and they had agreed on Mary going to Albany. She did not know that Mary was planning to return to Tallapoosa, and she had not see Reuben lately.

Mrs. Nicholson was a strong woman, and she did not back down from Mrs. Sherwood's aggressive attack on herself and her daughter. She stated that no one in this situation was without fault. Mary was her daughter and the baby was her granddaughter and she would do everything in her power to see that they were cared for. They were not wealthy people, but Reuben had been sending Mary a little money. She told Mrs. Sherwood she did not know what Reuben's intentions were and she did not know if Victoria knew about the situation. She assured her that she would see to it that Mary and the baby stayed in Albany until things were settled in Tallapoosa. She said firmly, "If you respect my wishes, I will respect yours."

Mrs. Sherwood left the Nicholson residence not knowing just who had called the shots, but at least she knew now that few people were aware of what had happened and that Mary would stay in Albany until they could figure out what to do. While the ladies had spent the morning in discussion, Dr. Sherwood had been visiting his daughter. He arrived just as Victoria was feeding little Vanessa her breakfast. Reuben's mother was busy in the kitchen and she offered Dr. Sherwood a cup of coffee. He declined, saying he would like to speak to his daughter alone.

Dr. Sherwood was a fair and just man, but at this point he did not know all of the details of the situation, and he was short with Mary Ann. Understanding his actions, Mary Ann took Vanessa outside with her so Victoria and her father could have some privacy.

Dr. Sherwood was shocked at his daughter's appearance. She was pale and seemed very frail. Her eyes filled with tears as soon as her mother-in-law left the house with the baby, and she fell into her father's arms. "Oh, Daddy, I don't know where Reuben is. He hasn't been home for two nights and I have had no word of where he is. Jessie came by looking for him and said he didn't go to work yesterday. Jessie said he would let me know if he found him, but I haven't heard anything. Is that why you are here? Do you know what has happened to my husband?"

Dr. Sherwood comforted his daughter and promised her that everything would be all right. He was gentle and kind as he questioned her about her marriage, and about how their life together was living in the house with her

54

mother-in-law. He realized immediately that Victoria did not know about her husband's affair with another woman. She was completely in the dark. She loved Reuben with all her heart and she wanted him home. He kissed his daughter on the forehead and told her he had to go to the office, but that he would come over after supper to check on her and Vanessa.

When Dr. Sherwood drove off in his car, he glanced in the backyard and saw Mary Ann with his grandchild. "Well, Mary Ann, just what do you know about all this? What role did you play?" Probably a mother protecting her son, he guessed. One thing he knew for sure, Reuben had left them. He knew why; he just didn't know to where or for how long.

Several weeks went by and there was no word from Reuben. Victoria was distraught, but Mary Ann told her nothing of what she knew about her son's disappearance. Mary Ann concentrated on taking care of little Vanessa. The two women were alone with a child to care for and had no means of support. Dr. Sherwood came by to see them every day and made sure they had food.

Finally he had a talk with them. He felt that Reuben was not coming back, and without him there to support them and keep up the house and yard it would be best if they moved out of the house on Head Street. He suggested they move in with him and his wife. After all, they were Victoria's parents and the child's grandparents and they certainly had enough room for them in their large home.

At first Victoria was reluctant to even consider leaving Head Street, and her mother threw a fit when Dr. Sherwood told her of his plan to move Victoria, little Vanessa, and Mary Ann into their home. She yelled at her husband, "How will it look moving that Kincaide woman into our home?"

She didn't mind Victoria and the baby moving in, but she could not accept Reuben's mother. Dr. Sherwood explained to his wife that Mary Ann would be there to take care of the baby. "God knows Victoria doesn't have sense enough to take care of a child these days. She is so frail, I am worried about her health. Most importantly, our grandchild needs a home. We will do this!" Dr. Sherwood would tolerate no further argument from his wife.

Reuben's mother understood that it was necessary to move in with the Sherwoods, but it broke her heart to leave the home that she had shared with her husband and son since 1909. Mary Ann decided she would take her personnel items and most cherished possessions and do as the

Sherwoods asked. The Sherwoods gave her a room in their home next to Vanessa's room. After Victoria had taken her things out of the house and they had moved all of Vanessa's toys and clothes, Mary Ann closed and locked the door, then wondered to herself if Reuben would ever come home.

The Sherwood home was in turmoil for several days as everyone settled in and adjusted to the new arrangements. Mary Ann fixed up her room. She had brought with her the wooden quilt chest that Reuben had made for her and she put most of her personal things in there. She cleaned and decorated Vanessa's room as well. The Sherwoods had bought all new furniture, bedding, draperies, and accessories for Vanessa's room. After all this was "their" grandchild, and she would have the best. On top of the new dresser, Mary Ann placed a beautifully designed porcelain shaving mug. Vanessa kept this mug all of her life because it belonged to her daddy.

Having the three women in one household was a disaster from the start. Mrs. Sherwood could not tolerate Reuben's mother's habits. She and Victoria laughed at her for putting cornbread in her coffee. They criticized everything she did. She only tried to take care of the baby and do as she was told, but the situation became unbearable for her. Mary Ann decided the best thing for her to do would be to leave. She put a few of her clothes in a small bag and dressed herself for walking. She went into Vanessa's room and watched her as she slept. "I must leave you while you are sleeping. I don't know when I will see you again. I know your grandparents will give you a good life, better than I ever could. I will miss you and I hope that you will remember me and always know that I love you with all my heart."

Mary Ann spoke these words, leaned over and kissed her grandchild softly on the cheek, then picked up her little bag and went downstairs to the dining room. Mrs. Sherwood and Victoria were sitting at the table having their morning coffee. They hardly glanced at her as she walked in the room. "You're late this morning. We had to get our own coffee," Mrs. Sherwood said curtly. Victoria just sat staring out the bay window.

Mary Ann stood tall for her petite size, and said in a firm voice, "I am leaving this house today. I won't be back. I ask only that you take care of my grandchild and that you see to it that she keeps the wooden chest with my things in it. I want her to have them. I feel I have done the best I

56

could. I know my son didn't mean to hurt any of you, and hope someday you will understand why he had to leave."

Having said this she turned and walked through the house and out the front door. Mrs. Sherwood was shocked; she couldn't say a word for several minutes. Then she jumped up and paced the floor saying all kinds of things about Mary Ann, about Reuben, about the marriage.

"Leave, go ahead leave. What else could we expect from the mother of a deserter!" she yelled out the window watching Mary Ann walk off down the road. Victoria had not moved from her seat. She just sat staring out the window. Her mother turned on her, saying "Oh, for God's sake, Victoria, what is wrong with you?"

After some time went by, the Sherwoods realized that Mary Ann really was not coming back. They still hadn't heard from Reuben and Victoria's depression was getting worse. They made plans for Victoria to go to Atlanta. They had wanted her to go to finishing school after her graduation from high school, but she had married Reuben instead. Now, even though she was already twenty years old, they felt she could still make a decent life for herself by getting a good education and meeting a respectable man. As she was, she couldn't take care of her child. The Sherwoods would keep their grandchild and Victoria would never have to worry that her baby wasn't well cared for.

Victoria was settled into school in Atlanta and Reuben had not returned to Tallapoosa. Mrs. Sherwood felt it was time to pay Mrs. Nicholson a call. She was very pleasant as she expressed her sincere appreciation to Mrs. Nicholson in keeping her word that she would keep her daughter, Mary, away from Tallapoosa until the Sherwoods had straightened things out. At this point, Mrs. Sherwood felt they had put a good face on the situation and so far no one seemed to know why Reuben left his wife and child.

Of course, the situation must be kept this way at all costs. Victoria had not been told about Mary and Reuben's affair. Mrs. Sherwood was confident as she told Mary's mother, "When Mary returns to Tallapoosa with Reuben's baby, my husband will see to it that the Kincaide place on Head Street is signed over to provide for them. If you ever reveal to our grandchild or Victoria the truth of this matter, I will promise you that neither Mary nor that baby of hers will ever receive any support from us. There is no need for anyone, especially the two children, to ever know about this. We want what is best for them. They will be raised here in

57

Tallapoosa, and after all what would people think? It is enough that we have to overcome the shame of Reuben's desertion. Do you understand?"

Mrs. Nicholson just nodded her head in acceptance. What else could she do? After all, they didn't have a lot of money, and Mary and the baby would need help. She assured Mrs. Sherwood that Mary would agree to her plan. She would send word to Mary in Albany to have her return with the baby to Tallapoosa.

Mrs. Sherwood left the Nicholson home feeling good about her plan for everyone's future. Today she was in control.

What happened after these negotiations to those involved:

- ▸ Victoria — stayed in Atlanta. She divorced Reuben on grounds of desertion.
- ▸ Vanessa — lived with her grandparents. She grew up believing her father was dead. At the age of 18 she married Jessie (he was 34 years old when they married).
- ▸ Mary Ann, Reuben's mother — lived on the Kincaide farm with Felix
- ▸ Mrs. Nicholson — would keep the secret
- ▸ Mary and her baby — returned to Tallapoosa. Mary guarded the secret, but the child, Annie Mae, would one day know her father.
- ▸ The Sherwoods — remained in respected society. They raised Vanessa. They never told the truth.
- ▸ Jessie — did as the Sherwoods asked him. He never told Victoria. He married Vanessa and protected her from the truth until his death.

CHAPTER FOUR

$\mathcal{R}$euben stepped off the train in Sanford, Florida. It was September, 1915, and he was only twenty-seven years old, although he felt like an old man.

As he looked around him he observed the maze of railroad tracks and the crowded depot. He had come in on the Atlantic Coastline train from Jacksonville. The railroads had opened up Florida to numerous commercial and agricultural opportunities. Many people poured into Florida's cities and rural areas. They were mostly farmers, laborers, merchants and professional people, although some were pleasure seekers, while others were Northerners seeking refuge from the harsh climate for health reasons.

Sanford was known as "The Gate City" because it had been the center of transportation for south Florida since the 1800s. Even before the Atlantic Coast had connected Sanford from the north, passengers and merchandise were brought into Sanford by steamboat down the St. John's River. In 1880, General Ulysses S. Grant, then president of the United States, turned the first shovelful of earth for the first railroad to be built from Sanford to Tampa. In 1886, the Jacksonville-Tampa and Key West Railroad was built into Sanford from the north, making this city the southern terminus of that railroad.

That day, when Reuben arrived in Sanford, he fell into the category of a refugee, not for health reasons, but looking for peace of mind and a job.

He reached into his pocket and took out a piece of paper. This was the folded paper Felix had given him the day he left the Kincaide farm in

Tallapoosa. Felix had told him he might find this paper useful if he headed south. He unfolded the piece of paper and read the information printed on it. "Celery farm workers needed. Contact J.R. Benson, Beardall Avenue, Sanford, Florida."

As Reuben folded the paper and put it back in his pocket, he was reminded of how Felix had always helped him out. He would go to this farm tomorrow, but for right now he was dead tired and thought he might find a place to wash up, get a good meal and a full night's sleep.

Reuben asked directions to a hotel in town. He was given directions to a historic tourist hotel on Oak Street, down by the edge of the river. It was about two miles and the railroad would provide transportation down there, but Reuben stated that he would walk. He was used to walking and although he was tired after the long train ride, he felt the walk was what he needed. He took the small bag his mother had given him when he left Tallapoosa and began trudging to the hotel.

As he walked the paved streets, past newly constructed business buildings, he noticed many automobiles and well-dressed people. He realized this was a prosperous town. Turning down First Street, Reuben looked up to see a majestic clock on the corner. It stood alone, towering over business buildings. Reuben reached into his watch pocket, removed his Elgin watch and held it out in front of him, extending the chain that attached the watch to his belt loop. Pausing, with a slight lean backward, he checked the time of his watch with the time showing in the grand old clock. He was pleased that they matched perfectly. Somehow this moment seemed to connect him with this place.

This old clock, that had been standing there since 1870, represented the era of thriving business in the town; Reuben felt good to be there. He thought of the booming years in his hometown, Tallapoosa, and sensed the same atmosphere there.

He had read in the Atlanta newspaper of Sanford's inestimable wealth. This town had an impressive historical resume as well.

Henry B. Sanford was a lawyer and United States diplomat. Under General Grant's administration, he was the minister to Belgium. He is credited with being the founder of Sanford circa 1871.

Mainly due to its location, Sanford became one of the most modern cities in the state of Florida. It was right on the St. John's River in central Florida, which provided great access for boat shipping, and it also became a railroad center. By the year 1893, Sanford was the largest orange shipping center in the world, but this area of Florida experienced a freeze in 1895, a disaster for the Sanford community, followed by a general exodus of people due to this catastrophic freeze.

This Southern city was down but not out. An early pioneer established a plant nursery, and the first attempt at truck farming was developed. Celery and lettuce were planted on a small scale and a system of irrigation novel at that time, 1898, was introduced. Several years later, crops were grown commercially, and profitable return gave impetus to the city's growth. By the early 1900s, Sanford boasted the title, "Celery Capital of the World."

This area of Florida was also prosperous because of the change in administration at the state level. When Napoleon Bonaparte Broward became Florida's governor in 1904, social changes in everyday life occurred more rapidly than in any comparable period.

Telephone service reached rural Florida and significantly altered the way in which farming communities related to each other. The average town of five hundred or more people had electric lights and women cooked on stoves instead of in fireplaces. Families ate grape-nuts, grits instead of hominy, and baked goods made of self-rising flour. Postum and coffee, already ground, were sold in pound packages. Homemade chairs, table and bedsteads were replaced by store-bought manufactured furniture.

Men began to get haircuts in "barber shops," and women changed their hair styles from bangs to a slight curl and put away their homespun bonnets. Women also began to wear skirts above the ankles and high-buttoned shoes. Men got out of the frock coat and set aside their celluloid collars in favor of the softer cotton. Businessmen began to use a contraption called a typewriter.

During the Broward era, the Buckman Act of 1905 was passed. This consolidated seven state-supported colleges and schools into four specialized institutions: The University of Florida at Gainesville (all male until 1947); The Florida State College for Women at Tallahassee (after 1947 the co-educational Florida State University); The State Normal School for Negroes at Tallahassee (after 1909 Florida Agricultural and Mechanical College, and after 1953 Florida A&M University); and a school for the deaf, dumb and blind at St. Augustine.

The college most familiar to the people of Sanford is the private institution of higher learning, Stetson University. This was Florida's first law school, and is located in DeLand, Florida, just north of Sanford. Stetson University was named after John B. Stetson (1830-1906), the man who originated the Stetson hat favored by Reuben and many others in the United States. A graduate of Stetson, Doyle E. Carlton, was Florida's first native son from a native institution to become governor of the state, in 1929.

Sanford was a well-known city in the state of Florida. In 1909 it sported a street car line. A railroad was built in 1908 through the celery delta.

If Reuben Oliver Kincaide had had a crystal ball, perhaps he could have looked into the future and seen that a half a century later something called tourism, most of it by automobile, would be the state's leading industry. Reuben had no idea at the time, but he would be a part of that era also.

Reuben checked into the hotel, ate a light supper and went straight to his room. He placed his Stetson hat on a small table by the bed, then removed his glasses and laid them next to the hat. Without undressing, he stretched out across the bed, rested his head on a pillow, and closed his eyes. Tallapoosa, and his life there, seemed a million miles away. He was exhausted and soon fell into a deep sleep.

The next morning he felt much better, but his mind was still racing with thoughts of whether he was doing the right thing. He had left his wife, his child, his mother and his home. Although it had been necessary that he leave the state of Georgia, he was unsure of what his actions would be now.

Reuben spent several days exploring the city of Sanford, but his money was running out so he had to make a decision.

In the late afternoon, Reuben walked down to the river. Always in the past when he had a serious decision to make, he would walk the woods of the Kincaide farm back in Tallapoosa. When he was young, he had been afraid to go near the grand river running past the farm, but since his encounter with a comforting love on the banks of the Tallapoosa, Reuben felt drawn to the river.

Today it was not the Tallapoosa, but the St. John's River. This river had connected this place in Florida to the rest of the world for many years. As Reuben stood watching steamboats going to and from the piers in Sanford, he wondered if he could sort out his life as systematically as the travel of these boats. They seemed to move with such ease. They accomplished their tasks with such grace. Why couldn't his life be so simple?

However, as Reuben walked along the edge of the river, he was some distance from town when his passage became difficult due to dense trees and underbrush reaching the water. He sat down next to the trunk of what he thought was a strange looking tree. It had upright stumps all around it. What he was seeing was a bald cypress tree, which develops unique upright "knees" near the base of its trunk. It has a feathery, light green, deciduous foliage that turns orange in the fall. He placed his hat on one of those "knees."

As he sat examining the tree, Reuben began to relax and became aware of the beauty of his surroundings. This place was so different from his home in Georgia. The land was warm, wet and lush. It had a deep green beauty that exuded an air of tranquillity, causing an inner strength to begin to stir inside of him. His mind cleared; he knew there was no turning back now. He would stay in Sanford, Florida. Reuben would get a job and contact Felix to let him know where he was. He would ask Felix to let him know from time to time about his mother, his wife, Victoria, and his daughter, Vanessa. He would send Felix money to give to Mary and ask Felix if she had returned to Tallapoosa with his baby.

Reuben had sorted things out; in fact, he had already made several decisions. Rising, he brushed off his pants and removed his hat from the "knee" of the tree. Just before he put his hat on his head, he tipped it to the tree and said, "Thanks for listening to my inner thoughts, old tree. I'll trust you to keep all this a secret so I can start a new life here."

It grew dark as Reuben walked back into town. This was a crossroad for Reuben's life. When he decided never to tell anyone about his past life he created the beginnings of a lifetime of secrets. The year was 1915.

The grand old tree remained majestic and laden with sweeps of Spanish moss. Forty-eight years later, Reuben's youngest grandson would run and play around the "knees" of this tree. Reuben never revealed his time spent here, and the old cypress tree kept its secrets.

Reuben awoke the next morning to a new beginning. He checked out of the hotel and asked directions to the J.R. Benson Celery Farm. The hotel clerk told him that if he was looking for work, he could go over to the freight depot or down by the docks and he would see farm trucks with the name J.R. Benson posted on their sides. He could probably get a ride out to the farm on one of these trucks. Reuben also inquired about the post office. Before looking for a Benson truck, he went to the post office and rented a box in his name.

Reuben then approached one of the Benson trucks just as it was pulling away from the dock area. "Hey," he yelled, "could I catch a ride out to the farm?"

The driver questioned, "Looking for work?"

"Need a job," was Reuben's reply.

"Jump in the back if you're ready to work."

It was a jeering response, but Reuben passed it off and climbed into the back of the truck, which traveled east of town for about five miles on a paved road, then turned south onto a dirt road. On either side of the dirt road, fields were being prepared for the growth of celery. The acres of flat land lay near the river, and the sandy loam and muck soil was perfect for this crop.

Reuben took the piece of paper from his pocket to double-check the name. It was the J. R. Benson Celery Farm. The truck stopped along the side of the road and the driver yelled back to Reuben, "You can get out here. You need to go over to that house across the road." He barely gave Reuben time to jump from the truck before he roared off, leaving a cloud of dust behind him. Reuben cursed as he took off his hat to brush the dust off his pants and coat.

Reuben looked across the road to see an English-style farmhouse. It was surrounded by trees and the interplay of light and shadow made the house look cool and inviting. No one was outside, so Reuben knocked on the front door. When the door opened, the roundest man Reuben had ever seen stood in front of him. He was short with a mustache, glasses, and gray hair. His belly folded out over his trousers. Reuben almost laughed; the man looked like Santa Claus. But before Reuben could make that mistake, the man barked, "All hired hands go to the back door!" Then, just as Reuben turned to find his way in to the back door, the man said, "Wait just a minute. You ain't from around here. No one 'round here dresses like that, and I don't know anyone who wears a hat like that in the fields. You got some kinda business here?"

Reuben offered his hand to the man and said, "Yes, sir, my name is Reuben Oliver Kincaide. I came from Georgia looking for work."

"Well, you don't look much like a farm hand to me," the man replied

64

not shaking Reuben's proffered hand.

A little perturbed, but determined not to leave, Reuben pulled himself erect and said forcefully, but politely, "No, sir, I am not much of farm hand. I worked ten years as a clerk in a feed store and another year in a dry goods store. I finished school and have a head for figuring as good as any man. I did live on a farm and I am not afraid of hard work. Today, sir, I need a job."

The man stepped forward and extended his hand, "J.R. Benson here, come inside. Maybe we can do some business."

It was as though some ground rules had been set, and Mr. Benson dropped his superior attitude. "I like your style, young man. I think you might just be the fellow I have been looking for to help me out. You say you can figure good, read, and write? Since you worked in a store, I guess you know about getting supplies. That right? I need a manager around here. Think you can do the job? Are you interested?"

"Yes, sir," Reuben didn't hesitate to answer. "I'll do a good job for you, Mr. Benson."

Mr. Benson pointed toward a chair in front of a desk that was in the corner of the front room. "Have a seat over there. We'll go over a few things. Mr. Benson sat down behind the desk. He was long-winded as he went on and on about the farm, the responsibilities, and his expectations of a manager. Reuben sat patiently with his hat in his hands. Finally Mr. Benson said, "Got any questions?" and before Reuben could answer, he called out, "Tasha!" Reuben jumped to his feet as a lovely young girl came into the room.

"Reuben," Mr. Benson continued his monologue, "this is my daughter, Tasha. She runs the household affairs around here. I noticed that little bag you are carrying. That your luggage? Will you need a place to stay?"

This Mr. Benson really didn't mince words, Reuben thought. All Reuben could get out of his mouth was, "Yes, sir."

"Tasha," Mr. Benson said as though he was giving an order, "take Reuben to the hired man's room in the back of the house. You can eat meals in the kitchen, Reuben. Three square meals a day. Same time every day. If you miss a meal, don't come around. Tasha can't be fixin' food all day. Meet me out back by the barn tomorrow morning at six. Breakfast is at five-thirty. I don't tolerate lateness, understand?" Mr. Benson didn't wait for an answer. He went out the front door leaving Reuben standing there holding his hat in his hands.

Tasha was the first to speak. "Don't be afraid of Daddy. He can be harsh at times, but he is a good man. Reuben? Is that your name?"

"Yes ma'am," Reuben replied.

"No need to call me ma'am, Tasha will be just fine. Come, I will show you through the house and to your room," Tasha said with a smile.

As Reuben followed her through the house, he noticed a bright living room filled with rosy colors. The furniture was dark wood. Some pieces of furniture were English in style with mahogany finish and some were cherry wood in the Colonial American style. There was a large sofa piled with pillows. Not one of the pillows was the same as another. They gave the sofa a plump look with their variety of fabrics and sizes. The dining room was simple with a plain table surrounded by antique chairs. There was a cabinet with some fine English china in it. The rooms were immaculate and vibrant with colorful pictures on the walls and many displays of ornamental objects. The windows were not draped. They had only a decorative valance at the top, allowing the Florida sunshine to pour into the rooms.

Tasha had Reuben follow her through the kitchen and down a short hall. There she opened the door to a small bedroom. Inside there was a small bed with a chenille bedspread, a three-drawer bureau, one cane-bottomed chair, a quilt rack with a quilt hanging over it, and a window that was covered with a faded chintz curtain. Tasha walked over and pulled back the curtain. The light, combined with the tumble of colors on the quilt, brightened the room. Then Tasha showed him the bath he could use across the hall. Reuben thanked his hostess and did not pay much attention to her as she left the room closing the door behind her. He was tired and relieved that he had a job. He was especially appreciative of the clean room. He had a place where he could hang his hat and, he hoped, stay for a long while.

Reuben's immediate future was mapped out. He became Mr. Benson's right hand man. He was the overseer for the celery farm's operations. He and Mr. Benson got along well. They had respect for each other, and Tasha was always there to help in any way she could. She read books in the evening and often shared them with Reuben. Reading together formed a common ground between them, and they became friends. Often in the late evening after a hard day of work, Reuben and Tasha would share stories about themselves with each other. Tasha told Reuben how her mother had died giving birth to her. She thought her father had always held that against her and wondered if this was why he treated her more like a hired hand than a daughter. But, she assured herself that she loved her father and was content with her life on the farm.

Reuben had to wonder if she really was happy. Sometimes he noticed a faraway look on her face as though she wished she were someplace else. He had tremendous respect for Tasha. She was a hard worker and a lovely young girl. He guessed that she was around nineteen years old. He enjoyed the time he spent with her, but he dreamed of the women in his past. Tasha never questioned Reuben about his past. She laughed at his funny childhood stories and accepted what he told her. They both realized the world would never be as they imagined life should be.

During the first year that he worked for Mr. Benson, Reuben never had to work in the fields. But in the summer of 1916, many of the laborers began to get sick with the flu. The laborers lived in small wooden houses with tin roofs. The houses were built in a straight row along a dirt road about a mile away from the main house. They were treated as migrant workers and their lives were consumed with working in the celery fields. When several of them became ill, it affected the production of the entire farm because the women and children had to take care of the sick instead of working the fields.

This meant that Reuben and Tasha had to put on field clothes and join the laborers in the fields. Neither of them hesitated to take on hard work, and they often worked side by side to get the job done. One sultry summer afternoon Tasha and Reuben rejoiced when clouds gathered to shield the field from the burning summer sun. When the first rain droplets came it looked like steam was rising from the soil. Then water began pouring out of the sky like a cool waterfall. The two workers dropped their tools and giggled as they turned around and around letting the rain touch every part of their bodies. Tasha took off her shoes and waded through the gullies between the rows of the field.

A loud crack of thunder came and Reuben yelled, "We better get to some cover, we shouldn't be out in the field in a lightning storm."

They ran for a barn at the far side of the field. Reuben was the first to run inside, shivering in the coolness of the shed. He turned around to see where Tasha was and laughed to see her standing under the eaves of the shed where water poured over her. She held her head back and let her sunburned skin soak in the coolness of the rain. Her cotton clothes clung to her body as though they were a sheer organza material. Tasha reached out for Reuben to join her under the steady stream. Their bodies touched blissfully. Reuben led her into the dark shed with its summer smells. She was cold and he covered her with his body as they found a bed of hay. Shafts of light came through the cracks in the boards of the walls, revealing their bodies. They began to play, to turn over in gentle careless rolls; they were soothed by the rhythm of their bodies. When they lay quiet, Reuben gazed into her dark eyes and parted her dark bangs, brushing them off her forehead. Tasha gave him a satisfied smiled. Reuben felt as though a part of him had come to life again.

When the rain ended and they strolled through the field to reach the house, they both felt that their meeting was fated. They had become good friends, and today they became lovers. The days after the rain shower were spent working in the fields, and on many nights Reuben came to Tasha's room. If Mr. Benson knew of these meetings, he never mentioned it to either of them. They were getting his field work done and he needed both of them. Reuben cherished his encounters with Tasha on those steamy summer nights.

Tasha would begin their twilight rendezvous by offering her lover a cool drink. Her arms would be empty and open to him as he entered her summer bed. The window was open to a breeze that ruffled the curtains. Reuben would close the mosquito netting around the bed before he caressed her cool skin. They shared many simple pleasures.

During the overnight stays, Tasha would whisper to him, "I love it dark and when it rains."

Reuben would say to her, "I love you in the summer sun."

CHAPTER FIVE

*A*lthough it seemed to Reuben that in this place perpetual summer reigned, cooler days eventually arrived as summer gave way to fall. The planting of the celery seedlings was finished, and the crop would grow during the cool Southern winter to be harvested in the spring. The Benson Farm had been lucky to get all the planting done before the flu had afflicted many of their laborers. Reuben was not spared from contracting the flu. When his fever began, he was afraid. He remembered getting typhoid fever when the epidemic ravaged Tallapoosa in 1893 and so many of his family members died. He had escaped harm — except for the weakness in his eyes. He wondered if he would escape death from this dreadful plague as well.

Reuben took to his bed while Tasha nursed him as best she could. Several days passed and Reuben's condition grew critical. Mr. Benson knew of a doctor who had come into town and was helping to take care of the flu patients. He sent for him. When Doc Lundstorm arrived he examined Reuben and said, "Well, son, you have the flu all right, but you are a young man and if you will do as I say you will get better. You have a wonderful thing in this Southern state of yours called oranges. You take these oranges and squeeze the juice from them. Fill a large glass full and put about a teaspoon of castor oil in it. Mix it up and drink this several times a day. Stay in bed and keep warm. In several days you should be feeling better."

With that, the doctor left. Reuben never forgot Doc Lundstorm. The doctor was from New Orleans and had been visiting his brother Charles, who had moved to Sanford from Virginia in 1898. Usually his visits were for pleasure, but this time he was called on to help fight a deadly virus.

The influenza epidemic began in Alabama and Georgia and, by 1918, it was a serious epidemic in Florida. Nearly 30,000 people contracted the disease and 464 died; it returned to take sixty-four lives in 1919 and seventy-nine in 1920. Doc Lundstorm had been right about the healing powers of Florida oranges. Oranges had been grown in Florida since the 1800s. The county in which Sanford is located was originally called Orange County. Later, oranges became the most valuable fruit crop in the United States and about two thirds of those oranges were produced in Florida. Although oranges remained important to the state of Florida, after Reuben survived the flu epidemic he would never drink a glass of orange juice again, and years later Reuben would tell his children about "Old Doc Lundstorm" and his orange juice and castor oil cure.

The winter of 1916-1917 was hard on Sanford. Not only had the flu epidemic begun, but there was a devastating freeze early in February. Reuben's health had improved, but now he had to worry about the farm's celery crop. He thought about all that hard work he and Tasha had put into this crop, and he realized that if it did not produce a good yield, he would probably be out of a job.

Immediately after the freeze, the Benson Farm celery crop looked as though it had been destroyed on the surface. But as the weather warmed again, the apparently lost crop came back to life. The new seedlings' foliage and the nearby water supply had shielded the crop from permanent damage. By March, the celery harvest was in full swing. The newspaper reported that on March 31 fifty-nine refrigerated freight cars moved out of Sanford. This was the largest one-day celery freight movement in the history of the Sanford celery delta. This single shipment represented 19,488 crates.

It was a time of rejoicing on the Benson Farm. Newspaper reporters contacted Mr. Benson and wanted to take a picture of his celery fields for the paper. All the managers of the nearby fields gathered for this picture. Reuben put on a suit and, of course, his hat. He stood proudly in the middle of the field, flanked by the other managers. The picture was printed in the April 3, 1917 Sanford Herald. An estimated 1,900 cars of celery were shipped from Sanford in 1917 at a value of $1,787,520.00.

Since Reuben was all dressed up for the picture taking, he decided he would take the day off. One of the reporters told him that on this day a new road was being opened from Sanford to Orlando. He said a lot of people were gathering downtown for the celebration. Reuben decided to go down to the road and see if he could catch a ride. The new road to Orlando was a nine-foot-wide, twenty-five-mile brick road. Reuben enjoyed his ride over the new road, and he had been wanting to see Orlando for sometime.

After he arrived, his stay was brief, and he didn't like it much. "Just a wide place in the road," he would recall later in life. This was his description of Orlando in 1917. Thirty-three years later, however in 1950, he would return to Orlando to live a life that was not in his mind or dreams in 1917.

When Reuben returned to the Benson farm it was late in the evening. Tasha was sitting outside in the shade of a tree. The light wind swaying the leaves on the tree branches filtered the setting sun's light on Tasha's hair. She was a picture of sensuous beauty as she sat there in her summer dress with a neckline that showed her tanned skin and the curve of her breasts. As Reuben grew closer to her, she stood, slim and long limbed, and embraced him. Tasha's dark eyes and long chestnut hair had a unique charm for Reuben. They abstained from fulfilling their desire for each other during Reuben's illness, and with all the work of the harvesting, Reuben had not experienced the sweetness of her flesh in many weeks.

After their embrace, they walked into the house. Tasha offered Reuben some supper from the kitchen, but Reuben took her in his arms and said, "I don't need supper to begin this night."

Tasha whispered, "Oh, Reuben, I have missed you."

They made their way to Tasha's bedroom. Their desire was so strong it was like a fever. Their love making was rough and passionate. Tasha directed his motion. She hungered for him so. Tonight Reuben would go further than he wanted to go, and he stayed longer then he should have stayed.

Three days later Reuben read this headline in the newspaper, "The US Enters World War I." The news spread throughout Sanford quickly, and every eligible man knew he would have to register for the draft. Reuben went to the designated place and filled out a registration card. It read:

Registration Card
Reuben Oliver Kincaide, Age 29
P 0 Box 1425
Sanford, Florida
Date of Birth: April 11, 1888
Natural born: Tallapoosa, Georgia, USA
He marked it "married" and signed his name.

In August 1917, Reuben's name was listed in the Sanford newspaper schedule for medical inspections. He was not recommended for early selection because of his poor eyesight. Since the declaration of war on April 6, 1917, Sanford had been experiencing hard times as the people there joined the United States armed forces in support of the war effort. Over 42,000 Floridians were called into the armed services and the civilians worked to support their cause. Sanford contributed to the wartime effort with the food it produced while at home food and other commodities were scarce and expensive. It grew increasingly difficult to keep up with the work on the Benson Farm. Then, because of the continuous need for soldiers, Reuben was called again for an examination. He was not drafted immediately, but the call did come. Reuben was working out in the field when Mr. Benson brought him the word. He was to report and be transported to Camp Green, Charlotte, North Carolina, on August 31, 1918.

Daybreak the next day brought rain, which was unusual for summer days when showers usually came in late afternoon. Reuben opened his eyes and lay there listening to the rain against the window pane. He held Tasha in his arms and gently ran his hand over her wonderful, responsive body. Last night had been a symphony of love making. They lay holding each other. Tasha whispered softly, "Reuben, don't ever forget me. I'll be here and I will love you forever."

Reuben kissed her on the forehead and said, "I love you, too."

The train was due to leave at 3:00 p.m. Reuben told Tasha that there was no need for her to go to the station, but she insisted. Tasha busied herself with getting ready. She wanted to look perfect for him. She wanted him to remember her always. After trying on every outfit she had, she decided on a slim gray walking skirt and a lace-trimmed white blouse. Around her neck she wore a string of pearls and attached to the pearls was a beautiful cameo that had belonged to her mother.

When Tasha turned sixteen, her father had given her the cameo and told her the story of a cultivated gentleman who had traveled from Europe. He had given Tasha's mother the cameo telling her it represented an ancient art form in which decorative seals were carved into gemstones. Many of these pieces could be seen in European museums. This particular cameo was made of inset chalk-like white powder in a figure that represented the Greek god Aries. Because of her father's memories of this gentleman, Tasha wondered if this man from Europe was her real father. She knew the cameo represented a true love shared between her mother and this stranger, and somehow it felt right for her to wear it today.

When it was time to leave the house, Tasha put on a tiny hat and a linen morning coat to shield her from the rain. Reuben had packed only a few things. He wore his suit, a white shirt, a tie, and his hat. When men were first drafted for the war in 1917, they left in groups. Reuben, however, would be traveling by himself to Camp Green.

Mr. Benson drove them to the train station. When they arrived he got out of the car and shook Reuben's hand. "Well, Reuben," he said, "I sure hate to see you leave. You have been a good worker. The best damn manager I ever had. Don't know how I'll be able to keep the farm running. May have to sell out. First the flu epidemic, now that damn war has taken all my help. Well, good luck to you."

Reuben said, "Thank you, sir."

Mr. Benson didn't wait for more of a reply. He turned to Tasha and told her he would pick her up when he got finished with his chores in town. Reuben and Tasha walked into the train station. After Reuben checked in at the ticket counter, they went back outside and stood beside a clock that signaled the departure time. They didn't talk much. Reuben paced, jingling the change in his pockets and stopping to pull out his pocket watch to check the time in his characteristic manner.

When the clock signaled that Reuben's train had arrived, Tasha reached for Reuben. He embraced her lovingly, and they stood silently looking at each other. Then he left his wonderful, exotic Tasha, boarded the train and found his seat. As the train pulled away from the station, he could still see her standing there. That beautiful face, her hair flowing beneath the tiny hat. She was still waving her hand. He answered with a wave of his hat.

In a matter of minutes the train turned to cross the St. John's River.

Three years had passed since he first crossed this river going south into Florida. Today he was going north, and, once again, he was crossing in the rain.

Reuben sat on the train and stared out the window, his thoughts of the past three years. He had not revealed his past to anyone in Sanford. Even though he and Tasha had developed a deep relationship, he never told her about his wife and child in Tallapoosa. He never told her about his mistress, Mary, and his baby by her. These secrets he kept to himself. Before he left Sanford, he had closed out his post office box. He wrote his last letter to Felix and his mother and told them to sell the property on Head Street in Tallapoosa. He gave his permission to his mother to sign the deed turning the property over to Mary. He felt this was the right thing to do for Mary and the baby. He had continued to send money to Felix for Mary. He had not written to Mary, nor had he written to his wife or her family.

Reuben had made good money working on the Benson Farm, and he opened a bank account at the People's Bank in Sanford. He even had a Christmas Club account for savings. When he left Sanford, he was going to war so he had no need of the money in this account. He left it there to be used later. If it had not been for the war, perhaps Reuben would have stayed in Sanford, but he had been drafted by the army and called to serve his country. Reuben had deep seated feelings about his country, and he had no regrets about entering the war effort.

As the train rolled through the countryside, Reuben felt confident about the new course his life was taking. His immediate destination was Camp Green, North Carolina. He only hoped this train did not stop in Georgia.

* * *

For a long time, Tasha stood on the platform of the train station. She didn't cry. There was only mist on her face from the rain. Reuben had been a stranger when he came to her and he was a stranger when they parted. Mr. Benson pulled the car up close to the platform and yelled, "Let's go home," to Tasha. Once they were home and after her father had left the house, Tasha buried her face in the pile of pillows on the living room sofa and cried. Her life for the past three years had revolved around Reuben, and now she felt lost without him. A month went by without a word from Reuben. Tasha's father told her to forget him, that he would never be back.

When the days of autumn set in, it became evident that Tasha was pregnant. If her father noticed, he didn't say anything. He treated her like a hired maid. His only comment to her was, "Guess you will be needing some help around here in a few months." Tasha spent her days taking care of the house and her father the best she could. In spite of the heartache, she was happy about the child inside of her. In the evenings when it grew too dark to read, she would sit and gaze into the sky. She had loved once. She thought, suppose you only saw the stars once in you lifetime, just think of the wonder of it. In her heart she knew she would never see Reuben again.

The days of January became crisp. It was time for the baby to be born. Mr. Benson sent for a midwife and he left the house. Tasha was put to bed and the hours of agony began. It was two days later when the midwife raised the shade to the window and the sun came peeking through. She held a precious little boy in her arms. Tasha was weak and could not raise her head from her pillow. The midwife laid the child by his mother's side and left the room to give the news to Mr. Benson. He was nowhere to be found.

The midwife did all she could, but she could not stop Tasha's bleeding. She asked Tasha what she should tell her father. Tasha touched her baby and said in a whisper, "I have no message to give." At the end of her life, she left just her spirit and what she had created. Mr. Benson buried his daughter beside his wife. He refused to even look at his grandson. He had blamed his daughter for the loss of his wife, and now he blamed his grandson for the loss of his daughter. He told the midwife to just give the child away. One of the migrant workers who lived on the farm heard about the baby. He and his wife had known Tasha and Reuben, and they knew that Reuben was the baby's father. They had always liked Reuben. He was good to their family when he worked as the manager of the farm.

They decided to take the baby and raise him until his father came back for him. The little boy was healthy and everyone called him "Lucky" because the family that took him in was so loving and caring. It did not matter to this family that Mr. Benson never acknowledged his grandson. Lucky grew up playing and working in the celery fields. He was told the story of his mother, Tasha, and of his father, Reuben.

Review and update:

- Tasha — Died giving birth to Reuben's son
- Lucky — Grew up never knowing his father
- Mr. Benson — Never acknowledged his grandson.
  He sold the Benson Celery Farm.
- Celery — The commercial growth of celery has moved to the muck soil of the Everglades.
- Doc Lundstorm — The Lundstorm house built in 1917 still stands in Sanford and relatives of the "Doc" live in it.
- Sanford, Florida — Remains an old-established community in Seminole County
- Orlando, Florida — No longer "just a wide place in the road"
- Old Bald Cypress Tree — Still stands on the banks of the St. Johns River
- Reuben never returned to live in Sanford, Florida. The old cypress tree kept the secrets as Reuben burdened himself with more.

World War I began in 1914 as a conflict between Germany, Austria-Hungary, and Turkey (called the Central Powers) and Britain, France, and Russia (called the Allies). The Americans aided the British and French by shipping large amounts of American goods for the war effort. When the German submarines (U-boats) began to sink American merchant ships, the United States joined the war.

On April 6, 1917, the United States declared war on Germany. By 1918 there were more than a million U. S. troops in Europe. Woodrow Wilson was the president of the United States at that time. When the war started there were just over 125,000 men in the U. S. Army. President Wilson called for the draft, and on June 27, 1918, the Secretary of War, Newton Barker, drew the first draft number.

Reuben had registered with the service when the war began in 1917 He was ordered to report to Camp Green, North Carolina on August 31, 1918. When Reuben arrived at Camp Green, he was bewildered by the disarray. He had no idea of what to do and no one seemed to notice him. Since he had arrived alone, it seemed as though he would just fall through the cracks. After his third day there, an officer noticed this odd looking little man still dressed in his suit and hat, wandering around the camp. He approached Reuben and said, "What's the matter fellow? If you're here to join this outfit, take yourself down to the uniform tent and get suited up.

Tell the sergeant that Lt. Long sent you. Make sure he gives you a good set of leggings. Report to me at the 81st Division." He did not add "That is an order," but Reuben took it as such. At least now he had a direction.

At the uniform tent, the sergeant instructed Reuben about how to wear the uniform. On this day Reuben became a "doughboy." This was the nickname given to US infantry men in World War I. Some historians say that the round brass buttons on the infantry uniforms reminded the men of balls of dough. Others suggest that the name came from the dough-like clay that infantry men used to clean their white belts. In times of war, things are often not done according to usual military procedure. The 81st Division's primary purpose was to get the unit ready to enter the fighting in Europe as soon as possible.

The basic training was crude, and half the time Reuben didn't know what he was doing. He just followed orders and learned that when an officer told you to jump, you didn't ask "why" but "how high?"

After only a few weeks of training, the 81st Division boarded a troop train for Hoboken, New Jersey. In just a short period of time, the leadership of this division had instilled in the men a sense of pride and commitment. All of the men, including Reuben, were focused on the task at hand and they felt bound together to serve their country.

In 1918, when American soldiers were leaving Hoboken in great numbers, it was noted that the members of the 81st Division wore a cloth patch on their left shoulder featuring a silhouette of a wildcat. Much comment arose about the right of any unit to so distinguish itself above all others. The 81st left for France and upon arrival this distinguishing insignia (unauthorized at that time) again caused comment and even orders for their removal. The matter came to the attention of General Headquarters which, upon investigation, decided that the morale and temper of this division were worthy of emulation.

In a short time each division, and finally each unit, in the American Expeditionary Force was ordered to devise its own shoulder sleeve insignia. Thus was born the present system of unit identity. The sea crossing from Hoboken to France was a traumatic experience for Reuben. He had always been afraid of the water, and on the sea he felt like he was in a washtub with water all around him. Needless to say, he was a happy man once his feet were on dry land again, even if it was on foreign soil.

The ship landed at Dieppe, France. The 81st Division formed its regiment and began its march. As it passed people along the side of the road, Reuben heard an Englishman yell out, "Glad you came, Yank, but the war is over!" For the rest of his life, Reuben never forgot these words, because for him the war had just begun.

In fact, the word sent to the United States in the spring of 1918 was that the British troops were in decline. The United States' decision to commit troops to the war effort resulted in a resurgence in hope that the war would end soon. The 81st Division was now on its way to the front lines in the area of the Argonne Forest and they would come under the command of General John J. Pershing. General Pershing insisted on keeping the American Army distinct from the other troops. When Pershing arrived in Europe to command the American Expeditionary Forces, General Headquarters wanted to disperse the American troops among the other allied forces. Pershing insisted that the Americans would fight better by themselves. He said, "The Americans are an earnest, serious people and their pride of race is strong. The term `keen as mustard' can be given to the private soldier for they are true crusaders, they came to do or die."

The American Army remained intact as the strategy for the deployment of the troops was formed for the battle of the Meuse-Argonne. This battle began on September 26, 1918 and was expected to result in a swift victory for the Allies, but it dragged on for over six weeks. The Argonne Forest presented a daunting tactical problem for the army.

Located in northeastern France, the main forest lies between the River Aisne in the west and the River Aire in the east. It is steeply sloped with thick woods and dense undergrowth. The attack went in on a forty-mile front equally divided between the American First Army under Pershing and General Henri Gouraud's French Fourth Army. The American attack would have to be made down a double defile since the 1,200-foot Montfaucon lay in front of them. Here the heights formed the watershed between the two rivers and commanded the valleys.

But it was more than ground that the Americans would have to overcome. The Germans had fortified strong points, dugouts, successive lines of trenches, and an unlimited number of concrete machine gun bunkers. They had the advantage of commanding ground and could pour artillery fire on any assailant advancing within range between the Meuse and the Argonne. It was no wonder that the enemy had rested here for four years without being touched. Victory for the Allies here would be a miracle.

The battle was extremely complex and all of the maneuvers were skillfully prepared. Many Americans fell beneath the scythe of the German machine guns as they fought in the heavily wooded area of the Argonne Forest. The Americans surprised the Germans in their all-out offensive, and the American army troops valiantly executed the decisions made by their leadership. The troops were strong and fit, disciplined, and skilled in the use of their arms. They performed precisely and heeled progressively forward. Gallant sacrifices were made by the fighting troops and, at one point, General Pershing had to pause to regroup and fortify.

On November first there was a call of "everyone to the battle." It was an American nation functioning like a machine with a drive that pushed the German army back to the armistice line. In the wake of this offensive through the Argonne Forest marched the troops of the 81st Division. It is true that the German forces were in retreat on all fronts and the armistice was to be signed, but word had not reached this area.

It was hard to be brave when one's regiment was in a battle zone being bombarded with guns and gas shells, but Reuben did the best he could. The air shook with the sounds of war, and troops hovered in their trenches. The advancement was slow and resistance was sporadic. Reuben was on his belly inching his way through the coiled snakes of barbed wire when he felt a sharp blow to his right side, then on his left side. He rolled his body to face the enemy. Through the mist he saw eyes blazing with anger, and as the German flipped his bayonet Reuben could see the blade of steel coming toward his chest. He clenched his eyes shut and threw up his arm to ward off the blow, but the blow never came.

An American soldier, the only American Indian in his regiment, had quietly, but forcefully stabbed the German in the back. Reuben opened his eyes and saw the dead body lying beside him. All the quiet soldier said was, "Lie still, I'll send a medic to you," and he was off to continue the fight.

The pain burned through Reuben's chest and movement seemed impossible. He lay in the mud until a medic came and bound his chest with tape and told him he would be picked up or if he could manage, to crawl toward the rear as far as he could. Somehow Reuben summoned his strength and determination and raised himself on his gun. He felt the earth spin around him, and, fortunately, two medics saw him and caught him before he fell. They put him on a stretcher and carried him to the truck to be transported to the rear medical tent.

When the truck got to the medical tent, there was no more room for the wounded inside. They laid the stretchers on the ground and attended to the most severe cases first. Reuben was not bleeding or screaming, so he was passed over. Finally a doctor checked him and told him he was a lucky fellow. The German had hit him with the butt of his gun and cracked his ribs on both sides, but he would mend. His chest was wrapped and taped and he was given crutches to walk with. He was told to go to the holding area and the first non-emergency outgoing truck would pick him up.

Reuben saw before him the horror of war: wounded and dying soldiers. He heard the screams of a man and saw the medic place a leather strip between the man's teeth. As the morphine began to soothe the pain, the doctor cut the man's right leg off below the knee. Still conscious, the soldier yelled, "Show me that leg!" The medic placed the amputated leg beside him and everyone paused to hear him say, "Oh, leg, thanks for being a good one. Sorry to see you go, but you are no good to me any more."

Reuben grew tired of waiting for a truck to carry him out of the war zone. His whole body ached when he walked, and the damn crutches were hard to maneuver in the mud. It seemed like it rained everyday here in this godforsaken place. Finally he was told that a troop from the 42nd Division was moving out and he could go with them. A few feet in front of the truck a board lay over a "mucky" area to cross over. Just as Reuben stepped on the board to make his way across, he encountered a French officer at the opposite end. The officer said, "Step aside soldier, an officer wishes to cross here."

In the stress of the moment, Reuben became enraged. He pulled the handgun from his side belt and replied to the officer, "If you put one foot on this board, I will shoot you."

The French officer stepped back as Reuben crossed the plank and proceeded to get aboard the outgoing truck. No military mention was ever made of the incident. After this Reuben was included with the 42nd Division. He never rejoined the 81st Division, and he never saw the American Indian soldier again. He would always remember him and wonder if he survived the war. One thing he knew-this brave soldier had saved his life, making it possible for Reuben to survive the war, return home to America, and live 71 more years.

On November 11, 1918, the armistice was signed ending a war of seemingly endless destruction. Germany was left in confusion. The forces mutinied and the German kaiser and crown prince fled to Holland. Germany had plenty of war materiel, but no food, and families were starving. The countryside showed devastating results from the war. The Allies had to wage total effective war in order to bring it to a quick and decisive conclusion. Halfway measures would not do and that was proven in the battle of the Argonne Forest.

Statistics show that 9,998,771 soldiers died in World War I and of those 107,284 were Americans. The real cost cannot be measured by direct money outlays. The effect on life, human vitality and the breakdown of modern economic society is the total cost.

The United States had in the beginning given economic aid to the Allies to ease the strain. Then they sent troops to turn the numerical balance. Above all the American soldier gave a moral tonic by coming to battle. Without this, victory would have been impossible.

In the end when the sun set on the battlefield and a sickle moon shone faintly over the tortured earth, America was deeply proud of its fighting men. They had done a job well and in a way we most admired. It was a magnificent victory, and the entire world rejoiced.

For Reuben, the armistice meant "this doughboy was going home," but it would be a long process. Reuben went with the 42nd Division to Brest, a seaport in western France, where he would wait for transportation home. Most of his time he spent wondering around the camp which had been set up for the troops. He was not ordered to pull any duty because of his injuries, and his body was healing well.

One afternoon a fellow soldier walked up to him, unwrapping a piece of pressed tobacco. Reuben said to him, "Hey, fellow, where did you get the tobacco?"

"Over at the Red Cross tent," the soldier replied. "You better hurry over there if you want some. They run out mighty fast."

Reuben hadn't had a chew of tobacco since he left the celery fields of Sanford, Florida. He had picked up the habit of chewing tobacco from his father, and during his work in the hot celery fields, the tobacco had kept his mouth moist.

When the aide in the Red Cross tent handed Reuben the three-inch-square piece of pressed tobacco, he felt like a kid that had just been given candy or an apple. In fact, on the tobacco wrapper was a picture of an apple. This was the manufacturer's logo. From that day on Reuben would purchase only the "Apple" chewing tobacco.

Reuben didn't have time to unwrap the tobacco when he walked out of the Red Cross tent. He was given an order to stand at attention. He dropped the tobacco in his pocket and brought his stout little body to the attention stance. Only a few feet in front of him stood several officers and with them was the legendary General John J. Pershing. This general had led two million troops in defeating the Germans, and Reuben was in awe of him. What an honor just to be in his presence. Reuben stood erect and looked straight ahead. There was a photographer there and he was taking photos.

After the general addressed the troops with a few words, he got into a jeep and rode through the camp. So caught up in the moment, Reuben was like a statue until an officer barked at him, "Dismissed soldier."

The photographer was from the *New York Times* and the photograph he took that day became one of the historical photos of World War I. Sixteen years later, Reuben would see this famous picture and would recognize not only General Pershing, but himself. He was so proud.

Both the American Army and the people back home made it manifestly clear that it was time to "Bring the boys back home" as swiftly as they had been sent over there.

French and British shipping was plentifully available for the American troops when defeat stared the Allies in the face, but once the shooting stopped, it became remarkably slow. Nevertheless, repatriation was achieved and beginning in December 1918 over 2,000,000 men had been returned to America.

However it was not until August 1, 1919 that Reuben would board his ship for passage home. All troops were deloused, that is run through a shower of disinfectant, and given a complete clean set of clothing immediately before getting on the ship. That was perfectly okay with Reuben. It felt good to get rid of the camp stench and he would do anything just to get home.

The troops were joyous during the sea crossing home and upon their arrival in New York, they were jubilant with their heroes' reception. The system of demobilization adopted was that of disbanding whole units. Soldiers were transported to a processing center nearest their home and for

Reuben this was Atlanta, Georgia.

CHAPTER SIX

*A*s he boarded the troop train to Atlanta, fear struck his heart. The war had been a frightful experience, but it had also been an escape from his past. Now he was taken back to the very place he had run from. There was no choice but to get off this train in Atlanta.

Reuben followed orders to report in at the processing center. The clerk asked him what job he had when he left for the war. Reuben replied, "'I worked as a manager on a celery farm in Sanford, Florida."

"Will that job be waiting for you when you get back?"

Reuben immediately said, "I don't know." Then he paused a moment. Since he left Sanford to enter the war he had not heard a word from anyone there. How could he be sure Mr. Benson would want him back? There had been no contact with anyone from his home town of Tallapoosa either. All he could think to say was, "No, no sir, I don't have a job."

The government gave the returning war soldiers top priority as railroad workers and anthracite miners. The clerk explained this to Reuben and handed him a document. He told Reuben he should go to Birmingham, Alabama. There he would find both railway jobs and coal mines in need of workers. He said, "Take this document and give it to the people in charge of jobs there. Here is a train ticket from Atlanta to Birmingham and $60.00 cash. Go across the hall and they will issue you a suit of civilian clothes. Good luck, Mr. Kincaide. Next!"

If Reuben had any second thoughts about these instructions he didn't stop to question them. The next thing he knew, he was at the depot looking for a train out of Atlanta to Birmingham and it couldn't come fast enough for him.

He boarded the train at 8:00 p.m. and took his seat. He had cleaned up and changed out of his "doughboy" uniform before he left the war processing center. In civilian clothing he would not be so conspicuous.

When the conductor passed through the car checking tickets, Reuben asked him if the train would stop in Tallapoosa. "No, not usually, any reason you ask?" The conductor was very polite.

Reuben showed him the document containing his military transfer and said "Yes, I'm going to Birmingham for a job, but you see Tallapoosa is my home and I think I would like to see my mother. I haven't seen her in four years."

The conductor said, "I will make arrangements for a stop and when you wish to get back on the train for Birmingham just give them this ticket." He handed Reuben the document and his ticket back.

Guess the decision has been made, Reuben said to himself. I'll get off this train in Tallapoosa.

The train came to a stop at the Tallapoosa depot. Reuben made his way through the car and stepped out onto the platform. The conductor waved from the train and yelled, "Welcome home, son!" It was 10:00 p.m. and only a few men stood on the platform, and Reuben saw only one man inside the depot at the desk, no one he recognized.

After the train pulled away, Reuben walked along the railroad tracks westward about a mile. There he found a familiar dirt road that would lead him down to the farm. Although it was night, the light of the moon provided him with sight of scenes he recognized. He didn't stop to think about how he was feeling at this time; if anything, his pace was quick as he walked past the barn up the road to the house.

All the lights were out in the house and the old dog lying on the front porch hardly moved when Reuben stepped up to the door. "Fine watch dog you are, Shep, or do you remember me?" Reuben reached to pat the dog and Shep responded with a yawn.

The knock on the door brought a man's voice in response, "Who the hell is it? Coming around here this time of night, better be a damned good excuse, I just got to sleep!" Felix opened the door and gazed with amazement, "What the hell? Reuben, is that you?"

"Damn Felix, don't be so happy to see me," Reuben said as he walked into the hallway.

Then they embraced each other and Felix ruffled Reuben's hair. "Where is your hat?" Felix questioned.

"Army don't issue any hats," was Reuben's response.

Felix led Reuben toward the kitchen. "Well, come on in, boy. What's goin' on? Where you been? I haven't heard a word since you wrote you were leaving Sanford over a year ago. Did you go to war?" Felix was just full of questions.

Reuben sat down on a chair at the kitchen table. He rubbed his forehead and said, "It's a long story, brother, how about you give me a bed and we talk all this out tomorrow?"

Felix patted him on the back and said, "Sure, sure, no need getting everyone up around here. Past midnight already. Little room in the back has a bed, suppose it will do for tonight. You go on back there and get some rest. We'll talk tomorrow."

Reuben started down the hall. "Thanks, Felix," he said quietly. "Glad you're home, Reuben," was Felix's reply.

Reuben was exhausted. He crawled into bed and laid his head on the pillow. He leaned up to take off his glasses and place them on a small table nearby. I didn't ask if Mother is here, he said to himself. He lay back on the bed and immediately fell asleep.

Daybreak came and a rooster in the chicken yard began to crow. Reuben sprang up as though he had heard a bomb go off. It took him a few minutes before he realized where he was. Inside he had ambivalent feelings. He had come home, but to find what? He got dressed and walked out of the bedroom. He reckoned he would soon find out.

As he approached the kitchen, he saw his mother standing by the stove. Her back was to him and for a moment he just stood there. Then his mother said, "Felix, you need to get some more coffee, we're just about out."

Reuben answered, " It's not Felix, Mother."

Mary Ann faced her son. She gripped the sides of her apron with both hands, "Oh my God, my God," she repeated. Reuben stepped forward and gathered her in his arms. He was trembling; tears were flowing down his mother's face. They held each other for a long while, then Mary Ann pulled back and looked at him. "My son, you've come home." She kissed him on the cheek.

"Don't cry, Mother," Reuben said to comfort her.

86

"It's only tears of joy," she said as she wiped her eyes with her apron.

"What's all this mushy stuff going on in here?" Felix said as he walked into the kitchen. "You don't see me all broke up, do you?"

"No, but I scared you to death when you opened the door last night," Reuben laughed.

Felix ruffled his hair. "Did not," he said.

"Now you two cut that out. Sit down there and I'll get your breakfast. Can't believe you let him in and he was here all night without my knowing." Mary Ann sounded a little put out.

Felix assured her, "Now, Aunt Mary, we just didn't want to git you up. It was way past midnight when this city slicker showed up."

Reaching into his shirt pocket, Felix took out a yellow piece of paper. Handing it to Reuben he said, "By the way, before I forget, I want to give you this. It came to the telegraph office in town and old man Clark gave it to me because he didn't know how to reach you. Sometime back in the spring. I kept it thinking you might show up one of these days."

Reuben took the paper and unfolded it. He read the words printed on the telegram:

"BENSON FARM SOLD. TASHA BENSON DEAD. CONTACT Y.R. GREEN.
SANFORD, FLORIDA"

To Felix and his mother's bewilderment, Reuben turned and walked out of the back door, across the back yard and into a thicket of trees. He kept going till he reached a little brook running through the back side of the farmland. Deciding not to jump across the stream of water, Reuben stopped just short of getting his feet wet. He stood staring at the water rippling over glossy stones. His heart pounded in his chest. He was clenching the yellow piece of paper in his fist. The words raced through his head — TASHA DEAD...TASHA DEAD ...

Dropping to his knees on the wet mossy grass, his hands opened and covered his face. The telegram dropped into the water and slowly drifted out of sight.

For a moment Reuben escaped from this world. He could hear Tasha's laugh, touch her teasing body, and feel her love. He remembered everything about her. His soul ached for her comforting arms.

This was the beginning of a pain he would feel over and over during his lifetime.

Without knowing about Tasha, he had made the decision in Atlanta not to return to Sanford, Florida. He knew now that he had made the right decision because he could not face a life there without her. He guessed that the flu epidemic must have taken her life. He could call that Mr. Green at the telegraph office in Sanford and find out. He would need to thank him anyway for sending the message.

Reuben washed his glasses off in the stream and dried them with a handkerchief from his pocket. He pulled his pocket watch from his pants pocket and saw that it was 7:00 a.m. He put it to his ear to make sure it was still running. It was a miracle that the watch made it with him through the war, but it was ticking loud and clear.

Reuben could see the brightness of the morning sun and as he turned from the meandering little brook to walk into the woods and back to the house, he could hear the morning birds singing their melody.

Felix became impatient waiting for Reuben to come back to the house. Mary Ann told him to sit still and have another cup of coffee; she was sure he would be back any minute. Felix couldn't wait. He said, "Now don't start making excuses for that boy, he is probably sitting in the outhouse reading the paper. When he gits back tell him to come on down to the barn. I can use a plow-boy today." Felix laughed at that thought.

Reuben was walking across the backyard when he saw Felix on his way to the barn. The dog, Old Shep, ran out to greet Reuben and walked with him down to the barn. Reuben said to Felix, "I see you still got old Shep."

"Yep, good for nothing but eatin' scraps." Felix busied himself with his morning chores. He looked up at Reuben and saw that the knees of his pants were wet and dirty. "What happened to you, did you fall down or you been prayin'?"

Reuben ignored the remark and took a stand next to the barn door.

"Well, I can see you're in no mood for working so let's get our talkin' done." Felix laid his pitchfork down and walked over and sat on a feed sack. Reuben remained standing in the door way. Felix broke the moment of silence. "The fellow with the telegram wasn't the only one looking for you. The sheriff came 'round here. Seems as though that pretty little wife of yours is getting a divorce. The sheriff mentioned a desertion charge against you. Says if they don't find you that is what she will get the divorce on. Now, I've never seen Victoria since her parents sent her to Atlanta right after you left. Some say she lives high in Atlanta with a job and all. I know she left your little girl for the Sherwoods to raise here in Tallapoosa.

"Don't mean to come down on you hard, Reuben, but it ain't right what you and Victoria done to that little girl. Even if it is her grandparents got her, still ain't right she don't have a daddy and only a part-time mother."

Reuben just lowered his head as his eyes filled with tears. Felix just didn't understand. Hell, he didn't understand.

Getting no response from Reuben, Felix continued to talk. "Now another thing. Don't git me wrong, I don't mind your mother staying here on the farm. God knows she does her share of helping out. She does all the cooking. That lazy wife of mine sleeps half the day and my youngins ain't no good. Anyway, I was glad to take Aunt Mary in when she left the Sherwoods. She came here with nothing but a little bag of clothes. She left everything she owns with them Sherwoods and in that house on Head Street that you gave away to that Mary girl.

"I used to go by to see Mary and the baby, but since your money quit coming last August, she don't want me around anymore. That little girl baby of yours is a cute little thing. Got golden hair just like her mother. Don't know how you do it, boy, but you pick some lookers. Mary is pretty as a peach and she still loves you. She thinks you will come to her and that baby. She says why else would you have them living in your place on Head Street... You goin' back over there, Reuben?"

Felix waited for an answer but Reuben just took out his tobacco plug from his pocket and bit off a chew. He made no remark.

Felix had not finished his say, so he continued. "That boy, Jessie, brags he will kill you if he ever sees you again after your taking money from his Pa's store and leaving that wife of yours in such a state. Somehow he found a letter between you and Mary and he gave it to the Sherwoods. He knows all about Mary and your baby. He told me himself that Sherwood's got the letter, but no one will dare tell Victoria the truth or they will answer to him. You would think he's in love with your wife. He spends a lot of time with the Sherwoods and with your daughter. What's her name, Vanessa?"

Again Reuben made no sound. "Oh, yeah." Felix remembered one more thing that he wanted to tell Reuben. "About a year ago, some men came here looking for you. Didn't say what it was all about. They looked like some kinda mob gangsters you see in them newspapers from Atlanta.

You're not in any trouble, are you?"

Felix was patiently waiting for Reuben to say something. But, this one-sided conversation was getting the best of him. He jumped to his feet and jerked Reuben by the shoulders, "Damn it, boy, what's the matter with you? Your life is a godawful mess and here I am trying to make some sense of it so I can help you, but I need some answers!"

Reuben grabbed Felix's hands and said, "Let go of me!" He was irritated that Felix had turned hostile and he was not used to explaining his actions to anyone.

Both men stood and stared angrily at each other. Then Felix reached over and gently placed his hand on Reuben's shoulder. "Look, Reuben, you can walk away, you don't owe me a thing."

"No, you're wrong there," Reuben said as he sat on the feed sack Felix had jumped up from moments ago. "I know you're the one person in this world who could possibly understand. You always did look out for me. From the early years when we were barefoot in overalls playing around the front porch and my brother, Frank, teased me all the time. I could never turn to Frank, he let liquor take over his life, but you have always been there for me. So if you've got the time, Felix, I will try to explain."

Felix leaned against a nearby tree. He picked up a straw and stuck it in his mouth to chew on, folded his arms in front of him and he was ready to listen.

Reuben began by going over the reasons he'd left Tallapoosa to begin with. The pressure put on him by a high-society wife. Trying to give her and their child everything. His affair with a sweet girl he loved and knowing she had his baby. The death of his Uncle Grier, which meant the loss of his job at the feed store, and he hated working for Jessie's Pa in that damn dry goods place. All the suspicions about him being at the hanging of Leo Frank in Atlanta, and he didn't want to hurt Felix's feelings, but no way was he ever going to live out here on this farm.

Reuben told Felix about his life in Sanford-what it was like working on the celery farm, and he explained in detail his relationship with Tasha and how he had left her in Sanford, Florida.

After a hug from this man he called his brother, Reuben proceeded to tell him all about the war and the hell of it.

Finally he said, "So, here I am."

Nothing more was said. They walked from the barn arm in arm to the house. When they reached the porch, Felix said, "Spend some time with your mother. I need to git to the plowing. Oh, by the way, Reuben, whatever you do, I will understand."

Reuben stared at his back as he walked away. What would he ever do without Felix?

When Reuben walked in the kitchen, he found his mother putting a pot of greens on the stove for supper. "I see you still start your supper early in the day," Reuben said.

Mary Ann turned and displayed a loving smile as she said, "I'm fixin' your favorites tonight. Still some biscuits here on the stove. You sit down there. I'll get some honey for you. You always did like biscuits and honey. Mighty late to be eatin' breakfast, but you need to eat. You're too skinny. I know you just don't eat enough."

Reuben sat down at the kitchen table. "Okay," he said. "I'll eat the biscuits and honey if you will sit here and talk to me."

Mary Ann stirred her pot of greens, wiped her hands on her apron, then sat down across from her son. "Reuben, I did the best I could with Victoria and the baby, but I was never wanted in the Sherwood house. I had to leave and come out here to the farm. I hated to leave my little grandbaby. I left her the wooden chest you made for me and some of our things in it. I don't go around to the Sherwoods now at all. I heard they told baby Vanessa that her daddy had died. Doc Sherwood put out the word that you died somewhere in Alabama during the 1917 flu epidemic. I knowed that was a lie. So did he. He got that sheriff to bring around a paper to find you cause that girl wants a divorce. They wouldn't be looking for you if they knowed you were dead.

"I'm glad we gave the old house to Mary and her baby. Mary's family sees after them. I don't go around them either. Just best I stay away. I just never go into town... Your brother, Frank, comes over to see me here on the farm. He's doing good. He has settled down some and built himself a log house down there on his place."

Reuben finished his biscuit and pushed back away from the table. "I've caused you a lot of trouble, Mother. I don't know what to do about it. I try to think over my life so as to straighten it out, but I just don't know how."

He got up from the chair, walked to the opened back door, and stood jingling the coins in his pocket. Mary Ann smiled as his gesture brought back memories of Reuben's father. She said, "Son have you been to Papa's

91

grave? I often go there when I'm lonely and afraid."

Reuben did not answer his mother; he just walked out the back door, across the yard and onto a little path that led up to the cemetery.

That evening Reuben joined Felix, his family, and his mother at the table for supper. His mother had prepared things she knew her son liked to eat: turnip greens cooked with some turnips and with a piece of fat back meat; sweet potatoes, baked whole; homemade butter and hot biscuits and black coffee. She had made a cake of cornbread even though she knew Reuben would not eat it. She enjoyed crumbling the cornbread in her coffee and eating it that way.

After supper the family sat around on the front porch and laughed and talked. Everyone sat quietly as Reuben would tell about the war, his life being saved by an Indian man, and the huge ocean waves.

When everyone had gone into the house and gone to bed, Reuben paced the yard. He had returned to Tallapoosa after being gone for four years. When he went to Sanford, Florida, four years ago, he had intended to change his life, start anew, but here he was back home. He knew now that his wife was divorcing him and they had told his little girl that he was dead.

He would be free to go to Mary and know his baby, but how could he do this with them living in the house on Head Street so close to the Sherwood home where his little girl, Vanessa, was? I can't get them and take them away. I have no place to take them. I don't even have a job yet, he thought to himself.

Reuben paced the yard until he grew tired. He went into the little bedroom in the back of the house and went to bed. As he drifted off to sleep, his last thoughts were of a lost love and he whispered, "Tasha, oh Tasha."

* * *

Morning came with the rooster crowing. Felix knocked on Reuben's door and called out, "There is a train coming through at eight. Better get up if you want to catch it."

Reuben sat up on the side of the bed and shook his head. That Felix always could read his mind. He answered Felix. "Is Mother up yet?" There was no reply, but he could smell the brewing coffee and knew that answered his question.

When it was time for Reuben to leave the house, his mother put her arms around him and said, "You don't need to stay here. You will never be happy here on this farm. Should I walk down to the train with you?"

Reuben hugged her and said, "Not this time, Mother."

Felix shook Reuben's hand and offered to walk with him into town or take him in the wagon, but Reuben responded by saying, "I had rather go alone."

Leaving the farm, he walked down the road to the railroad tracks, then followed the tracks into town. As he was approaching the crossing located near the Bailey's Dry-Goods store, he noticed a man crossing the track going toward the dry goods store. When he got closer, he realized it was Jessie Bailey. He started to turn off the track when he heard Jessie yell, "Reuben, Reuben Kincaide, is that you? You bastard." As he walked toward Reuben he continued swearing.

Once they were face to face, Reuben said, "Jessie, I don't want any trouble. I'm just going to catch the train out of here."

Jessie shoved Reuben off the rail track cursing with every breath. "You low-life coward, you. Where the hell have you been? I'm going to make you pay for what you have done. I'll kill you for what you did to Victoria."

With each shove Jessie's anger increased and without leaving time for Reuben to say a word his anger became rage. He hit Reuben on the jaw. Reuben staggered backward, but didn't fall. He took a swing at Jessie and hit him in the stomach. Jessie folded in half. He was quite a bit taller than Reuben, so Reuben took advantage of this bent position and hit Jessie on the back of the head. This did not take him down. He grabbed Reuben by the knees and they tumbled into the kudzu down the banks of the railway tracks.

One break away and Jessie pulled a knife from his pocket. He waved the steel blade at Reuben and plunged forward. Reuben ducked and the knife went flying through the air and landed point up in the thick kudzu. Jessie bent forward to pick up the knife. Reuben kicked him in the back. Jessie fell forward and onto the blade of the knife. He rolled into a ball and moaned, pulling at the knife stuck in his stomach. Reuben scrambled up the banks of the tracks.

He looked all around and saw no one. He could see the train waiting at the depot so he ran till he reached it. Once inside, he brushed himself off and made his way through the station to the outside track.

93

Reuben boarded the 8:00 a.m. train leaving Tallapoosa. He showed the conductor his ticket and paper from the military, then took a window seat. As the train pulled away from the depot, the whistle blew several times. In town, on the north side of the railroad track, Reuben's little girl, Vanessa, was up, dressed and ready for her grandmother to take her to school.

In the house on Head Street, another little girl was still asleep.. Her golden curls were in ringlets around her little face and tossed softly on the pillow.

Neither knew that the sound of this train whistle meant that their daddy was leaving.

Once again, leaving Tallapoosa seemed the only thing Reuben could do. Damn that Jessie, he thought. Now Reuben knew he could never return home. "Lie or die, Jessie Bailey, makes no difference to me," Reuben muttered under his breath.

It was a cloudy day and when Reuben noticed the raindrops on the train window, he remembered another time he'd left, and this brought more memories, especially since he remembered he'd never contacted Mr. Green in Sanford, Florida, regarding his letter about Tasha's death. He was now leaving Tallapoosa, Georgia, once again, going to Birmingham, Alabama this time, and once again he was crossing in the rain.

CHAPTER SEVEN

$\mathcal{R}$euben always wanted to go to Birmingham, Alabama. It was only 60 miles from his home town, but when he left Tallapoosa in the past, he had always gone in the other direction, toward Atlanta. Today, a short stay in Birmingham would become one of the most important parts of his life.

Birmingham, named after an English city, is the largest city in the Southern state of Alabama. Here you will find huge reserves of the three most important raw materials used in steel-making: coal, limestone and iron ore.

The mines in Birmingham became productive in the late 1800s when the steel industry began. Birmingham also became a major railway center since the railroad was used for shipping the raw materials to factories in the North. Andrew Carnegie built the first large steel plant in Pennsylvania and in the early 1900s Henry Ford began the automobile assembly lines in Michigan.

During and after the first world war (1914-1917) thousands of men were needed to work in the mines and on the railroads. Many of the returning soldiers were sent to Birmingham for jobs. Reuben Oliver Kincaide was one of them.

Process stations had been set up in Birmingham where soldiers could go to find out about the available jobs and where they could work. At this center, Reuben was given a choice of either the railroad or coal mines. He knew the railroad job would be the better choice. He was given a location where he could report to work. Since he had no place to stay, he was also given the name of a boarding house where he could get a room.

Reuben wasted no time checking in at the boarding house. Once in his room he refused to think about his troubles. He felt like going out and getting drunk, but he was too tired to do that. A good night's sleep was what he needed most.

* * *

He reported for work at the railway office. The clerk behind the desk said to him, "You're one of the late ones. Only thing we got left is a flagman's job. Can't guarantee that but for six months. You can check with the mines after that."

Reuben had news for this fellow, he would never work in one of those bottomless pits. For right now he needed the job, so he told the clerk, "I'll take the flagman's job." The clerk gave him instructions and he went to work.

After working a week, Reuben received his first pay check. Come Saturday morning the first thing he wanted to do was to buy a suit of clothes, especially a hat. He walked the streets of Birmingham looking for a Stetson hat. Only one style would do, and that was the narrow-brim, low-crown, felt with a wide band around the crown. He saw a sign that read "Everyman's Hats," and he entered the store.

He was looking around when he heard a husky voice say, "Can I help you, sir?"

Without looking at the man, Reuben said, "I'll take a look at that brown one on the top shelf." He pointed to the hat.

Mr. Bogart got a step ladder and proceeded to retrieve the hat off the shelf. He had his back to Reuben, then he turned and handed the hat to him. Reuben's face grew pale and his hand trembled when he took the hat. He recognized this man! Mr. Bogart made no mention of the recognition and said, "Are you going to wear this, or do you want me to put it in a box?"

Reuben's mind raced. All he wanted to do was get out of there. He sat the hat on the counter and as he took his wallet from his back pocket he said, "I'll wear it. How much do I owe you?"

"That'll be six dollars and I thank you for your business, sir." Mr. Bogart was waiting by the cash register. Reuben handed him a ten dollar bill and Mr. Bogart gave him change. Reuben put his money away, then picked the hat up and started for the door.

"Say," Mr. Bogart questioned, aren't you going to try it on?"

Reuben hesitated for a minute, then, facing Mr. Bogart, he put the hat on.

"Wait a minute!" Bogart said as he rounded the counter. "Don't I know you? Can't recall your name, but I never forget a face."

"Think you are mistaken this time," Reuben replied.

"Now don't give me that." Bogart was inches away from Reuben. "Every so often I run into one of you boys and you all say the same thing. You know as well as I do you recognize me. Been a few years, but hell, no way you forget what went down in Atlanta. So, let your guard down boy, no one around here cares what happens in Georgia."

"Okay, Okay," Reuben said. "What are you doing in Birmingham? I thought you were a big shot in Atlanta."

Bogart stepped back and relaxed against a stack of boxes. "Were, is right," he said. "They kinda put the heat on some of us after the hanging, so most all of us left the state. I came over here, but some of the gang went to Indiana. What brings you here anyway? Didn't you live somewhere near Atlanta?"

The instant fear had left Reuben and he began to talk openly to Bogart. He told him about the job with the railroad and Bogart told him to look him up when the job was finished. Maybe he would have something for him, or if he was interested he might think about going to Indiana. After talking for some time, they parted friends, saying how good it was to see each other. "By the way," Bogart said as Reuben stepped out the door. "What is your name?"

"Reuben Kincaide," was the reply.

"Call me George, George Bogart and Reuben you come around anytime."

Reuben tipped his new hat and walked down the street.

* * *

Three months went by and the first of January meant that the year 1920 had arrived. This was the year that a new census of the population of the United States was to be taken. The census taker showed up at the boarding house in which Reuben was living. The landlady provided him with a list

97

of the roomers. She guessed at their ages, but she did know the occupations of each one. She listed Oliver Kincaide, male, white, age 25, roomer, worked on railroad.

Reuben put in long, hard days working in the railroad yard, but he didn't care. It kept his mind off other things. He had obtained a post office box and was sending Felix some money to give to Mary and the baby. He really regretted that he had not seen Mary when he was home, but somehow sending her money eased his conscience.

Felix had told him that the divorce papers the sheriff showed him stated the divorce would be final in January if it was not contested. Victoria Sherwood would be free of her husband, Reuben Oliver Kincaide. Reuben thought of his beautiful, wonderful, delicate Victoria. His heart ached. He would always love her.

He had loved two women, Victoria and Mary. They were different in every way. They had both satisfied a need in him. Now he must live without either of them. After his leaving them the first time, he had been blessed with another love. This had been a passionate, unrestrained love, but Tasha had been taken away from him also.

Reuben put aside matters of the heart and concentrated on working and making money. He had gone to a bank in Birmingham and checked on how to obtain the money he had left in the People's Bank in Sanford, Florida. The bank told him they would send the necessary papers for a transfer of funds to Florida, but it would take some time. Reuben agreed for them to make the transaction.

He showed up for work on the last day working as flagman for the railroad. They were sorry that they had to let him go, but they were trying to give all of the soldiers a few months' work. They suggested he go to work in the mines, or if he didn't want to do that, they would give him free passage on a train wherever he wanted to go. As of March first, Reuben had not received his money from the bank in Florida. His guess was he would never get this money unless he returned to Sanford and there was no reason for him to do that. He thought about what his friend Bogart had said about giving him a job, but he just didn't want to get mixed up with that group again.

Birmingham was a big, dirty city and Reuben still had that country feeling in him. He had not had a decent meal since he got there, six months before. The boarding house was a rathole and all-in-all this was not the place for Reuben. He said his goodbyes to Bogart, the landlady, and closed his post office box, but left his bank account open. With no unfinished business there in Birmingham, he walked to the train depot. He was going to take advantage of that free train ride.

After boarding the train and taking a seat, he removed his new hat and placed it on the vacant seat next to him. He folded his hands in his lap, his fingers interlocking, and twirled his thumbs around and backward, then forward. His little body was thin and he looked forlorn as he wondered, What am I going to do? Where am I going to go?

The train meandered its way through the city and picking up speed, it headed north. The conductor walked down the aisle of the car calling out, "Next stop Decatur. Next stop, Decatur, Alabama." It was the beginning of spring, 1920. In a couple of weeks, on April 11, Reuben Oliver Kincaide would be 32 years old.

He would live 69 more years!

CHAPTER EIGHT

*J*essie had lost consciousness and his body lay curled in thick kudzu. His hand still gripped the handle of the knife that was stuck in his stomach. The bank of the railroad track shielded Jessie's body as the train rambled past leaving Tallapoosa. The man who had fought with Jessie was on this train. He made no effort to look out the window in search of the spot where he had fled only minutes before.

Reuben noticed only the raindrops that peppered the window of the train. He was escaping more than just his fight with Jessie. He was leaving his tormented past. Just as the tangled kudzu vines covered the banks of the Georgia railway track, Reuben would forever hide the life that began here in this country town, a town nestled deep in the southland.

The sign on the train depot read Tallapoosa, Georgia. It was just past eight o'clock in the morning and a farmer was on his way into town to pick up some stock feed. He was guiding his horse and wagon along the dirt road that ran next to the bank of the railroad track. At first notice, he thought he saw a large sack of something partially hidden in the kudzu at the edge of the road. Then when he got closer, he realized it was a man's body. He pulled his horse to a halt, jumped down from the wagon, walked over and touched he man on the shoulder.

Jessie moaned and the farmer jerked back, startled. Jessie tried to straighten his body and the farmer yelled, "Holy, Jesus, you have been stabbed!" The farmer then went with his first instinct. He unfolded Jessie's fingers gripped around the handle of the knife, then he slowly pulled the knife blade from his stomach. Blood poured out, running down into Jessie's trousers. The farmer took his shirt off, folded it the best he could and wrapped it tightly around Jessie's abdomen and tied it, putting pressure on the wound.

"I've got to get you to a doctor," the farmer said as he put his hands under Jessie's arms and pulled him to the wagon.

He then hoisted the body like a sack of feed onto the wagon. Jessie had passed out again. Wasting no time, the farmer took Jessie straight to Doctor Sherwood's office. He reigned in the horse and leaped from the wagon shouting, "Doc, git out here quick!"

The doctor heard the racket outside and opened the door to his office. "What's going on out here?" he questioned.

The farmer was annoyed as he yelled at the doctor, "Lands sake, Doc, don't just stand there. This man has been stabbed. Bleeding something awful, but he is alive."

The doctor shifted into action. "Help me get him into my office." As they carried Jessie through the door, the doctor called out to his nurse, "Get in here, Rosemary. I'm going to need your help." They placed Jessie's limp body on the examining table and the doctor and nurse went to work.

All attention was focused on saving this man's life, therefore the doctor hadn't even noticed who this person was. The farmer had walked back outside to straighten up his horse and wagon. Once the doctor had secured the bandage, he realized who his patient was. "Jessie! Why it's Jessie Bailey! Keep an eye on him," he said to his nurse as he whirled around to get outside. He called out to the farmer, "Hey, what happened here? Who the hell are you and how did Jessie get stabbed?"

The farmer climbed up on the wagon and said to the doctor, "Don't know nothing, Doc. Found him alongside the road right down yonder." He pointed down the railroad track west of town. "The fellow going to be all right?"

"Yeah, he'll recover. You better stick around, I have to report this to the sheriff, you know. What did you say your name was?" the doctor questioned.

"I didn't," was the farmer's reply as he maneuvered his horse and wagon away from the doctor's office.

The doctor walked back into his office to check on Jessie. It was several hours before Jessie woke up as the doctor had given him a sedative.

He and the nurse had put him in a bed there in the examining room so they could watch him closely. Jessie opened his eyes and saw Doc Sherwood standing over him. "What the hell's goin' on?" he said as he tried to raise himself up off the bed.

"That's what I'd like to know," Doc Sherwood said, encouraging Jessie to lie back down. The doctor got close to Jessie's face and said in an irritated voice, "You, tell me, boy. What happened before I get the sheriff over here? I already sent for your daddy."

"Damn it, Doc, can't you see I've been stabbed? That bastard Reuben Kincaide attacked me with his knife. Don't need no damn sheriff. I will take care of this myself. Don't need my daddy either. Just tell everybody to keep the hell away from me," Jessie shouted, and grabbed at his wounded stomach.

At that time the door flew open and in walked Jessie's daddy, Mr. Bailey. "What you yelling about boy? What the hell's goin' on, Doc?" Mr. Bailey was red in the face and slightly out of breath, indicating he had rushed right over as soon as he got the word that something had happened to his son.

Doc Sherwood stepped between Mr. Bailey and Jessie. "Your boy is all right. He has been stabbed in the stomach, but it wasn't too deep and he will be fine in a few days. He says that Reuben Kincaide did the stabbing. You know anything about this? I am obligated to report this to the sheriff."

"Boy's lying, Doc. You told me yourself that Reuben died during the flu epidemic over in Alabama. Dead men don't stab people. I'll go get the sheriff. You better tell him the truth, Jessie. Can't put the blame on a dead man." Having said this, Mr. Bailey turned to walk out the door.

Doc Sherwood took hold of Bailey's arm and said, "Hold on, I'll go with you." Jessie had not said one word to his daddy and even though Mr. Bailey had rushed over to the doctor's office, he seemed to ignore his son's condition. Once outside the office, the doctor stopped Bailey and said, "No need to get the sheriff. He's already looking for Reuben. If Jessie is telling the truth and Reuben is here in Tallapoosa, then the sheriff will find him."

Bailey looked puzzled. "I don't understand. Thought you said Reuben Kincaide was dead."

Doc Sherwood answered, "Let's go over to the cafe and have a cup of coffee and I will explain. My nurse will take care of Jessie. Did you close your store up?"

Bailey replied, "Yep, closed her up. No dry goods will be sold today. Means no money to pay you, Doc. You can make that boy work off your fee for fixing him up. Maybe you'll have better luck at making him work than I do. He's just no good; now he is in trouble again and, as usual, lying about it."

"Don't be so hard on Jessie. I believe he is telling the truth about Reuben stabbing him." The doctor continued the conversation once they were settled at a table in the cafe with their coffee.

Bailey was confused. "All I know, Doc, is that Reuben was to lock up my store one night. Next morning he didn't show up for work and money was missing from my safe. This was about four years ago and I never saw him after that. Now you say he could be back in town. If so, what's the deal? You telling me he died?"

"Let me try to explain," Doc began. "As you know my daughter, Victoria, was married to Reuben and they gave my wife and me our precious grandchild, Vanessa. On the same day that Reuben left your employment, he also left his wife and child and even his own mother. We couldn't imagine what had happened until one day shortly after he left, Jessie told us he had found a letter that Reuben must have dropped while removing money from your safe. I won't go into all the details, but it seems as though Reuben had gotten a girl pregnant. The girl went out of town to have the baby, but she was threatening to come back to Tallapoosa with the child. Guess Reuben was afraid his wife would find out, and he didn't know how to handle it, so he disappeared. I think he had other troubles, too, but to tell you the truth I was glad he was gone. He should never have been a part of my family.

"I tried to tell my daughter that her marriage to this Kincaide boy would never work. You can take a country boy out of the country but you can't take the country out of the boy. Even though Reuben and his mother and papa moved into town, they never did fit in here. That kind will always belong out on the farm... Anyway, he broke my little girl's heart when he left her. I had to move her and the baby into the house with me, because they had no means of support. After awhile I convinced Victoria to go to Atlanta for schooling. My wife and I agreed to take care of our grandchild so Victoria could get a fresh start.

"When the child was about three, she began to ask questions about her daddy. Wanted to know where he was. So I thought it best just to tell her he was dead. Since I heard about the flu epidemic about that time, I figured best thing was to tell everyone Reuben died during the epidemic. I could have left it at that, but just this year, I realized Victoria would need to get a divorce from Reuben if she was to ever be free of him, because I could not prove he was dead. So, when the divorce papers were filed, it was the law that a warrant be issued to search for Reuben, because in order to grant the divorce, grounds of desertion had to be proven.

"What I am trying to tell you, Bailey, is that the sheriff has been out looking for Reuben Kincaide for several weeks now. Your son, Jessie, has kept the promise he made to me that he would never tell Victoria the truth about why Reuben left her. As far as I know, she does not know about the other woman and child. I never thought I would have to tell anyone the truth about all this. The only thing I ever wanted to do was to protect my family. So, go easy on Jessie. There is only one person to blame for all the trouble caused here and that person is Reuben Oliver Kincaide."

Bailey stood up and held out his hand for a handshake. "Thanks, Doc, for fixin' up Jessie. You can rest assured all you've said to me today won't go any further. I'll just go over and pick up my boy and take him home."

Several days went by and Jessie was recovering from his wound. Mr. Bailey had a talk with him. "I don't understand how you got mixed up with all this but if you know where that Reuben Kincaide is, you best tell the sheriff and let him handle it. It's a crime to stab someone and Reuben should not be allowed to get away with what he has done to that Sherwood family."

Jessie muttered under his breath, "I'll kill that bastard. He will pay for what he has done."

"What did you say, son?"

"I said, I'll find Reuben myself. I have a score to settle with him. I'll bring him in to pay for what he has done to everyone here."

"I still think you should have the sheriff take care of this."

But Jessie couldn't go to the sheriff, because he had lied about Reuben being the one who attacked him with a knife. The first thing Jessie had to do now was to find that knife because it had his initials carved on the handle. He had questioned Doc's nurse about who brought him in and if they had found the knife. The nurse told him there was no knife with him when he was brought into the doctor's office. She did tell him the name of the farmer who brought him in.

Jessie went to visit the farmer, using the excuse it was to thank him for saving his life, but his real purpose was to find out what happened to the knife. The farmer told him that after he pulled the knife from his stomach, he threw it over in the weeds. He didn't think anything about it. He just wanted to get Jessie to the doctor.

Jessie returned to the stabbing scene over and over again in search of the knife, without success.

Several weeks went by and there had been no sign of Reuben Kincaide in Tallapoosa. When Jessie had exhausted his contacts in search of Reuben, he knew there was only one thing left to do. He would pay a call on Mary. He was sure that Mary would know where Reuben was hiding, because she was his mistress.

After Reuben disappeared in 1915, Mary had returned to Tallapoosa with Reuben's child. Those who knew about the situation had kept their mouth shut. Reuben's wife had moved to Atlanta, and both families involved had guarded the secret. Mary and her child now lived in Reuben's house on Head Street. Reuben had seen to it that his mother signed the deed over to Mary so she and the baby would have a place to live. Reuben's mother had gone back to the farm to live with family and, of course, Reuben's wife and child had moved into the house with her parents before she went to Atlanta.

It was a cool evening and the autumn sun had set beyond the Tallapoosa River. A romantic time for most people in this quaint little town, but for one man who walked the streets, only anger and revenge found room in his heart. It was dark, almost eight o'clock when Jessie knocked hard on the door to the house on Head Street. Mary opened the door and Jessie's first thought was, what a sweet little thing this is.

Mary was twenty-five years old but she still had that teenage charm about her. Her little body was a bit fuller. She wore a gingham dress gathered tightly around her tiny waist. The neckline of the dress was cut low, revealing her voluptuous breasts. Her golden curls tossed about her forehead as she tilted her head upward to look into the face of the man standing at the door.

Jessie wanted to put his hands all over her and devour her on the spot, but he controlled himself because his real purpose here was to find her no-good boyfriend, Reuben. So he was polite when he said, "Good evening, Miss Mary; I'm Jessie Bailey. I'm looking for a friend of yours and just wondered if you've seen him."

Mary was friendly with her answer, "I know you. You're Jessie, Mr. Bailey's son. Mr. Bailey, the man who owns the dry goods store. Come on in. Who are you looking for?"

Jessie walked past Mary into the living room, his eyes searching the room. "Lookin' for Reuben Kincaide. Got some money to give him." Jessie was lying, but he thought the money angle would assure his finding out where Reuben was.

Mary was still standing by the open door when she replied, "I haven't any idea where Reuben is. The last I heard he was in Sanford, Florida, then I reckon he must have gone to the war. You might check with Felix Kincaide out on the farm. I think Reuben's mother lives out there now."

"I've already been out there and couldn't get any straight answers and it looks like you're not going to be straight with me either. You tellin' me a little lie, Mary? Is he here?" Jessie walked through the house looking in every room. "You hiding the bastard?" His voice got louder as he checked each of the rooms.

Mary followed Jessie, saying to him, "Please, he's not here. Please keep your voice down; my little girl is asleep."

About that time Jessie opened the door to a small bedroom and saw the little girl in her bed. "That's your kid? That the bastard child?" he jeered at Mary.

That was it; Mary had had enough. She yelled at Jessie, "You get out of my house, now! You hear me? I said leave!"

He walked out of the little girl's room, but did not leave. He pushed his way past Mary and went into the kitchen. He began to throw things around. Mary went around picking things up off the floor. "What are you doing? Why are you doing this? I told you I don't know where Reuben is. Stop this! Leave us alone!" She picked up an iron skillet and hit at Jessie. "Get out of here!" she screamed.

Jessie dodged the skillet. He grabbed Mary's arm and threw her up against the kitchen counter. "Stop, leave, now thems not the words you said to your lover boy, Reuben, so don't waste them on me," he said, as he pinned her arm against her back and pressed himself against her.

"Telling me the truth? Huh? Mary? Reuben's not here? Well, well just you and me. Can't find the man, but looks like I found me some kinda woman."

Jessie towered over Mary. He held her backward on the counter with one hand and used the other hand to feel her. He tried to kiss her, but she resisted. She muttered, "Please, please Jessie, stop. Please leave me alone."

She clawed at him, scratching his face and in her struggle she fell to the floor. Jessie towered over her and laughed, "Don't worry, honey pie, I don't want you giving me a bastard child."

Jessie continued to laugh as he made his way through the kitchen. He yelled back at Mary, "You see that lover of yours, Reuben, you tell him I'm looking for him. I plan to hurt his ugly face and you, Mary, you tell anybody about this and I'll be back." On his way out the back door he jeered, "Yum, yum, good stuff."

Mary lay curled up on the kitchen floor. A little girl walked into the kitchen crying, "Mommy, Mommy, are you hurt?"

Mary struggled to sit up. She reached for her daughter and Annie Mae went to her. They cradled each other. "I'm okay, sweetheart. Mommy just had a bad fall," Mary said, comforting the child, praying she had not seen what had happened.

At that time they heard a man's voice call out, "Mary, Mary you home?" Mary was terrified; the man's voice startled her. But when she saw the man walk through the open door, she realized it was not Jessie returning.

"Hey, Mary, it's Robert Wilson. You all right in here? Your front door was wide open. Why, Mary you've been hurt," Robert said as he rushed across the room and helped Mary take a seat on the sofa.

Mary sobbed a little, but she tried to gain her composure because little Annie Mae was standing there. "I'm okay," she said, taking Annie Mae onto her lap. "A stranger broke in the front door and tried to rob the house. I fought with him and when he ran toward the back door I went after him and I fell on the kitchen floor."

This was not the truth, but Mary was convincing. Robert accepted the explanation since he was too much of a gentleman to question Mary any further. He was a tall, thin man and his actions always displayed compassion for people. Everyone in Tallapoosa knew Robert. He was a fine Christian man, and at one time or another had given a helping hand to most everyone who lived there. He had recently lost his wife during childbirth. Several of their children had died shortly after birth, but this time the child survived its mother. Robert still showed signs of grief on his face, and everyone in town was doing all they could to comfort him.

Mary felt good that it was Robert who had walked into her house right at this time. She felt a sense of understanding from him. "I'm glad to see you, Robert," Mary said. "Let me put Annie Mae back to bed, then we can talk."

Mary tucked the child under her covers, then she went into her bedroom and changed her dress. She combed her hair without looking into the mirror. She couldn't bring herself to look at this woman who had just been attacked. Her tiny shoulders trembled as she took several deep breaths. Robert was waiting for her out in the living room. Jessie's last words to her rang in her ears, "Never tell or I'll..." Although she wanted to rush into the living room and tell Robert what had really happened to her, she knew she must not.

Robert had sat down in a large chair waiting for Mary. His elbows rested on his knees as he leaned slightly forward with his hat in his hands. When Mary walked into the room, she tried to smile as she said, "Well, Robert, what brings you out this time of night? Trust the baby is doing okay." Mary sat on the sofa opposite Robert.

"The baby is fine," he said. "And that is my reason for being here. I am in desperate need of someone to take care of my baby. I haven't worked a lick since my wife died. I gotta get back on the job. I talked to your mother and she said you might be willing to help out. I'd be glad to pay you whatever you ask."

Robert knew that Mary lived alone here with her child. He knew she was not married. If he knew who the father of the child was, he would never say anything about it. It was just the kind of person he was. He never judged anyone and guessed that with Mary's situation, she could use the money.

Mary didn't have to even think about her answer. "Of course, Robert, I'll be glad to take care of the baby if you are sure you want me to. No one round here seems to want to give me a job because of my reputation. I'm a good worker though and heaven knows Annie Mae and I can sure use a little money. But, really Robert, I'd be glad to take care of the baby for free. Least I can do for you. You've always been there to help my family in times of need."

Robert looked relieved as he said to Mary, "I know you're a good mother and right now my child needs the care of a good woman. I'll be happy to give you whatever you need. If you want to bring the baby here during the day, you can, or you can come over to my place. Whatever arrangements you want to make will be fine. You have taken a big burden from me by saying you will look after the baby."

Robert got up and walked toward the front door, which was still not closed all the way. "You going to be all right here? Don't think that man will be back, do you? You want me to go get the sheriff?"

Mary immediately jumped up and said, "No, don't do that! I mean, no, I'll be okay. It was just some kid looking for some money. Found out I didn't have any, so he left. I'll tell the sheriff about it tomorrow. Don't worry about me here. I'll be over to your place early in the mornin' and don't you worry about the baby; I will take good care of her."

"That will be fine, Mary. God bless you," Robert said as he walked through the doorway and closed the door behind him. As he walked away from the house, he knew there had been trouble there tonight and he also knew that the front door had not been broken into.

Mary sat up on the sofa the rest of the night. She cried because Jessie had hurt her and she cried because she knew that Reuben Kincaide must be there in Tallapoosa and he had not been to see her. Mary knew the sheriff was looking for Reuben because Victoria, his wife, was getting a divorce from him. Maybe after the divorce he would come to her and take Annie Mae and her away to be with him.

It was dawn and Mary had not slept. She gathered her things together, got Annie Mae ready, and went over to Robert Wilson's house to take care of the baby as she had promised.

* * *

The baby was not healthy and in November she died. Mary was there to comfort Robert. He was such a kind and gentle man and now he had no family. He begged Mary to stay with him. She felt compassion for him and at this time they both had needs. Mary and her daughter, Annie Mae, stayed most of the time with Robert, but Mary would not give up her housekeeping on Head Street. Although Robert and Mary's hearts ached for others, they shared their pain. Robert wanted Mary to become his wife and he adored little Annie Mae. His wish was that they become a family.

Mary felt a need for the security of Robert's offer, but her heart was not free. She was 26 years old and as long as she could remember had loved Reuben Oliver Kincaide. They had shared a passion and now she was raising his child. Reuben had never seen Annie Mae, but circumstances in his life had kept them apart.

Unlike others in this town of Tallapoosa, Mary knew that Reuben had not died during the flu epidemic. Until this year, he had kept in touch with her through his cousin, Felix. He had been good to send her money and she was sure the reason he had not sent her any during the past year was because he was overseas in the war.

On a cool, brisk morning in February, Annie Mae walked along holding her mother's hand, her golden curls dancing on her little shoulders. They were on their way to school. Mary always walked with her daughter to make sure she got to school safely. She was a very protective mother. She never told anyone, except her parents, who the father of her child was. She did not know if Victoria, Reuben's wife, knew. She was not in the same social standing as the Sherwood family, so there was never any contact between them.

When she registered Annie Mae for school, she marked *father unknown*. After sending Annie Mae off at school, Mary walked into town to buy a few things for Robert. As she passed a newsstand, there on the front page of the Tallapoosa newspaper — printed in black, bold, lettering for the whole world to see — were the words: DIVORCE FINAL: Socialite Victoria Sherwood is granted divorce from Reuben Oliver Kincaide. Mary grabbed a paper and read every word of the article printed in fine print under the headlines. All search had been ended and the court was satisfied that the defendant has been publicly notified. The defendant is hereby informed that divorce is granted. The divorce states: willfully deserted and abandoned without cause; leaving her without means of support for her or daughter 5 years old; name she bared prior to marriage be restored to her; custody of child be awarded to her."

None of this meant anything to Mary. She didn't care about the details. Her heart soared, her mind raced — Reuben was free; now he would come. She glided through her task and returned home to her house on Head Street. As soon as she was alone inside the house Reuben had given her, she shouted out loud, "The waiting is over. Reuben loves me. He will always take care of our little girl and soon he will come and get us, Annie Mae and me. We will be ready for him."

CHAPTER NINE

*R*euben's mother was with Felix on the Kincaide farm when they got word that Reuben's divorce from Victoria was final. The last they had heard from Reuben, he was living in Birmingham, Alabama, working for the railroad company. They never had any contact with Victoria's family. The Sherwoods were prominent people of Tallapoosa and would surely be embarrassed by the news of their daughter's divorce.

Reuben's mother, Mary Ann, had tried to live with this family five years ago after Reuben had first left Tallapoosa. She had suffered great humiliation living with them and when she couldn't take it anymore, went out to the farm to live with Felix. It broke her heart to leave her granddaughter, but she knew the Sherwoods would take good care of little Vanessa. They had no use for Reuben, but they doted on their grandchild.

Mary Ann grieved for the love of her son and her granddaughter. She wondered if, now that the divorce was final, would Reuben return to Tallapoosa?

Victoria had filed for divorce from Reuben at the insistence of her father. She had established a new life in Atlanta. She had finished her schooling and now worked as an interior designer. Her parents had persuaded her to leave her child with them in Tallapoosa. She came back, though, for short visits, usually on holidays. The Sherwoods believed that if their daughter stayed alone in Atlanta, she would meet someone and get over Reuben. Victoria couldn't seem to make them understand. She had but one love in her heart. She would love Reuben all of her life.

Jessie meanwhile was consumed with the idea he would find Reuben, and he boasted about the plans he had for their next encounter. Most of the time, he spent hanging out with the local boys at the billiard parlor, and some days he worked in his father's dry goods store. Often he could be found at the Sherwood home. He had convinced them that he would be their protector from Reuben Oliver Kincaide. He threatened anyone who might even think about telling Victoria the truth about her husband's affair, and he would have killed anyone if he knew they told little Vanessa she had a half-sister who attended the same school as she did. Vanessa was convinced that her father had died in the flu epidemic in 1917. She was seventy-nine years old before this explanation would be challenged.

Reuben's two little girls were growing up with an obsession of protection from the truth about their father. Thoughts of his knife's whereabouts haunted Jessie. He kept returning to the scene of the fight where he last saw Reuben. The knife remained buried deep in the kudzu, and no one told Jessie that Reuben was in Alabama.

People from Alabama and every state had just been through a devastating war in Europe. Woodrow Wilson was president of the United States. He had led them to victory in the war; now he wanted the nation to take up new responsibilities of world leadership, but Americans had grown tired of crusades. They wanted to escape the rigors of problem solving. They turned to a kind of romantic cynicism, appearing to be suspended between the innocence and security of childhood and the wisdom and weariness of maturity.

The country entered a period that would be labeled as "The Roaring Twenties" or "The Good Old Times." The birth of a full-blown consumer-oriented economy resulted in a radical change in lifestyles. The gaiety of the times was evident in the fashions and notoriety of dances. In fashion, the ladies' hemlines went up and they became known as Flappers. Their hair was bobbed, they wore long strings of beads and beltlines falling off the hips. If women wore galoshes, the more buckles the better. The buckles were worn undone and made a flapping noise when walking. Hence the name Flappers.

The most famous dance was called the Charleston, named for a city in South Carolina. People were in a frenzy over this dance. Children would go through the motions while playing, while older people were warned of health hazards the dance involved. Everyone was aware of the Charleston's impact. One thing for sure was the Flapper and the Charleston livened the 1920s and Reuben Oliver Kincaide was living during this savoring of time that was shaping the history of a country.

Reuben sat still in his seat and gazed out the window of the train as it picked up speed, leaving the town of Birmingham, Alabama. The conductor had said the train would make its first stop in Decatur. Reuben knew this town was located about 80 miles north, so it would be several hours before the stop. He pulled his pocket watch out and figured the time. He calculated that they would arrive in Decatur around noon time. The next couple of hours would prove to be important to him.

When Reuben boarded the train, the events of his past life weighed heavily on him. He tried to put his past to rest in his mind. The one positive thing that Reuben possessed was a sense of adventure. As the train rolled through the landscape of northern Alabama, Reuben relaxed and absorbed the scenery. It was a beautiful sight to see: dramatic rocky, wooded hills, and in several places, cascading waterfalls which were evidence of rivers and lakes. Springtime had brought forth a showy stand of wildflowers and these could be seen in abundance when the train dipped into the low plateau areas.

Reuben had only seen the big city of Birmingham, but now he could see what a beautiful land this was that made up the state of Alabama, the twenty-second state to enter the nation (in 1819). Traditionally, it had been a major farming region of the South and is one of the most historic of the Southern states due mainly to the issue of slavery. Alabama seceded from the union in 1861 and became a member of the Confederate States of America. It survived the turbulent years of the Civil War, which ended in 1865, and by the year 1870 prosperity began with the building of the railroads. During World War I (1917-1918) the farmers of Alabama supplied vast quantities of cotton and food to the war effort.

It was now 1920 and if Reuben was to leave the state of Alabama, he would have to cross the Tennessee River. In Reuben's life, there seemed to always be a river to cross. He had grown up near the Tallapoosa River in Tallapoosa, Georgia. The memory of an evening on the banks of the Tallapoosa River brought a loving ache to his heart.

When he left the Tallapoosa River area, he traveled south where he would live near another river. This river, called the St. John's, flowed past the town of Sanford, Florida. Tears filled his eyes. He had memories of pain shared when he was last seen at that river crossing in the rain.

Now Reuben was approaching the Tennessee River. The Tennessee River begins in the southern Appalachian Mountains, near Knoxville, Tennessee. The streams, fresh from the mountains and the master stream sweep southward, then bend down in northern Alabama forming a rich valley, then turn due north across Tennessee and Kentucky and flows into the Ohio River. Located in the middle of the river's bend into northern Alabama is a town called Decatur, Alabama. This is where the train stopped before crossing the Tennessee River.

The conductor told Reuben they would be there for awhile because they were having some trouble with the engine. He said they would blow the train whistle when they were ready to leave.

Reuben decided to get off the train, stretch his legs, and get something to eat. He spotted a small cafe across the street from the railroad tracks. When he entered the cafe, he removed his hat and gazed around the room for a place to sit. The room had several small tables and a lunch counter near the back. The tables were mostly occupied with men. He made his way toward the lunch counter. Everyone stared at him because it was evident he was a stranger in town due to the way he was dressed. He had on a suit and tie and new leather shoes.

The men in the cafe were mostly farmers in overalls and those who were local shop keepers didn't wear suits. The plump little lady behind the luncheon counter spoke to Reuben kindly. "Have a seat stranger. I'll be with you in just a minute." Then she gave Reuben a friendly smile.

Several of the men at the counter nodded to Reuben, and he felt a sense of friendliness and acceptance. The waitress was quick to bring him coffee and take his order. The man seated next to Reuben wasted no time in starting a conversation. "You just get off the train from Birmingham?" the farmer asked.

"Yes," was Reuben's short reply.

"Just passing through, are you?" the farmer continued to question.

Reuben again gave a short reply, "Guess so."

The farmer was not disturbed by Reuben's short answers; he wanted a conversation. "Lot of strangers come to town lately. Most of them looking for work. They come to the right place. Since the war this place has really been busy. Lot of Yankees moving down here, opening up businesses. I'm having a hard time supplying them with enough lumber for their building.

By the way, my name's Baxter, Jim Baxter." He turned sideways and reached out his hand to Reuben.

Reuben sat down his coffee cup and shook Baxter's hand. "Reuben Kincaide," was his reply.

Baxter felt the door was open for more conversation. "I own a sawmill about 20 miles outside of town. Came in today for a few supplies. Always git a bit of lunch here when I come to town. I have to stop by to see my Rhoda. Ain't she a pretty little thing?" He winked at the waitress behind the counter and she returned his attention with a little giggle. "Too bad you ain't looking for work. I sure need a good man to help me out. Guess you gonna git on that train and keep on goin'. Well, done with my eatin'. Guess I better git on down to the feed store and load my wagon. Gonna be late now before I git home tonight. No need to beg me Rhoda, no time for any of that hanky-panky today." He laughed as he stood up and made a kissing noise toward Rhoda.

"Nice to have met you, Reuben Kincaide. You ever come back in town look me up."

Reuben turned slightly and said, "Thanks," as Baxter walked away. Reuben finished his meal and looked at his pocket watch. It had been over an hour; he wondered if the train was ready to leave. Then he heard the train whistle signaling for everyone to get aboard. He paid Rhoda, thanked her for the nice meal, walked back across the tracks and down the platform of the train station. He put his hand on the railing of the steps to the train, stepped on the first step, then hesitated.

This hesitation was a moment in time in which Reuben made a decision that would determine his future. He stepped back onto the platform of the train station and spotted a porter who was standing there. "Will you get my bag off that train? I won't be going any farther." Reuben would not cross the Tennessee River that day.

He stood on the station platform with his small suitcase in his hand as the train pulled away. When the noise of the train had quieted, Reuben said to a railway worker, "I met a man called Jim Baxter, runs a sawmill, said he was going to a feed store. Would you know what feed store he was talking about?"

"Sure thing," the man replied, "it's down on Bank Street. Just a couple of blocks from here. You go straight down this street to Bank Street, turn left and you will see it just across the street from the State Bank. State

Bank is a big building with large columns in front. You can't miss it."

Reuben thanked the man. Reuben wasn't giving himself time to think about what he was doing. It was an impulsive action. This Jim Baxter had said he needed a good man, and Reuben was looking for work. When Reuben found the feed store, he saw Mr. Baxter loading his wagon. Mr. Baxter looked surprised when he said, "Hey there, young fellow. Thought you would be on the train that just crossed the river. What changed your mind?"

Reuben's tiny frame remained stately as he said, "Truth is, sir, I am looking for work. I had a job with the railroad in Birmingham, one they give me when I got back from the war, but that job ran out so they gave me free passage on the train if I wanted to go someplace else."

"So you're one of those soldier boys?" Baxter questioned. "I wouldn't have figured that, you being all dressed up the way you are. Well, like I told you, I run a saw mill and I need some help. If you're willin' to work, I'm willin' to hire you." Baxter patted Reuben on the shoulder.

This made Reuben relax and he began to talk freely. "I don't know much about sawmills, but I'm willing to learn and I'm a hard worker."

"Okay, then it's a done deal," Baxter said as they shook hands. "Throw your bag in the wagon and grab the reins on those horses. We got to git a move on or it will be midnight fore we get out to the mill."

Once they were seated on the wagon, Baxter took the reins from Reuben and said, "Here, I'll do the drivin." Reuben, remembering the conversation in the cafe, knew that Mr. Baxter would do the talkin' as well! It wasn't an easy task guiding a wagon with two horses down streets. The streets had to be shared with cars and trucks. Baxter made mention that soon he planned to replace "Old Shorty and Slim," the two horses with one of those fancy new trucks.

Reuben commented on the nice buildings, and his attention was drawn to several beautiful Victorian-style houses. Baxter informed him that a lot more of these types of homes were being built in this area, and he was having a hard time keeping up with the demand for lumber.

"So, Reuben, you say you never been to Decatur before?" Baxter asked.

"No, sir, never," Reuben replied.

This was Baxter's cue for dialogue. "God's little green earth is what I call it. The town sits in the middle of what is called the Tennessee Valley. Long before the first white man ventured down this river, several native

American tribes — Cherokee, Creek, Chickasaw and Tuskegee — found a valley teeming with game. Many of them settled here farming, hunting and fishing. You like to fish, Reuben?" Baxter didn't wait for an answer. "River's a great place for fishing. They say you can catch large mouth bass, small mouth bass, channel catfish, crappie and fresh water drum. Also this river area's a great place for ducks and geese. Thousands of them can be found over on that peninsular cross town.

"Course I don't do much fishing or hunting. Seems like all my time is spent at the sawmill." Baxter paused to ponder those words for a minute. They had reached the end of town and it was a good thing Baxter knew the right road to take because the countryside was laced with trails. They were still in a low plateau area, but Reuben could see a mountain in the distance.

He said to Baxter, "Looks like a mighty big mountain ahead. We got to cross that?"

Baxter was amused. "No, my boy, that is the forest. The sawmill is just at the foot of that mountain. We do get a lot of timber out of there though."

The horses began a slow trot down a long stretch of road and Baxter continued his Decatur story, "When the Europeans began to explore this area they drove the Indians out. They first called the town Rhodes Ferry, then in 1820 the president, James Monroe, renamed it Decatur in honor of his friend Commodore Stephen Decatur. This Decatur fellow was a decorated navy officer and he was challenged to a duel by a Commodore James Barron, at whose courtmartial Decatur had presided. Barron had accused certain officers, headed by Decatur, of persecuting him. The duel took place near Bladensbury, Maryland, and Decatur was killed. It was shortly after that when the president changed the name of the town.

"The government finally succeeded in pushing out most of the Indians, then Decatur got all mixed up in the Civil War. Union troops came in, made raids and almost destroyed the place. The Yankees tried to burn us out, but the people here were resilient. After the Civil War, the people here felt like they helped patch things up between the North and the South. Because of the town's location on the Tennessee River, the rail and highway lines grew and economic prosperity brought wealthy Yankees to the area.

"Things slowed down when World War I came, but now that's over, things have picked up again. Yeah, the people here relish their history."

It was late afternoon and Reuben was almost lulled into sleep with the slow, continuous motion of the wagon. It was only when the wagon hit a bump in the road did he return to the sound of Baxter's chatter. As it grew dark, Baxter stopped talking and concentrated on maneuvering the horses and wagon. Reuben was wide awake as the terrain became rocky and hilly. They approached a thicket of trees and as they came through the trees, Reuben saw a small house. He couldn't make out many details of the house, but be could see a dim light in the window.

Baxter pulled the horses to a halt in front of the house and said, "Sure is late, but I see my wife still has the light burning for me. I'll go in and let her know I'm home, then we'll go down to the barn and put the horses away."

Baxter returned in a few minutes and they drove about fifty yards to a barn that was quite large compared to the house. Reuben made the comment, "Huge barn you got there, don't think I've ever seen one as big."

Baxter replied, "Well, I use part of it for a barn and part of it for my sawmill work. The actual sawmill is in back of the barn. You'll see all that tomorrow, but right now, we gotta off-load this wagon, bed the horses down and see about fixin' you a place to bed down."

After the chores were attended to Baxter showed Reuben a small room attached to the side of the barn. It contained a single bed with a blanket on it, a small wash table with a pitcher for water and a wooden cane-bottomed chair. "Nothin fancy, son," Baxter said as Reubn stepped into the room, "but you can stay here free of charge as long as you give me a good day's work. I'll give you your wages on Saturday morning and if you need to go to town that will be the day to go. There's no workin' on Sundays. My wife will expect you to go to church. See you got good enough clothes for that. Got any overalls in that little suitcase you holding there?"

"No sir, but if you can loan me a pair, I will get some on Saturday when I get my first pay. I'll need to take care of some business in town on that day."

"Okay, sure, that'll be fine. Now, you get a night's sleep and come up to the house early. My wife will have you some breakfast. The old rooster out there will let you know when to git up." Baxter was still talking when he closed the door behind him.

When Reuben stretched his body on the bed and closed his eyes, he wondered, *what in the world have I gotten myself into now?* He had no purpose, no direction, no real reason for being here. Why was he here when everyone he loved was someplace else? He was confused, but his body was tired so he had no trouble falling asleep.

The sawmill was located higher up the mountain than Reuben had realized the first night he was there. Baxter had said it was near a forest and in the light of day, Reuben was amazed at what a magnificent forest it was! It was a wilderness of shades of green. Southern pines and white oak trees reached high out of the forest darkness for the light. Deer, wild hogs and wild turkeys roamed in the underbrush, and deep within the forest a stream wound mistily away to meet the river.

In the late afternoon, Baxter would find a quiet spot by the stream to dangle a fishing line to catch some red eye bass. Reuben would join him, but Reuben never fished. Mr. Baxter told Reuben how the forest had provided all their essentials for living and it was evident there was a bountiful supply of timber for the sawmill.

Reuben didn't talk much and never said anything about his past life. Baxter never asked him any personal questions, but he must have sensed that Reuben had a troubled past. One afternoon as they were walking out of the forest, Baxter said to Reuben, "Hope you decide to stay here with us, son. Perhaps the forest will provide what you're searching for, a new beginning."

Reuben gazed down the long valley and said nothing. In his mind, he wondered how this could be. He wasn't sure how long he would stay there.

The first week went by quickly. The work was not all that hard and Reuben really enjoyed Baxter's friendship. Mrs. Baxter was nice to him and concerned about him not eating much. She also reminded him everyday about church on Sunday. He could ride there in the wagon with them. Flat Creek was only a couple of miles down the mountain. Reuben made her no promises.

Saturday morning came and Baxter gave Reuben his week's pay. He told him that a friend from Moulton, a little place near them, would be by in his truck and he could catch a ride into Decatur with him. That is if he still wanted to go. Reuben asked if the man would be bringing him back and Baxter said, "I'm sure he will. He always goes into town on Saturdays, gets himself liquored up and is in need of someone to drive him home."

The two laughed at this image. Reuben put his suit on and slid his suitcase under the bed. When he arrived in Decatur, he had the man drop him off at the post office. They agreed on a place to meet later that afternoon. Reuben went into the post office and told the clerk he needed to rent a post office box. He also needed paper, pen and an envelope. The clerk was polite and took care of his needs. Reuben wrote a short note to his cousin, Felix, and his mother in Tallapoosa. He just wanted to let them know where he was and give them his mailing address so they could get in touch with him. He didn't have any extra cash that week, but he would send some later for Felix to give to Mary and the baby. In the letter he shared no details of what he was doing.

When he left the post office, he walked to the State Bank and explained to the bank president about the money he had left in the bank in Sanford, Florida, before he went to the war and how he had asked the bank in Birmingham to try to get it for him. The bank president said he would contact the Birmingham bank and see what they could do. Reuben gave him all the information he needed and said he would come back every Saturday to check on his money.

Having finished this business, Reuben bought himself a pair of working denim overalls. He then walked around town and noticed a theater. The sign out front read, "Princess." Reuben bought himself a ticket and went inside. The Princess Theater had been renovated in 1919 from a hotel's livery stable into a 1,500 seat theater. High-class road shows, silent pictures and vaudeville were the attractions of the day. Reuben enjoyed these things. He had been exposed to this sort of entertainment during his young life in Tallapoosa. His wife, Victoria, was from a cultured family and Reuben had been a part of that life for a short while.

When Reuben sat in the Princess Theater, his eyes saw the shows, but his mind remembered the past. He came out of the theater when it was late afternoon. Then walked toward the railroad station. A train was sitting there getting ready to depart. Looked like it would be going north. North, south, either direction, did it matter? The train whistle echoed in his ears. He walked across the tracks to the little cafe where he had met Baxter. Perhaps, just perhaps, the forest meant something to him already. One thing he knew, being in the forest, working at the sawmill and having the Baxters as his friends had promoted a sense of peace. That was all he could hope for at present.

The man he was to meet was waiting outside the cafe. He was drunk, so Reuben drove the truck home. Sunday morning came and Reuben accompanied the Baxters to church at Flat Creek. Mrs. Baxter was eager to introduce Reuben to several of the young ladies at the church. After all Reuben was a handsome young man, and very well mannered. The girls were interested in this stranger from the start. They told him about a church social being held the following Sunday and hoped he would be there.

Reuben said to the young girls, "Next Sunday, April 11th? I will remember the church social if you will remember that it's my birthday." The girls all giggled.

CHAPTER TEN

$\mathcal{W}$hen the new work week began, Baxter told Reuben that a neighboring farmer had asked him if he could help him out preparing his land for this year's cotton crop. Reuben and Baxter willingly went to help the McCormick family.

When Lousinda and James McCormick married, they homesteaded one hundred sixty-five acres in the forest. Lousinda had grown up in the forest. Her grandmother was a Cherokee Indian named Martha. Martha's ancestors were part of the mighty and powerful Cherokee nation. Before Martha was born, parties of the Cherokee had pushed down the Tennessee River and formed settlements around the Tennessee-Alabama line. Some of the tribe lived in scattered villages along the banks of the Tennessee River, but the tribe that Martha was born of, ventured into the nearby forest, and found something mystical about this ancient forest.

It was a wilderness, once the floor of an ancient sea. There were canyons and caves in the mountain and waterfalls and abundant wildlife. In its wild glory it provided all the essentials for the Cherokee's freedom-loving lifestyle.

Martha, as a little girl, ran free through the tall trees and splashed and played in the flowing streams. Her brothers tracked deer along rock cliffs that rose from the waters of the lake and captured some raccoons who also traveled here.

Canyons and caves beside the Sipsey River provided shelter for the families. Martha's family used hardwood that came from the rich soils of

123

sheltered caves to build houses, and pine trees that grew on the drier slopes and ridges to make furniture. Their life in the forest seemed peaceful but even before Martha was born, the encroachment of the white man came and would change their lives forever.

In 1820, the federal government seized the Cherokee land that became Decatur and many visitors and white men began to settle there. At the same time gold was discovered in the nearby Georgia territory. When these things happened, there was a powerful agitation to remove the Indians. In 1835, the Treaty of New Echota was established. This ceded all land east of the Mississippi River to the federal government. The Indians were to be removed and they were to go to the territory of Oklahoma. Their exodus began and was completed in the winter of 1838-39. The reason is not known, but Martha did not go with her family on this TRAIL OF TEARS.

Several years later, a Viking man came on a raft down the Tennessee River. He pulled over to shore near Decatur. He was adventurous and eager to behold the wilderness so he ventured out into the forest. To him it was a place untouched by time and the beauty of nature possessed him. He spent days exploring this unique and primitive environment.

One morning, having made his way through a laurel thicket, he saw an Indian girl gathering nuts off the ground. Her incredible beauty captivated him. He approached her cautiously. She was not afraid as she raised her body to observe him. His appearance was something she had never seen before. He had blazing red hair, white skin and was tall with broad shoulders. She could not help but stare into his blue eyes. She did not know that a person could have eyes of this color.

"I hope I didn't startle you. I mean no harm. I didn't know anyone lived here. I haven't seen anyone for days. My name is John. What is your name?" He stood still as he talked to her.

Then as though she had hardly noticed him, she continued to gather the nuts and place them in a basket. John could not walk away from her. He began to gather the nuts also and placed them in her basket. After a few minutes of silence she said, "Martha, my name is Martha."

"Oh," he said, "You can speak."

She seemed a little irritated as she said, "I can speak your language; my mission mother taught me."

"So, you live near here?" John stood and leaned against the tree trunk.

Martha was hesitant to answer his questions, but she didn't want him to leave her so they talked until the basket was full of nuts. John offered to carry the basket for her, but she said "no." They parted knowing that they would return to meet again and again under this chestnut tree.

The chestnut tree was the most valuable tree in the forest to the Indians and early settlers there. The trees were straight trunked and tall, reaching over 150 feet in height and some fifteen feet in diameter. They could be compared to the majestic redwood groves of the Pacific Coast. Traditionally, the Indians used the bark, which could easily be stripped from the tree trunks, for cover for their homes. Then, with the use of tools in the 1800s, they built log cabins from the wood. The wood was also used as posts and fences and furniture. The nuts from the tree made zesty food and were used in soups, stews and prized stuffings. Also the Indians and old-time settlers picked the nuts and traded or sold them to local merchants.

When John found the chestnut tree, he had found two jewels of the wild. For it was in this enchanting setting he also found romance.

It was not long until John took Martha as his wife. They were married in a little church built of logs, nestled in a grove in the forest and that had been built in 1808. They called it, "Pine Torch Church," because they burned pine knots which were placed in holders to provide light during night services. Martha had grown up going to church there with a woman whom she called her mission mother.

John etched out 1200 acres of the forest. It encompassed majestic hardwood trees, undisturbed gorges, sandstone cliffs, swift streams and waterfalls. There were creek bottoms where John and Martha grew cotton and flax, corn and a vegetable garden. Martha had a loom for making cloth, and for John there was an abundance of animals for hunting and fishing. In the springtime, John would walk with Martha as she picked wildflowers. They would watch the streams cascade over the rocks, and John would watch his wife as she washed her long black hair in the waterfalls.

In 1857 they had a son and christened him John Allen Sanderson, Jr. In 1861, the Civil War began and John felt it his duty to go fight for what he thought was right. He made Martha promise to marry his brother, Charles, who came to live with them in case he didn't return from the war. Having made this promise, Martha stood in the yard holding the hand of their four-year-old son and waved goodbye as John walked off through the forest. Martha was pregnant with another child who would never see her father. John was killed in the Civil War and was buried in Nashville, Tennessee.

Martha married Charles.

John Jr. grew up with his mother and step-father in the forest. When he was twenty years old, he married a girl twelve years of age. Her name was Rodha. They had a girl and named her Lousinda. At the age of eighteen, Lousinda married James Clark McCormick. James was an Irishman who had come to northern Alabama with his five brothers from the state of Georgia. The brothers were headed west, but once arriving in this wonderful forest area, they decided to stay.

Like John before him, James found his wife living in the forest. In 1901, Lousinda and James married and lived on their homestead in the forest. The next year, 1902, they had their first girl child and named her Rebekah. Lousinda had passed to Rebekah the blood and bones of her ancestors. She taught Rebekah the ways of life she had learned from her grandmother, Martha.

Rebekah spent her early years in the forest. Lousinda had her grandmother's loom and Rebekah would play around her feet as she would weave the threads.

The forest became a target for federal ownership when Theodore Roosevelt became president. He preserved vast areas of forest lands for national parks. He said, "There's nothing more practical in the end than the preservation of beauty." Federal funds were appropriated for the purchase of forest lands.

On January 15, 1918, the forest that Rebekah lived in was designated "Alabama National Forest."

The Indian girl, Martha, who had stayed behind during the Trail of Tears, the removal of the Indians to Oklahoma, did not live to see the final exodus of her people from the forest. She did not live to see the day when the Cherokee Indians were declared U.S. citizens by the federal government. The citizenship had made no difference to Martha's people. It had taken generations, 81 years, but the federal government finally moved all of them from the forest.

Lousinda and James sold their 165 acres to the federal government in 1916. They were paid $4.75 per acre. They moved to a 40 acre farm in an area called Flat Creek. When they moved, Lousinda had to leave her grandmother's loom behind. Rebekah cut a clipping from the rose bush which grew wild in the yard of her home in the forest. Lousinda and Rebekah cried when they left the forest. Rebekah was 14 years old.

By the year 1918, Lousinda and James had eight children. One night their home caught on fire. They got all the children out of the house and James rang the dinner bell. Neighbors heard the bell and came running to help. They couldn't save the house, but everyone helped to rebuild the McCormick home. The people of Flat Creek were generous in caring for each other.

In the spring of 1920, Reuben had come with Mr. Baxter to help the McCormick family with their cotton crop. It took a lot of hard work to produce a cotton crop. Everyone in the family had to work, and it was not uncommon for neighbor to help neighbor. Reuben didn't know much about growing cotton and he had always hated working on his family's farm in Tallapoosa, but if Baxter wanted to go help these people out it was okay with him. Just another days work.

McCormick asked Reuben if he could handle a mule and plow. He explained that he had five daughters who could do the hoeing, but plowing was a man's job and he needed help with that. The fact that plowing was man's work implied that it was harder work than the hoeing. This notion was to be questioned when one day, one of McCormick's daughters decided to do some plowing. She then discovered that the men had been getting away with doing the easier job.

Reuben didn't think it hard or easy, he just began the plowing. It was reaching the noon hour when Reuben looked up and out across the plowed field. In the distance, he saw a young lady standing between the cotton rows in the red clay. She was wearing a dress that reached to her ankles; a bonnet covered her hair. When he got closer, he stopped the mule and looked upon her. Her face opened crimson to the sun, blushed with rosy health. Her lips parted with the freshness of smiles, and her eyes sparkled of good humor. She possessed a rare blend of natural ingredients. She was a lovely lady and Reuben knew at once he had discovered an exceptional woman.

Neither of them said a word to each other. Reuben continued his plowing. He didn't say a word to anyone about the girl, but the rest of the week he did his work in the cotton field watching her from a distance. The only thing he knew about her was that she was one of McCormick's daughters. He also knew that the McCormick family went to the Flat Creek Church and come Sunday, he was anxious to go to the church social the giggling girls had asked him to attend.

Rebekah McCormick, daughter of Lousinda and James Clark McCormick, would be eighteen years old, October 15, 1920.

Nineteen twenty was a banner year for the women of the United States. Woodrow Wilson was president and had signed into law the 19th Amendment to the Constitution which gave women the right to vote.

Many aspects of women's lives changed, but Rebekah was somehow removed from these roaring twenties. She was the daughter of a farmer. She was a country girl and knew no other way of life. She was the oldest of her parent's ten children and was obliged to work hard. She did not have leisure hours to perfect her looks. She still wore her dress down to just above her ankles. Her hair was not bobbed and she wore no jewelry. She was definitely not what was called a flapper girl. Her father would never allow her to dance. And although Rebekah did not fit the descriptive roaring twenties flapper, she possessed a simple elegance.

When she arrived at the church, Reuben was already there. Several girls were around him, but when Rebekah reached the group, they parted and one of the girls introduced them. He had seen her only in the working field, now he saw before him a beautiful girl dressed in a violet calico dress. Her hair was chestnut brown, her eyes green like the sea when the sunlight glistened on it, and she was delightfully sweet and young. He addressed her with tentative pleasantries, and Rebekah was smitten with this handsome polished young fellow.

The giggling girls left Reuben and Rebekah alone for a few minutes and when they came back, they were carrying a cake and singing "Happy Birthday" to Reuben. They had not forgotten that Reuben told them April 11 was his birthday. Someone shouted, "Where are the candles? Can't have a birthday cake without candles!"

One of the girls remarked, "We don't know how old he is, so we couldn't put candles on the cake." Everyone laughed and Reuben thanked them for the cake. He told them to cut it so everyone could have a piece.

Again Reuben and Rebekah found themselves alone when everyone continued their socializing. Rebekah was curious so she asked, "Tell me Reuben, how many candles should have been on the cake? How old are you?"

Without hesitation, he looked straight into her eyes and said, "I'm twenty-five. Yep, I'm twenty-five years old today," Reuben lied to Rebekah.

He had seen in her smiles, an alluring coquetry and he knew that such a girl would be a challenge for his passion. His time as a married man had failed to dampen his ardor for sex or destroy his spirit for adventure. He had no plan of play. So without forethought, he wiped away his seven years of married life.

He was now thirty-two years old. He was twenty-five years old when he married Victoria. He was seven years older than she. Ironically, it was now seven years since he had first married. Would it be possible to wipe away those seven years of his life? Rebekah went on smiling and beaming at his sallies. Yes, when he stood here before this beautiful young girl, he was twenty-five again. If there ever was a time to start over, it was now.

Reuben did look young for his age. Proof of that was when the lady at the boarding house in Birmingham had told the census taker that Reuben Kincaide lived there and she guessed his age to be twenty-five. This had taken place only four months before.

He and Rebekah had a wonderful time that night at the church social and when they said goodbye to each other, they both knew they would see each other again. Reuben had met Rebekah and had turned back the hands of time. I can do this! he resolved, and began with a mental housecleaning, letting go of old, worn-out beliefs and making room for new, positive thoughts. He would take charge of his life now. He had a reason to do so and her name was Rebekah.

Reuben continued to work at the sawmill and continued going into town, Decatur, on Saturdays. He would check his post office box for news from Felix in Tallapoosa.

Things remained the same there. His mother was there with Felix on the farm. She rarely went into town and when she did, she would walk past the school yard and search for her granddaughters. Watching the two little girls from afar, she marveled at how precious they were. Both were six years old now. Vanessa, Reuben's daughter by his wife, Victoria, was a delicate little thing. She had shiny dark hair pulled away from her face with a ribbon that matched her dress. Her dress had ruffles with a trim of lace and in her play, she never looked untidy.

Annie Mae, Mary and Reuben's child, sported golden curls that bounced as she twirled and turned in her zestfulness. Her little dresses were gingham plaid and she had no ribbons for her hair.

Mary Ann could never approach her granddaughters because she vowed to Reuben she would never reveal the secret between them. They would go to school together not knowing they had the same father.

Vanessa was being raised by Victoria's parents while Victoria remained in Atlanta. Mary still lived in the house on Head Street and worked for Robert Wilson. The money from Reuben did help Mary in taking care of Annie Mae. Mary felt the money was still her connection to Reuben, and she waited for his return.

After Reuben read the letters, he immediately threw them away. He then purchased a money order, put it in an envelope with a letter and mailed it to Felix.

Having taken care of this business, he went to the bank to check on the money he hoped to be getting from the bank in Sanford, Florida. The answer to his question was always the same, "Nothing yet, sir, but we are working on it."

Next stop would be the Princess Theater where he could enter a land of make believe. There he could escape the memories of his life in Tallapoosa, Sanford, Florida and the horrible war.

These days when he walked out of the Princess Theater, he had only one thing on his mind. Tomorrow was Sunday and he would see Rebekah. After several Sundays of seeing Reuben at church and one would guess some prompting by Rebekah and her four sisters, James and Lousinda McCormick invited Reuben home for Sunday dinner.

The McCormick's forty acres sat just outside the forest in a valley below the foothills. They had moved here when they left their land in the forest. Their hewn log house was rain riddled and too small for their family, but here they had weathered many a storm. They had a cotton crop from which they could get cash, they had a bountiful vegetable garden, a field of corn and some livestock.

In the yard about ten feet from the front porch stood a large pole with a large iron bell attached to it. The bell was mounted about eight feet high on the pole, but it had a long cord so that even a small child could pull it to ring the bell. This was the bell that James had used to call for help on the night their house burned down, and this was the bell he rang on that day in November 1918 when the war was over.

Also in the yard, right next to the porch, was a beautiful rose bush. Rebekah had planted it there after taking it from their home in the forest.

Everything that surrounded this house showed that they were a caring, loving family. When the children gathered around the home-made wooden table for dinner, James would say a blessing. He was a religious man, and it was said that he should have been a preacher. His brother John was a Baptist preacher. Some said that James was called to preach, but John answered. This was a joke shared by family members.

Just as John took charge of preaching, Lousinda took charge of most of the family matters. Her folk wisdom was namely that of her grandmother, Martha, the Indian girl.

Both James and Lousinda took a liking to Reuben. During Reuben's visits, his attention went mostly to Rebekah while her younger sisters would giggle and flirt. The boys were all younger than the girls so mostly they would run and hide from Reuben. His time spent with this family was a time of comfort, good food and warmth. He was touched by their friendship and he knew he had found a place called home. They asked nothing of him and he told them little of his past.

Spring turned into summer and Reuben was always eager to go help the McCormick family with their cotton crop. The hoe was used for chopping cotton and as Reuben chopped the cotton his thoughts were untangling the chaos of his past to make room for his future. As Reuben and Rebekah worked side by side in the field, they shared there special glances and Rebekah nurtured her dreams. Reuben had an irresistible charm and his romance with Rebekah was enhanced as they shared more time together. When possible, they would find a place to relax after a day spent working.

Sitting under a tree at the edge of the field, they would watch butterflies sprint over the patches of crimson clover. They could feel the velvety summertime breezes. To Reuben, Rebekah had a soothing spirit about her.

Often times, they would walk through the coolly shaded forest where gentle breezes brought echoes of the romance Rebekah's ancestors had found. They paused beside rocks draped with honeysuckle vines. They could smell the sweetness of the flower. It was there they tasted their first kiss.

The two were enraptured as they walked hand in hand out of the forest down the dirt road toward home. The hour grew late as they reached the yard. Reuben picked a rose from the bush beside the porch. As the cool breeze of the evening blew cross the rose, Reuben knew he had found the girl he wanted to share the rest of his life with. He handed Rebekah the rose and Rebekah gave him her heart.

The onset of cooler weather was welcomed by Reuben. The sultry summer heat had made his work in the sawmill and in the farm field miserable. He would not miss the steamy mornings, the biting flies and the sweat. It was October and the cotton fields were in full bloom. The landscape looked like a blanket of fresh fallen snow.

Everyone was called to help with the cotton picking. Even the children were taken out of school to pick. Each picker was given a burlap sack. This sack was called a pick sack or tow sack. It had a large strap, which was worn over the shoulder. The sack was dragged along behind the picker as he or she filled it with cotton. The size of the pick sack usually depended on the age of the picker and, how much cotton they could pick.

Everyone was expected to pick from one-hundred to two-hundred pounds of cotton a day. Many parents would whip their children if they did not pick at least one-hundred pounds in one day. The stalks of the cotton plants were used for these whippings. The parents felt this was teaching their children responsibility. The amount of cotton taken to market meant cash money for the family. The men would buy supplies for the farm and the women would take the Sears and Roebuck catalog and order items they needed, mostly material for making clothes.

In this year of 1920, they would pay ten cents a yard for dress material, gingham or calico. The few dress patterns that were bought were passed around and shared with neighbors. They bought little underwear. Usually the underwear was home-made using sacks that flour and sugar came in. These sacks held one-hundred pounds of flour or sugar, were white, and were boiled and washed. Later the flour sacks came in printed material and these were used for making dresses and bonnets.

Even though the brassiere for women first appeared in style in Paris in 1889, the ladies on the farm did not wear them nor did they wear corsets. They usually got two new dresses a year. The old dresses they wore out in the fields. The children always made a list up from the catalog, but seldom were any of these items ordered.

On a cool, crisp, October morning, Reuben looked up from his cotton picking and saw Rebekah walking toward him. Her hair was pinned up under her bonnet and she wore a faded dress with an apron tied around her tiny waist. She was carrying a little bucket. Looked like a syrup or lard bucket to Reuben. When she got close, she said, "Reuben, I brought your lunch. My sisters think you are too skinny, so I made you some biscuits and a baked sweet potato. I'll sit it over there under that shade tree so when you get ready you can eat."

As she walked away, Reuben called to her, "So you think I am skinny? That's what you think about me? That all?"

Rebekah turned her head and gave Reuben a teasing smile. After placing the little bucket in a safe place, she returned to the field to work beside Reuben. As the noon hour approached, Reuben pulled his pocket watch from his pants pocket, leaned slightly backward and said, "Guess it's time for that lunch pail. You ready to quit, Rebekah?"

"I'll race you to it when I finish picking this row," she answered.

On reaching the end of the row, they dropped their pick sacks and like playful youngsters, they ran, whirled and raced across the field. They shared the biscuits and sweet potato and displayed their delight in each other. This young girl had rejuvenated Reuben and he encouraged her nurturing. The golden leaves of fall danced away. Rebekah was eighteen on the fifteenth of October.

Reuben had come to Decatur a lonely man running from lost loves, the horrors of the war and other things. He found work and caring friends. The people knew nothing of his past. They asked no questions. Reuben appeared to them to be a fine young man. He was always clean and neat, well-mannered and well-spoken. On Saturday, he always bought a newspaper in Decatur and his name was first on the list when they started delivering the paper to rural areas. It was said there was never a newspaper brought to these country people till Reuben Kincaide came.

Reuben always read the paper cover to cover. He wanted to have full knowledge of current events. He was interested in what the government was doing and he kept up with baseball. He was an avid fan of Ty Cobb, who was not only the best baseball player at that time, but he was from Georgia and only two years older than Reuben. Reuben remembered when Ty Cobb made his debut with the South Atlanta League in 1903. Now, however, Reuben began to read about a challenger to Ty Cobb's records. This new player had signed with the New York Yankees in April. They called him Babe Ruth.

133

Reuben was an interesting fellow to the McCormick family. His appearance into their lives intrigued them, and his courtship with their daughter Rebekah was constant as winter time approached. He came to their home every Sunday and even though work in the fields had ended for the season, Reuben could always find an excuse to come around. Finally James McCormick took Reuben aside and plainly said to him, "Look, young man. Either marry my daughter or quit coming around here."

Reuben had not thought of marriage. He would have to spend some time thinking about that. Rebekah's father had spoken to him on Sunday and the events of the following Saturday would change everything. As soon as Reuben stepped into the bank the bank president called to him, "Mr. Kincaide, I have some good news for you. Your money arrived from Sanford, Florida." Reuben couldn't believe it. He had little hope of ever getting the money he had saved while working on the celery farm.

A bank cashier counted out to him one thousand dollars. He thanked everyone in the bank and walked out feeling like a rich man. He went straight to the post office and sent Felix one hundred dollars. He told himself that with the remaining money he could do exactly what he wanted to do. He could go anywhere he wanted. He'd had a hell of a life up until then, but with the help of his money he was taking control of his life again.

The past was over for Reuben. He would now concern himself with the present. He had an incredible feeling that his life was just beginning. He bought some new clothes, then he went to the train station. He had heard about a local train that went through the countryside and made a stop at Trinity, a small town near where the McCormick family lived. He boarded this train, got off at Trinity and walked to see Rebekah.

He would take Rebekah, this girl from the forest, make her his wife and this time he would be head of his household. When Rebekah said "yes" to this marriage, it was a personal milestone for Reuben, a moment in time when his whole life changed. With his money in his pocket and the promise of a new bride, he had found a place where he could be happy.

It was late Saturday evening when Reuben told Rebekah that next Friday, he would borrow Mr. Baxter's horse and wagon and he would pick her up. They would go to Moulton where the courthouse was, get their marriage license and be married. He told her he was buying a set of mules for farming and he was going to build a house on a little piece of land near the sawmill. James McCormick had agreed they could stay there with the

134

family until the house was ready.

On Sunday, Reuben did not come to the McCormick home for his usual visit. It was the first week of December and the weather had turned cold. Lousinda McCormick sat by the fire surrounded by her children and her husband. She was the mother of a large brood: ten children. Rebekah was the oldest of these children. She was an elegant young lady who had shared her mother's responsibilities of taking care of the home and the young children. Now her time had come to have her own family. Lousinda did worry that her daughter was marrying a man they knew nothing about. But, Reuben had an irresistible charm and had captured her respect. She told Rebekah, "This week I will prepare a room for you and your husband. You are so young, but your ancestors have given you root and now your father and I give you wings."

Throughout the week, Rebekah's four sisters would not leave her alone. They confided in each other. They told secrets, talked of love and desires. When they had gone to bed at night, they hugged their pillows and giggled at Rebekah. They told her that Reuben was too skinny, but if she didn't want him, any one of them would take him. Rebekah would always have this joyful image of her sisters as children skipping along with their ruffles and laughter. But childhood is not forever, and now Rebekah would become a woman.

CHAPTER ELEVEN

$\mathcal{W}$hen Reuben prepared himself to leave the sawmill on Friday morning, he got rid of his small suitcase. He kept nothing — no pictures, no letters, not even a piece of clothing from his past. He took with him only the new things he had bought in Decatur. Rebekah was waiting for Reuben when he arrived. He pulled the wagon and horses up close to the porch and she walked out to greet him. He called out as he stepped down from the wagon, "Are you ready to go?"

She was ready. She turned to wave goodbye to her mother and sisters and brothers. They were standing on the porch. James McCormick was in the woods hunting.

Rebekah was wearing a coat and she had a blanket for her lap. The air was crisp and chilly. As Reuben wrapped the blanket around her feet and legs, he said to her, "These shoes the only pair you got?" Rebekah nodded her head yes. "Well," Reuben said, "first thing we will do when we get to Moulton is buy you some shoes."

The shoes Rebekah wore were white summer shoes. She wore white stockings also, but there was a reason for this: it was her wedding day. She didn't say anything to Reuben about the shoes. When they got to Moulton, they went straight to a dry goods store for her new shoes. While Rebekah was picking out her shoes and getting fitted, Reuben stood in the doorway jingling the change in his pocket. When they left the store, Rebekah was wearing her new shoes.

They went into the courthouse and told the clerk they wanted to get married. The clerk said they could fill out the paper work and if they didn't want to wait, they could go across the street to the feed store because that is where the judge went and he would have to sign the licenses.

Reuben and Rebekah walked into the feed store and the owner asked if he could help them. Reuben replied, "looking for Judge Kumpy."

"That would be me," a stately looking gentleman said as he approached them from the back of the store. "What can I do for you?"

"We want to get married," Reuben said.

"That right, young lady?" the judge questioned Rebekah.

"Yes, sir," she replied.

"You get your license yet?" the judge continued to question them.

"Right here," Reuben said as he handed the paper to the judge, "We need you to sign."

The judge took the paper, looked over it and said, "You two want to get married today?"

"Yes, sir, if that's possible," Reuben said and Rebekah nodded in agreement.

"Sure, young man, it's possible. I'm the judge. I can marry you right here and now. That is if you don't mind getting married in a feed store."

The owner of the feed store yelled out, "Hey, I heard that. Nothing wrong with my feed store. Good a place as any for a wedding."

Reuben glanced around the feed store. It brought back memories of the feed store he once worked in. Memories flooded him of Uncle Grier. Why not get married here in this feed store? Uncle Grier would be proud. "We're ready if you are, sir," Reuben said to the judge.

"Okay, young fellow. You talked me into it. Mr. Whipple, you gonna be our witness? Let's fix a place back here by the stove where we all can stand." The judge was talking while preparing a place for everyone to stand.

Reuben took Rebekah's hand and led her to the back of the feed store. As she removed her coat, the atmosphere of the feed store became chapel-like. A luxurious quiet filled the room as the men gazed at Rebekah. She was a beautiful bride. She had chosen to wed in white linen. She and her mother had cut carefully and stitched evenly the clean linen of the pristine white dress. There was no lace or beads, no satin or bows, only the fresh, white, treasured fabric of linen. The dress yielded a sense of a new life.

She wore nothing in her hair, which was pulled away from her face and into a bun in the back. Her arms were free of flowers. There had been no design to the ceremony and no fancy lists made. Only his discovery of her and her intrigue of him. Rebekah's face shimmered with a cheerful glow. She stood before Reuben with grace and dignity, like sun in the rain.

The judge took a little book from his coat pocket and began to read. It had been seven years since Reuben had heard these words. Seven years ago the vows had been the same but today, Reuben stood in a different world.

Rebekah said, "I do," as she took Reuben for her husband to love, honor and obey till death do they part. Reuben said the vows to Rebekah, but he made no promise in his mind.

The judge asked if there was a ring for the bride. Reuben took off the ring he was wearing on the smallest finger of his left hand and slipped it over Rebekah's finger. The judge then said, "Okay, young man, you may kiss your bride."

Rebekah turned her face to Reuben. He kissed her gently on the lips and they embraced. They held each other tenderly as their hearts passed one to the other. It was a moment they would remember all their lives. The marriage license was dated December 14, 1920, and signed by Judge J. E. Kumpy. The newlyweds got into the wagon and drove the horses toward Rebekah's home. Here her mother would have a nice warm supper and a room prepared for them.

The wagon ride was terribly bumpy and the late evening, December air was cold on Rebekah's face. She sat silent as Reuben drove the horses and talked about how he didn't intend to live with her parents long and his plans to buy some mules next week. As Rebekah's husband, he did not intend to share with her his past. His past life became his secret. Rebekah made no mention of it. She looked ahead, down the road. She held the ring in her hand. It was too big for her finger.

The family lingered by the fire till Lousinda told all the children it was time for them to go to bed. The girls giggled as they disappeared under the covers and the boys protested at their noise making. After everyone had settled, Reuben and Rebekah went to their room. Reuben closed the door and they prepared for bed. Rebekah opened the lid to a box her mother had given her and took from it a gown. It was not an exquisite gown, but it felt soft and warm. It was made of flannel and trimmed with a pale yellow ribbon. She slipped it over her beautiful, young body and quickly climbed into bed, because the room was cold and she shivered.

Reuben got into bed wearing his underwear. They teased each other as they covered themselves tightly with the handmade quilts. Her sense of innocence was fleeting as he inspired her with his affectionate touch. Rebekah, his wife, became his succulent vine. She made him feel healthy and whole. She filled his soul and on this night she became his life-long blessing. He would dwell with her forever.

The early light of the morning came and they lay awake wrapped in their delicious cocoon. They were kissed with the wedding morning dew and they loved again.

Reuben bought his pair of mules one month later, but the plan to build a house near the sawmill failed. Instead he made a deal with a land owner not to sharecrop, but to be a furnishing tenant, the difference being a sharecropper lives and works on a place fully furnished with all the necessities for farming and support for his family until the crops are sold. Then, he gets one-half of the selling price of the crops raised. The furnishing tenant has a landlord, but he furnishes equipment for farming, supports his own family and at the sale of the crops, he receives two-thirds of the cotton and three-fourths of other crops raised.

Reuben had his mules and money in his pocket to support himself and Rebekah for a while, so he fit into the latter group.

It was the end of March when Reuben and Rebekah prepared themselves to take their mules and move into a place of their own. On the day they were leaving, a friend was visiting the McCormick family and he had a camera. He took a picture of Reuben and Rebekah and their two mules. Reuben was dressed in a white shirt, a pair of overalls, his suit jacket, last year's shoes, and, of course, his hat. Rebekah wore a black denim skirt with pockets, a white denim jacket, black stockings and the new lace up high-top shoes Reuben bought her. They stood in the back yard of the McCormick's place holding the reigns to the mules. Reuben looked proud with his right hand cupping his pocket. Rebekah was pregnant with their first child.

This photograph taken in 1921 documented the beginning of Reuben Oliver Kincaide's life with Rebekah McCormick. The photo would withstand the perils of time and their children would each cherish a copy.

The house they moved into was plain with rough, unfinished walls. There was a large room with a fireplace, one small bedroom on the side, a kitchen in the back, and there was no front porch.

Family and friends helped to provide them with some furniture. There was already a wood-burning stove in the kitchen, and someone gave them an old wooden kitchen table. Reuben built a bench to put at one side of the table, and Mr. Baxter gave them two chairs. Both bench and chairs had been made from pine wood at the saw mill. Rebekah's mother gave them a four-poster bed and other small things such as a wash stand.

They didn't have much, but it was a beginning, and Rebekah took pride in keeping her house clean. She spent most of her time in the kitchen. She was mistress of this room. Her intent was to nurture her husband and later, her children. She picked vegetables from the garden, killed and dressed chickens in the back yard and on any given day, the aroma of slowly baking bread filled the house. Bread was known to be the "staff of life" but in Reuben's household it was coffee. The enameled coffee pot always sat on the iron stove. He liked his coffee strong. He said if you couldn't practically cut it with a knife, it wasn't any good.

In the late evening when the day's work was done, Reuben would come home and Rebekah was always there when he would open the door and call out, "Is supper ready?" Usually he would add to that, two words "ole' woman." Throughout all their years together, Reuben and Rebekah called each other "ole' woman" and "ole' man." It was a term of endearment they used for each other. Most likely it was derived from an old Indian custom. Many of the Indian customs still lingered with Rebekah. One such custom gave Reuben a fright.

It was shortly after they had moved into their home. One night they were already prepared for bed, but had not yet turned out the lamp, when a knock came on the door. Reuben opened the door and there stood ten or twelve people, neighbors from the countryside. They spoke not a word. Rebekah invited them all in and they each sat down around the front room, some on chairs, some on the floor. They took nothing to eat or drink. They sat in silence for about an hour, then they all stood up and left the house. This custom was called "dry-sitting" pronounced, "dry-setting." It was always done to newlyweds or as a welcome to someone moving into the area.

It was a good thing that Rebekah knew about this custom because Reuben had never heard of such a thing. He was ready to take his shotgun out. Needless to say he was not in favor of the idea or custom or whatever it was.

Summertime came and Reuben continued to work the fields during the day, and in the evenings he would sit and read the newspaper. He could hear the sweep of Rebekah's skirt across the wooden floors as she cared for him and their home. Often they took time to nurture themselves by walking through a field of wildflowers or resting beneath a shade tree.

Rebekah could see that little-boy twinkle in Reuben's eyes. She was carrying his child and he seemed to be very happy; that is why the event that followed was so perplexing to her.

It was terribly hot and the rain came in the middle of the day. Rebekah thought no one would be watching as she stood under the eaves of the house to let the rain fall on her. She had taken the pins from her hair and it fell to her waist. The rain poured over her face and through her beautiful chestnut brown hair. She loved washing her hair in the rain because the rain water gave a shine to her hair.

Having left the field because of the rain, Reuben came to the house. As he came around the corner of the house, he saw her silhouette embracing the rainfall. Time raced backward as his heart leaped with joy. It was Tasha! He was again in the celery fields of Sanford with his beloved Tasha. The rain was still caressing her body. His whole being filled with ecstasy as he remembered the joy of her. He leaped as he wanted to catch her, to hold her once again.

The moment he touched her, he knew it was not Tasha. He shoved Rebekah away from the spout of water, shouting at her, "What the hell are you trying to do? You want to make yourself sick? You go in the house and get some dry clothes on."

Rebekah started to cry as she said, "Why, Reuben, what is wrong with you? I've done nothing wrong. It won't hurt the baby, if that is what you are afraid of. I've seen my mother wash her hair in the rain many times when she was with child. It was so hot and I was enjoying the cool rain."

Reuben's answer to her was, "Well, you can just go and enjoy something else. I don't want to catch you doing that again."

Rebekah had no way of knowing what had just happened to Reuben. She only knew he had hurt her feelings. Reuben could not tell her. She just wouldn't understand how hard he had tried to let go of the past. She just wouldn't understand. Maybe someday he would be free of the memories of Tasha.

Every season was beautiful and so it was as summer turned to autumn. Reuben was an accepted stranger among these people of northern Alabama. Here he felt a deep satisfaction and a sense of a full world unfolding with Rebekah to savor by his side. It was Rebekah who had introduced Reuben to the finest and rarest pure love. Beauty transpired through her as she awaited the wonders of motherhood. Reuben gave the impression that this was all he ever wanted.

It was time for the birth of their first child. Reuben took Rebekah to her mother's house so she could be comforted and cared for. The hour drew near as Reuben kept pulling out his pocket watch, but time seemed to stand still. He kept a fire in the fireplace all night as the October nights were cold. The firelight gave the room an amber glow as he watched his wife bear the pain with her mother by her bedside. A baby's cry awakened the golden sun.

The small miracle was wrapped in a blanket and laid in his arms. "A son, my son," he whispered as he held him close to his heart. Then he placed him on his mother's bosom and she pressed her husband's hand to her lips. They held in their hearts this link between generations and a son they could not bear to lose.

As Reuben gazed upon the mother and child, the spirits of his past seemed to inhabit his soul and his eyes held the image of another time. He turned his head as tears expressed his thoughts of two baby girls. Rebekah only guessed they were tears of joy. She said to him, "Reuben, what will you call our son?"

Without hesitation he replied, "Marion Harding, his name will be Marion Harding Kincaide."

She smiled and said, "I think that is fine. It is a fine name for our son."

Later the family asked Reuben why he named the baby Marion Harding. He said he chose the name Marion because his father's name was Francis Marion and he had been named after an American Revolution officer, Francis Marion, who was nicknamed the Swamp Fox due to his cunning guerrilla-style attacks on the British in South Carolina during the Revolutionary War. Francis Marion (1732-1795) was a hero from South Carolina. Reuben's grandfather had come from North Carolina before he moved the family to Tallapoosa, Georgia. The war hero, Francis Marion, was popular all through the South. The famous Castillo de San Marcos fort in St. Augustine, Florida, was renamed Fort Francis Marion and there is a

Francis Marion National Forest in McClellanville, South Carolina.

Reuben gave Marion the middle name Harding, because at the time, the President of the United States was Warren Harding. Reuben was patriotic and proud of his country, and he expressed that pride when he named his son, Marion Harding.

At the time he did this, he had no way of knowing that this was not his first son. Another boy had been born three years before in Sanford, Florida. Tasha had given him his first son. The celery farm workers, who took the baby to raise when his mother died and his grandfather did not want him, loved the boy very much. They knew who his father was, but they had no reason to try to find him, nor did they have the means to do so. They figured he went off to war and since he didn't return to Sanford, he was probably killed. If they ever needed to, they would tell the child his father's name, Reuben Oliver Kincaide. They called the little boy, Lucky.

By the end of 1921, after Reuben had labored so hard, his income for the entire year was less than $350. This was due to the severe drop in farm prices. The index of farm prices plummeted and the farmers of the South were the worst hit. Reuben had invested everything he had into this farm life and now he had a wife and child, so he decided to try another year's crop. At the sale of the second year's crop, the landlord demanded 75 percent of the profit. Reuben had a big fight with him because these were not the terms he was supposed to be working under. The landlord won the argument by refusing another year's contract and ordered Reuben to move off his property. This left Reuben broke and with no house to live in.

As he stood at the window watching the whirl of winter leaves catch falling rain, he was jingling the coins in his pocket. Coins, this is all he was left with after two years of hard work and trying to do the right thing. He had such high hopes after he received his money from the bank in Sanford and married a wonderful Christian girl and now had a beautiful baby son. Reuben questioned himself, *what happened to my dream of letting go of my past, living in the present and planning for a good future?*

Rebekah could tell something was troubling her husband, so she asked, "Reuben, what's wrong?"

Reuben turned from the window with his hands still in his pockets and said: "It's this damn farm. Can't make a living at it. I tell you ole woman, it's no good. What we need to do is get out of here." Reuben paced the floor as he raged on about refusing to be an aged farmer stuck to a plow,

143

trying to make a living off worthless ground. He grew more restless by the minute and finally he grabbed his hat and slammed the door as he left the house. Rebekah sat quietly holding the baby boy in her lap.

Reuben went to the barn, got his two mules ready and took them to Trinity. Here he sold the mules, bought a train ticket to Decatur and boarded the train. As the train pulled away from the Trinity Depot, Reuben said to himself, "There has got to be a better life out there. I will find it! Guess I've learned my lesson about farming. I hated that damn farm in Tallapoosa. Don't know what made me think it would be any different here. One thing for sure, I promise myself I will never try it again, not even if I live to be a hundred."

Reuben would live to be one-hundred, and that is one promise he would keep.

When Reuben got to Decatur, he went into the office at the train station and asked about a job. He told them he had worked for the railroad in Birmingham after the war and he needed a job now. The only thing they had was the job of a car knocker. He would have to take care of the railroad cars, see that they were cleaned out and hook them up as needed. He accepted the job. He made arrangements for an apartment in town and moved Rebekah and Marion into it. Rebekah did not question his decision to leave the farm.

Only fifteen months passed before Reuben and Rebekah had another son. Reuben was not content with his job, but he went to work everyday. While working around the train station, he overheard many conversations of travelers that came through there. The speakeasies were the most popular subject discussed. "Speakeasy" was the slang word given to the one-time saloon where alcoholic drinks were sold illegally. Their secretive atmosphere was created due to the Prohibition law passed in 1920. This federal law forbid the manufacture, transportation and sale of alcoholic beverages in the United States.

The worst aspect of this law was that people who would in no way be criminally bent, and were ordinarily law-abiding citizens, found themselves in speakeasies in order to have a drink. There was big money to be made in speakeasies and the racketeering of alcohol. Gangsters were organizing as never before. Their big ports of operation were large cities such as Chicago, Detroit, Cincinnati and New York, but they involved many men from all over the country.

As Reuben walked through the station one day, he heard a familiar voice. When the man turned so Reuben could see his face, he recognized him immediately. It was George Bogart. They made eye contact at the same time and Bogart called out, "Hey, Reuben, where's your hat?"

"In my locker. I don't wear it when I am working," Reuben replied as he crossed the room and shook Bogart's hand.

"You working here in this rinky-dinky town? You working for the railroad here in Decatur? I wondered what became of you after you left Birmingham. You should have stayed there. I told you I would see you got a job and from the looks of this place you would have been better off." Bogart continued to talk as they walked toward the train he was to leave on.

"Maybe you were right about the job," Reuben said. "Things didn't work out quite like I wanted them to here, but one good thing, I found me a good woman and now I'm married and have two sons."

Bogart congratulated him and they stood outside the train car and talked for about twenty minutes. "Tell you what," Bogart said, "I got some business in a couple of Northern cities, but I'll be passing back through here in a couple of weeks. If things work out like I expect them to, I will be closing up my hat store in Birmingham. Tell me how I can contact you when I come back into Decatur. We might be able to work something out."

Reuben wrote his address on a slip of paper and gave it to Bogart. He told him he could also ask at the depot office; they would know where to find him if he was working. With that Bogart boarded the train. Reuben thought what an odd fellow this man he had once met in Georgia and came across again in Birmingham was. He wasn't sure just what he was all about, but the idea of working for him might not be such a bad one.

Three weeks later, George Bogart returned to Decatur. He made Reuben an offer to move to Jeffersonville, Indiana. He told him he had purchased a house there and Reuben and his family could live in it. He said the house needed some repair work and a good paint job. He asked Reuben if he could paint. Reuben's reply was, "I haven't done much of it, but I'm a quick study."

That was good enough for Bogart, so they made plans for Reuben to take Rebekah and his two sons to live in the Bogart house in Indiana.

When Reuben told his railroad bosses he would be quitting his job and going to Jeffersonville, Indiana, they informed him that Jeffersonville was a big railway center and he could probably get a job there with the railroad.

They assured him of free passage from Decatur to Jeffersonville because he did work for the railroad.

So once again, Reuben would take advantage of this free railway pass and if the deal with Mr. Bogart didn't work out, he might just wind up working for the railroad in Jeffersonville.

Rebekah sat on the porch with her mother as she watched her two little sons play in the yard. It was springtime and she had taken their shoes off so they could feel the fresh green grass beneath their feet. Rebekah's younger brothers, Thelton and Nathan, stood at the side of the house watching the little boys also. The brothers were wearing bib overalls made out of denim and long-sleeve shirts. They were barefooted also.

Rebekah said to her mother, "I don't know why Reuben wants to move to Indiana. I just don't know if I am up to traveling with the boys. We don't have many clothes and I don't have anything to carry what we do have in. I don't seem to be able to talk to Reuben about my needs."

Lousinda stood up, reached out to her daughter and said, "Come in the house, the boys will watch your babies for a few minutes." When they got inside, Rebekah saw a traveling trunk sitting in the middle of the room. Lousinda walked over to it and said, "I thought you might be needing this. I told your father when you married Reuben Kincaide that it wouldn't be long before you would be leaving. Rebekah, Reuben is not like us. We are just country people. Never been anywhere and will never go anywhere. Which is okay for us, but Reuben is different. He's a man of the world. His thoughts go far and beyond this place of your ancestors. He's a stranger to us. But, I like him. He has showed us that he is a hard worker and he is intelligent, always reading the newspaper and always interested in what is going on. Go with him, Rebekah. He will take you away from this place and someday, you will have more than you ever dreamed. Be understanding of him; he is just a man, and no man listens to his wife. You put your things in this trunk. I have already put a few things in there for you and the babies."

Rebekah hugged her mother and said, "Thank you, ma." She then reached into the trunk and picked up a photograph. It was a photo of her that her father had taken the morning she got married. She was standing in the sun, in the front of a window on the side of the house. She was wearing the clothes she would be married in except for her white shoes. Her right arm was bent to her waist as she held a dark felt hat in that hand. Her left arm fell gracefully to her side and her hand caressed the folds of her skirt against the crisp breeze that blew on that December day. Her waist-length hair was pinned back away from her face and up off her neck. She wore no jewelry. Her beautiful face was young, fresh and pure. She stood tall and proud caring the dignity of her ancestors. She showed strength beyond her years at only eighteen years old.

In the trunk there was also a Bible. Rebekah opened the Bible and placed the photograph between its pages. She started to cry. Her mother said, "Now, there will be none of that. You've got a trip to take. I'll tell you what; ask Reuben if it is okay that your sister, Mattie, goes with you. She can help you out on the trip, then Reuben can put her on a train and send her home whenever you don't need her anymore. How does that sound? See, everything is going to be all right."

When Rebekah got home, she asked Reuben about Mattie going to Indiana with them. He was in complete agreement with the idea. Rebekah also told him that neither she or the boys had good enough clothes to travel in. Reuben's reply was to go down to the dry goods store in Moulton and buy whatever she needed. She could tell the owner of that store he would get his money when "hell freezes over." Reuben was bitter and blamed everyone for his failure as a farmer.

The day for leaving Decatur could not come too soon for Reuben. He closed out his post office box at the Decatur post office. He had never told Rebekah about the post office box. He sent Felix a letter saying he was going to Indiana and that he would be in touch. In the letter he did not mention Mary or anyone else and he sent no money.

This decision to move to Indiana meant he could distance himself even further from his past. He told Rebekah very little about his past only that he was born in Tallapoosa, Georgia, that his father had died and his mother lived with his brother and was well taken care of.

* * *

There was a light rain on that early Spring morning when Reuben, Rebekah, the two boys and Mattie boarded the train in Decatur, Alabama.

Immediately the train turned north onto an iron bridge that had been built across the Tennessee River in 1856 before the Civil War. The little boys delighted in the sight of paddle-wheel steamboats on the river, while Rebekah and Mattie settled themselves down for the long train trip.

147

Reuben sat in a seat alone. He had intended to cross this river four years ago, but instead, he had found someone and a way of life that postponed his travel. Today Reuben was a different man. He wore his suit, tie and hat. His small body sat tall in the seat. He held his head high with confidence. His wife asked him if everything was okay. His sons played and called out, "Look, Daddy, look."

As the train rolled on the tracks across the river, Reuben smiled as he gazed out the window. He could see sun through the rain.

CHAPTER TWELVE

*A*fter news of the divorce of Victoria Sherwood and Reuben Oliver Kincaide was published in the town's newspaper in February of 1920, talk of Reuben settled down.

Jessie Bailey had been the last person to see Reuben in Tallapoosa. Jessie continued to brag about how he would handle Reuben if he ever saw him in that town again. Jessie never told the truth about the fight he had with Reuben. He seemed to feel it necessary to spend a lot of his time at the Sherwood home, and he went along with them in telling Vanessa that her father was dead. Everyone was very protective of little Vanessa.

Jessie seldom saw Mary, but when he did he joked about their encounter that night when Jessie was searching for Reuben. Mary never told anyone about what happened to her. After Mary saw the notice of the final divorce in the newspaper, she waited for Reuben to come to get her and Annie Mae. When Felix came to her and showed her the letter from Reuben after he had gone to Decatur, Alabama, she still had hopes of him coming back to her. After all he kept sending her some money even if he didn't write directly to her. She wrote letters to him and gave them to Felix to send to Reuben, but not one was ever answered.

Mary continued to work for Robert Wilson and they remained friends. Once in a while, Robert would bring up the subject of marriage, but Mary always turned him down until the day Felix came over with the news that Reuben had married someone in northern Alabama.

On Christmas day, eleven days later, Mary got married to Robert. She told her daughter that even though Robert was not her father, he loved them

149

both very much. He was a good provider and would take care of them. She also told her that her real daddy had not forgotten her because he had sent her money.

"Annie Mae," Mary said "someday your daddy will come to you. You must remember he loves you and you must always be good to him. In my heart, I will always love him. I promise, my darling daughter, one day he will come."

The little girl was six years old. She would wait twenty-four years, to realize her mother's promise.

The day after Mary's wedding to Robert, she moved her things out of the house on Head Street. She kept the house and it was two years until she heard from Felix that Reuben had a son. Reuben had stopped sending money and the news of his son put a closure to Mary's humiliation. She sold the house. She was going to make sure that Annie Mae would never have to share this property with one of Reuben's heirs. This was the least Reuben could give her because he was never going to give her his name. In the beginning it had been everything for Victoria and Vanessa; now she was being passed over for another wife and child.

One day, when Annie Mae was old enough, Mary would tell her the complete truth about her father. She would never tell Victoria or Vanessa the truth about her baby by Reuben. For now she would live and let live.

Victoria remained in Atlanta and visited her daughter in Tallapoosa on holidays. If she knew about Mary and Annie Mae, she never acknowledged it.

Reuben's mother stayed on the Kincaide farm with Felix and waited for word from her son. She never made contact with Victoria, Mary or either of her grandchildren.

Reuben escaped his past for many years. He continued to lie about his age and seven years of his life. He became an expert paint contractor. This would be his occupation until he was eighty years old.

Rebekah continued to have children (ten in all). She remained a devoted wife and mother, although she never wore the ring Reuben gave her on their wedding day. She never again washed her hair in the rain, but would catch rainwater in a bucket. The rose became a symbol of devotion to her. She returned to the forest for a cutting to plant in a special place. Just as her father had done, she rang the bell at the end of another war. The ringing of the bell would once again declare the house burning. She also kept the photograph of herself that her mother gave her. One day, all her children would have a copy.

This same photo would be used in a published book that was dedicated to her, Rebekah McCormick Kincaide.

Of the McCormick family, many members of Rebekah's family live near the forest today.

The feed store in Moulton, Alabama is still open for business. One day three ladies would come to this store where Reuben married their mother.

What happened to those in Ruben's life:

George Bogart — Reuben's mentor. They shared a lifetime for better or worse.

- ▸ The knife Jessie pulled on Reuben remained buried in the thick kudzu on the banks of the railway track. The knife would be found thirty-four years later, but not by Jessie.
- ▸ Felix — The last time he heard from Reuben was in 1924 when Reuben left Decatur headed for Indiana. Felix died 4 years later.
- ▸ MaryAnne — Reuben's mother moved off the Kincaide farm when Felix died. She went to live with Frank, Reuben's half-brother. MaryAnne was Frank's step-mother. She died in 1936 without ever seeing her son again.
- ▸ Victoria — After her divorce from Reuben, she continued to live in Atlanta. She visited her daughter Vanessa in Tallapoosa on holidays. If she knew about Reuben's mistress, Mary or the child, Annie Mae, she never acknowledged it. Her cries in the night for her lost love would one day be answered.
- ▸ Vanessa — In 1924, when Reuben moved to Indiana, his daughter Vanessa was ten years old. She was doted on by her grandparents and Jessie.
- ▸ Mary — She had waited for Reuben until she heard he had married another. She was twenty-five years old when she married Robert. She gave her daughter, Annie Mae, a step-father. In her heart, she knew that one day Reuben would return to them in Tallapoosa.
- ▸ Annie Mae — Reuben's daughter by his mistress Mary was a beautiful little girl with golden curls, like her mother. She was a happy child and would love her real daddy, no matter how long it took for him to come to see her.
- ▸ Lucky — was three years old when Reuben had another son.

Reuben had no idea that Lucky was growing up in the celery fields of Sanford. He would not know of Lucky until one day Lucky would use his father's name.

- ▸ The Mule Photograph — The photo of Reuben and Rebekah standing in the barnyard with their two mules, documented Reuben's life beginning with Rebekah. This photo taken in Alabama in 1920 would one day be compared with the photo Reuben had taken in Tallapoosa in 1913 before his marriage to Victoria. These two photos were taken seven years apart.

- ▸ Reuben's Age — His first lie to Rebekah had been about his age. He told her he had been born in 1895 when in fact he was born seven years before that in 1888. Years later Reuben would reveal his true age to governmental authorities. To Rebekah and his family there would be no explanation given.

CHAPTER THIRTEEN

*I*t was 1924 and once again Reuben Oliver Kincaide was on a train. He was traveling, yearning to be free from his past, and searching for a better life.

After crossing the mighty Tennessee River, the train stayed on a route north. The weather had cleared and in the distance to the east, Reuben could see the Great Smokey Mountains. He pointed them out to his wife and two little boys.

Rebekah had heard of the Great Smokey Mountains because it had been told to her that her great-great-grandfather, Richard Sanderson, had crossed these mountains to make a land deal with the Cherokee Indians in 1775. The Cherokee Indians called the mountains a name that meant "the place of the blue smoke" because the tops were nearly always covered with a blue-gray haze that looked like smoke.

These mountains were part of the mountain range that had been a barrier to the migration of white man to the west. Richard Sanderson was living in North Carolina and was interested in the territories beyond the mountains. He formed a land company and employed the services of a skilled woodsman named Daniel Boone. Boone marked trails into the unexplored mountains. He cut a trail known as the Wilderness Trail, and this was used as the main route into Tennessee.

When Richard Sanderson was dealing with the Cherokee Indians he exposed his son John Allen to a way of life that would spark his interest of exploration and adventure and would lead to his marriage of a Cherokee Indian girl named Martha.

While growing up in the forest in northern Alabama, Rebekah had often sat and listened to the elder members of her family tell the story of John Allen Sanderson and Martha. Rebekah had pictured in her mind the great mountains that John Allen had crossed before venturing down the Tennessee River. She never dreamed that one day she would see these mountains.

The rail tracks left the hilly region and ran down into a deep basin. Somehow Rebekah felt a kinship to this place. She knew that her great-grandfather had left his wife Martha and little boy, John Allen, Jr., to join the Confederacy during the Civil War. What she did not know was that at this moment, the train she was on was crossing the site of the Civil War battle of Murfreesboro. This battle was fought between December 31, 1862 and January 3, 1863. John Allen Sanderson had died here.

As Rebekah looked out the train window, she could see the rows of small white crosses marking the Stone River National Cemetery. She would never know how close she came to her great-grandfather's grave.

The train stopped in Nashville, Tennessee. Reuben checked with the conductor to see if he could get a Pullman sleeper car so they could put the boys to bed for a nap. Their playfulness had worn Mattie, Rebekah's sister, completely out. The conductor was pleased to accommodate them and everyone settled down for the continuing train ride.

Rebekah sat next to Reuben, while Mattie and the boys slept. She reached over and took his hand. She spoke softly to him. "Reuben, I am enjoying this trip. I never thought I would leave the farm. You are showing me a whole new world and I am grateful." Reuben removed his hand from hers and said nothing. The train approached Kentucky.

Although Reuben sat in silence, it did not dampen Rebekah's spirit. She could feel her great-grandfather's adventurous spirit and marveled at the sights outside the train window.

Fields of blue grass covered the rolling hills. It was the tiny flowers of the grass that gave entire fields a blue cast. Horses could be seen running free in their pastures.

When Reuben looked upon Rebekah's face, he could see the pleasure the sight of these wondrous things brought to her. Perhaps when he looked into her bright shining eyes, he could see his hope for the future.

The train crossed another great river, the Ohio, and immediately stopped at its final destination, Jeffersonville, Indiana.

Reuben, Rebekah, their two sons and Mattie, Rebekah's sister, were hesitant to leave the train.

They were a poor Southern family and today they found themselves walking into a major railroad center in Indiana. It was like watching an ant hill, seeing everyone racing around and not knowing what direction they were taking or what they were doing.

Reuben yelled to Rebekah, "This gives new meaning to The Roaring Twenties." Because of its central location, Indiana was the crossroads to America and everything that affected the country passed through there. A sign of the times was the excess of prosperity.

Progress for Indiana actually began in the 1850s, when the railroad pushed into the state and provided farmers with new markets for their crops, the largest of these being corn. During this time, other industries grew. The Studebaker brothers, Clement and Henry, formed a company that became the largest wagon manufacturer in the country. Later in 1904, they began to make gasoline-powered cars.

In 1862, Richard Gatling invented the first practical machine gun, and James Oliver invented and improved a hard-steel plow that could easily cut through tough prairie sod. By the 1920s, Indiana's automobile and other metal-products industries had expanded rapidly.

Understanding the progression of this state and its easy access to the rest of the country, it was not hard to understand how this area became a melting pot for all the elements of the times, which included social behavior as well as inventions.

A spirit of gaiety raged through the country. Radios could be found in living rooms and movies gained popularity. Even though it was during the Prohibition days, drinking and breaking the law were acceptable things to do for the great middle-class, for women as well as men.

Organized crime flourished because of the bootlegging and smuggling of alcoholic beverages. Large amounts of money could be made so it became a way of life for crime gangs.

Calvin Coolidge became president of the United States when Harding died in office in 1923. He was a common and honest man and even though he could not control organized crime, he was admired and stayed in office until 1929.

Reuben could identify with Calvin Coolidge. Reuben, like President Coolidge, was known for using few words. Coolidge was nicknamed

"Silent Col." Once during a baseball game, he spoke only four words, "What time is it?"

Like Reuben, Coolidge enjoyed the game of baseball. He opened the World Series in 1925.

A personal habit Coolidge had was pouring his coffee into a saucer to cool, then drinking it from the saucer. Reuben noted this idea from his president and began doing it himself. For the rest of Reuben's life this was one of his traits. Wherever he went he asked for a second saucer when he was served coffee. Rebekah never prepared the table at home without making sure there was a second saucer at Reuben's place. The practice may not have been appreciated at social gatherings in the White House, but Calvin was the president of the United States. Therefore if Calvin could do it, so could Reuben.

Reuben proclaimed that Calvin Coolidge was the best president this country ever had. Reuben knew for sure that the years of Coolidge's presidency (1923-1929) were the best times of his life.

This period of his life began once he stepped off the train in Jeffersonville, Indiana.

Reuben guided his family through the mass of people and luggage at the train station. Bogart had given him the address of his house in Jeffersonville and Reuben, with his family, was to live there.

Reuben's heart filled with excitement! This was a new world! Their life was going to be great here. He took Rebekah's hand and promised her this. Rebekah trusted her husband and shared his excitement.

A man tapped Reuben on the shoulder and asked, "Are you Reuben Oliver Kincaide?"

Reuben replied, "Yes".

"You are to come with me. Mr. Bogart said to transport you to his place."

He was a powerfully built man of formidable girth, a stranger, but without hesitation Reuben followed him out of the train station. They loaded Rebekah's trunk into the back of a large black car, then the family got inside the car with the rest of their things. Reuben sat up front with the stranger.

The family gazed out the windows of the huge black car as it wound its way down streets of the city on the banks of the Ohio River. The stranger drove the car out of the city into a rural setting. It was only a short distance before he brought the car to a stop.

There on a gentle rise sat a large two story house. It was painted white with green shutters. There was a porch across the front with ornate wood trimming and carved spindle posters. The front yard was spacious and tree-shaded. To this family, who had been living in a Southern tenant farm house in Alabama, it was a hill-top mansion.

After parking the car, the driver helped Reuben carry the trunk and place it on the front porch. He then shook Reuben's hand and Reuben thanked him for the lift. As the black car disappeared down the road, Reuben took off his hat and scratched his forehead. He never found out how this man found him among the crowd at the train station.

The boys had tumbled out of the car and Mattie was chasing them to the back of the house. Reuben and Rebekah held hands as they followed the playful children into the backyard. They strolled through a blossoming apple orchard. They were enticed to sample the fruits of a grape arbor. Reuben pointed out the barn and explained to his wife where he would fix a place for some chickens. They explored a plot for a vegetable garden and together they wandered down behind the barn into a meadow filled with wildflowers. It was sunny and warm and their life suddenly seemed sprinkled with magic.

When Rebekah lifted her head to Reuben, her face was powdered with sunshine and her eyes expressed a fulfillment of a lifetime of dreams. Reuben was astonishingly intense as he lay with Rebekah. She was a beautiful and fertile woman and as he immersed himself in her, they blended together into a deep, delicious place. Sun drenched violet petals were scattered by a breeze and with the whispering of promises to each other, they left their field of dreams.

Over the coming years, Reuben and Rebekah would return to this spot with their children to have picnics. Before the children, their feeling of delight would be shared by special glances at each other. All of Rebekah's life, she enjoyed having picnics with her children.

When Reuben and Rebekah returned to the house, they found the two little boys banging on the door, yelling at Mattie to open it. Reuben said to them as he stepped up on the porch, "Get away from that door. I have the key; Mattie can't open it. I'll let us all in, but there will be no running or yelling in the house."

The family went from room to room, amazed at what they found. The wooden furniture was splendid in its simplicity and most adequate for their needs. They marveled at the Victrola in the living room and the telephone on the wall in the kitchen. Rebekah was pleased with the supply of utensils for housekeeping. She and Mattie began their work immediately, preparing beds and arranging the house for their use. There was only one room upstairs that was locked and Reuben did not have a key for that room. He gave the explanation that the room had Bogart's personal belongings and it was not to be disturbed.

On his inspection of the house, Reuben could see there was a lot of work to be done. It was a good sturdy house, but the clapboards on the outside needed painting and there were some plain, unfinished walls on the inside. He told Rebekah to make a list of all the things they needed, and the next day, they went into town.

Reuben made no attempt to be alone in town. There would be no secret post office box opened, no secret letters mailed to Tallapoosa, no contact at all with his past.

Together they bought materials from the dry goods store and gardening supplies. Then while Rebekah shopped for groceries, Reuben went to the paint store. He told the owner of the store that he did not know much about painting but he was going to paint Bogart's house. The store owner told him, he had come to the right place. He gave his guidance to Reuben in selecting paint, brushes, a ladder, and so on. He even advised him on wallpaper and Reuben picked out some that had printed roses and clematis.

The store owner told Reuben he would have all the supplies delivered to the Bogart house and when Reuben offered to pay, the man said, "Put your money in your pocket. I'll be well paid for this job!" Once again Reuben found himself lifting his hat to scratch the top of his forehead. He didn't know what to think of that remark, but he gave no argument.

When Reuben returned to Rebekah, she had finished her grocery shopping and the man who owned the grocery store told them his delivery boy would give them a ride home. He also told Rebekah to call him on the phone when she needed something and he would have it delivered. With a sarcastic voice, Reuben said, "I suppose you will pay for my groceries, too."

The man sorta chuckled and said, "No, sir, you will pay your own grocery bill."

Rebekah didn't understand what was going on, but from then on what food and items she didn't get from the garden or make on her own, she ordered over the telephone.

Reuben settled in to make the coming years the happiest time of his life, and he knew it was up to him to make this happen. His emphasis was on his family. He dedicated his time to working on the Bogart place and after many trips to the paint store, he became an excellent painter. He enjoyed painting more than any other job he had ever done in his life.

Rebekah awoke to a time when her whole life changed and she was shaping her destiny. She created a warm and happy, spirited refuge for her family. With cheery gingham curtains and soothing aromas infusing the kitchen, it was a welcoming house for friends.

At the end of each day, Reuben and Rebekah retired to their private chambers where they shared their nest of comfort.

Nine months after their arrival in Indiana, they filled the house with happiness when a baby girl was born. It was in the fall of that year that Bogart brought his wife to pay a visit to Reuben. Originally Bogart had planned for Reuben to take care of his place in Jeffersonville until he came to live in it, but his plans changed. He bought a place in Louisville, Kentucky, which is located just across the Ohio River from Jeffersonville, Indiana.

Seems as though Bogart had gotten involved in horse racing. He and his wife attended The Kentucky Derby on the first Saturday of May, 1925. The Kentucky Derby began in 1875 and became the best known horse race in the United States. The year Bogart and his wife attended, a sports columnist gave the race a nickname — the "Run for the Roses." Since 1904 it had been the tradition to decorate the winning horse with a blanket of roses. The roses draped over the horse and the proud jockey astride provided a wonderful snapshot for Stella Bogart. She enjoyed taking photographs and took her camera everywhere.

On the day Stella accompanied her husband to the house in Jeffersonville to visit Reuben, she became fond of Rebekah and the three children. She and Rebekah became good friends and she returned to the house often. She provided them with clothes and things that they ordinarily would not have had. She always had her camera with her when she came and on one visit she insisted the family dress for a nice photograph.

Stella positioned the family on the front porch. She spread a quilt out, draping it down over the edge of the porch. Reuben dressed in his suit, white shirt and tie, sat down and placed his oldest son, Marion, directly in front of him. Reuben wore his glasses but no hat. Marion was wearing a child's sailor suit and black knee stockings and shoes. He sat with his legs over the edge of the porch and his feet on the ground.

Rebekah sat down beside Reuben. She was wearing a plaid gingham dress she had made herself. Her long hair was pulled back away from her face into a bun in the back. She wore no makeup or jewelry. She put her arms around her second son and placed him at her knees. The little boy sat with his legs straight out and his little hands in his lap with fingers touching. He had on a short-sleeve shirt, short pants, knee socks and shoes.

Stella placed a knitted blanket between the two boys and sat the baby girl down in the middle. The baby was wearing a white sweater with matching baby cap and booties. Underneath the sweater she wore a dress made by her mother.

There Reuben sat with his beautiful wife, Rebekah, and their three healthy, happy children. He was a proud, happy man; a man free of his past, looking forward to a bright future.

Stella took the photograph. It was in the fall of 1925. Reuben was thirty-seven years old. Sixty-nine years later, this photo would be used to unite Reuben's past with his future. Reuben would live through sixty-four of those years.

The years spent at the Bogart house were happy times. The first Christmas after Rebekah and Reuben's first girl was born, Reuben bought a unique, glass-like Santa Claus ornament to hang on their tree. This Santa Claus became a symbol of Reuben and Rebekah's love for their family. Even though the Santa was made of a fragile material, it survived the fifty-one Christmases they shared together.

Reuben and Rebekah also started the tradition of The Sacks.

In the early years of their marriage, with a new child arriving approximately every two years, it was not easy providing for them. When Christmas time came, they pondered over what to do to make the children a special treat. Hanging stockings seemed to be a good idea, but truthfully they didn't have that many extra stockings so they came up with the idea of taking small paper sacks, rolling the tops over once and filling them with whatever they could come up with. Usually it was some candies, especially a peppermint stick and a chocolate drop, then they would add an apple, a banana and an orange and some nuts. Each SACK was placed under the tree with a child's name on it. Somehow this SACK became each child's possession. All year everything had to be shared with each other, but this was from Santa Claus and it was theirs alone.

This tradition of having the SACKS was to be carried on every year without fail during their lifetime with their children. Now, although their parents are no longer with them, the children gather together at Christmas and each year the SACKs are placed under the tree, each SACK with each one's name on it. A prized possession for each one alone! It is as though each SACK holds a magic gift. Not just candy, fruit and nuts but the real spirit of Christmas, from their parent's hearts, the gift of LOVE.

1927 brought the birth of another baby girl. Shortly after the baby was born, Rebekah received word from her family in Alabama that her father was very ill. She and Reuben discussed the fact that as soon as the baby could travel, Rebekah and the children should take the train home to see her father.

Four months later, the time had come and Bogart and his wife, Stella, came to help Reuben put his family on the train. After the train left, the Bogarts took Reuben back to the place in Jeffersonville. Bogart told Reuben he was really pleased with all the work he had done there and he was mostly impressed with the paint job he had done on the house with all the ornate trim work.

Bogart said to Reuben, "Well, Reuben you have everything in good shape here so while your family is away I have some other jobs for you to do." Reuben asked no questions and offered no resistance to this statement. A few days later he found himself in Bogart's car traveling north. Shortly, they arrived at a place called Mooresville, just southwest of Indianapolis, Indiana.

When Reuben got out of the car, he observed a small white farm house. The paint on the outside was peeling, and upon entering the house he could see faded paper decorations hung dejectedly from unpainted walls.

Mr. Bogart introduced Reuben to John Wilson Dillinger. This was not the John Dillinger Reuben had read about in the newspaper. It was the infamous Dillinger's father.

Shortly after the warm greeting, Reuben understood that he was there to restore, repaint the farm house and to help out in anyway requested of him. Seemed as though Dillinger and Bogart were old friends.

Dillinger provided Reuben with a room in the back of the farmhouse, and plans were made for him to begin his work. Reuben liked the man. They often talked about current events, such as Charles Lindbergh's flight from Roosevelt Field, Long Island, to Paris. The day Lindbergh landed in Paris, May 22, 1927, Reuben had a lengthy conversation with Dillinger and some other men that hung out around the farmhouse. They were all amazed at this tall, slender, young air-mail pilot's solo, non-stop flight across the Atlantic. They discussed how this would be the age that air transportation would begin.

Reuben remembered that when he was fifteen years old, the Wright Brothers built the first airplane and flew it in Kitty Hawk, North Carolina. He had said then that he would never be caught flying in one of those contraptions, and now Lindbergh's flight hadn't changed his mind on that.

As Reuben finished his cup of coffee, he said to the guys, "Well, today, boys, a man crossed the ocean in 33.5 hours, but I'm not interested even if it were to the moon and back!" Reuben had no idea that on July 20, 1969, this trip to the moon would actually happen and he would live to see it! He kept his word to his final days: he never flew on one of those airplane contraptions.

Most of Reuben's talks with Mr. Dillinger were about sports. Babe Ruth hit sixty home runs for the New York Yankees and was dubbed the greatest ball player that ever lived, and Reuben made a wager that Jack Dempsey would beat the current heavy-weight boxing champion, Gene Tunney, in the fight to be held in Chicago in September.

Reuben lost that bet, but he never paid the wager because by the date of the fight he had returned to Jeffersonville.

Rebekah was returning from her trip to Alabama because their first son would be starting school.

On September 7, 1927, Rebekah's father, James Clark McCormick, died. Rebekah was grateful she had spent some time with him before his death. He had given her a set of knitting needles: an Excelsior Pin set belonging to his mother that was over 200 years old.

Mattie, Rebekah's sister, did not return to Jeffersonville. Reuben began to help with the care of the children. When the baby girl was crying, Rebekah would hand her to Reuben. She would stop crying and look up at Reuben and smile. Rebekah would say, "This child is your favorite, Reuben." He formed a special bond with this daughter and maintained it all of his life.

Seasons went by and every season was beautiful. The first rays of spring sunshine welcomed morning glories, holly hocks, bridal wreath and violets. Crabapple trees shaded a gentle slope behind the house. In May the trees transformed into soft, sugar candy clouds of red, pink and white blossoms.

The children ran and played under the canopy of the grape arbor and searched the fields for four-leaf clover. Reuben and Rebekah played with the children and created a warm and welcome home for friends.

Rebekah took the children to church every Sunday. She had promised her father that she would always go to church and take her children. She kept that promise all of her life.

Reuben did not go to church, but during the years in Indiana he gave the children money to put in the offering plate at Sunday School and he read the Bible at home.

When summer came, Reuben lined the porch with baskets of fruits and vegetables, and Rebekah preserved the season's harvest. Rebekah had learned from her mother the art of canning and preserving foods. All of Rebekah's life, she nurtured Reuben and her children with good nutritious food. Most of the time she made up her own recipes. She made cottage cheese by letting milk clabber, taking the cream off the top, then poured the clabber milk over a piece of cheese cloth that was placed in a gallon pail. She then tied the cheese cloth together and hung it on the clothes line. The whey would drain out. She would crumble the whey when it was dry, put it in a bowl and pour some of the cream on it. The rest of the cream she used to make butter by beating it till all the milk was out.

She delighted her children with making snow ice cream during the winter and she was an expert at making apple butter. Most of her self-created recipes would later be found in a published cookbook, which was dedicated to her.

Rebekah would start her supper about three o'clock in the afternoon. She wanted it to be ready as soon as Reuben got home. Later in the evening, she would call the children in and tell them to sit on the front porch and wait for their daddy.

Reuben had started doing painting jobs for other men besides Bogart. He was an excellent painter and made good money at it. When he worked in Jeffersonville, he rode the bus, since the bus line came within about a quarter of a mile from the house.

When the bus stopped, the children could see it and they would race across the open field to get to their daddy. Reuben would always have a little paper sack of candy. He would hold it out and the first one to reach him, got the sack. That child got to divide the candy — one piece each. The children would toddle playfully along beside Reuben. When they reached the house, they sat on the porch and enjoyed their candy. These children never forgot the race for the candy sack.

Reuben was a caring father but he was also very strict. He taught his children to do the best they could at whatever they were doing, whether it was their school work or picking up sticks out in the yard.

When the two little boys fought, Reuben made them run around the outside of the house in opposite directions. Then he would tease them by asking them if they saw the little white calves following them. The boys were much older before they figured out their daddy was talking about the calves of their legs. One day when they had to run around the house, the boys ran into each other and hurt themselves. Reuben never made them do that again.

As the trees turned a beautiful gold in the fall, the children went to school. Their hair was cut by their mother, and she also made the girl's dresses. They had to walk over a small hill to catch the school bus. A black man they called Old Man Franklin looked out for them because he had a place on top of the hill. His yard was fenced in, and inside the fence were some apple and pear trees. He told the children any fruit that was outside the fence they could have. When they got off the school bus they looked forward to picking up the fruit. They guessed Old Man Franklin let them pick up the fallen fruit so they wouldn't climb his fence and pick from the trees. The strange thing was that during the winter months, when the trees had no fruit on them, the children would still find apples outside the fence on the ground.

Being from the South, Reuben and Rebekah were not used to the harsh winters of Indiana. To chase a chill, Reuben would drink his coffee and say, "Just like Maxwell House, `good to the last drop'." This slogan of Maxwell House Coffee long outlived its creator, Theodore Roosevelt, and Reuben preferred Maxwell House coffee all of his life.

Rebekah would sit by the fire quilting, her hands mimicking her female ancestors. When it was weary out of doors, she would add cheer to a gloomy day by planning her spring garden and enjoying the fruits of her summer labor.

When the snowfall brightened the dreary landscape, Reuben, Rebekah and the children were enticed out of doors and delighted in a time of playfulness.

Just before another girl child was added to their family, Stella Bogart took a photo of Reuben and Rebekah's two boys and two girls. The children were dressed in their Sunday best. The two boys had on white, long-sleeve shirts and ties, the youngest one a bow tie. Their pants were knickerbockers, dress knee breeches for that era, and they wore knee socks and dress leather shoes. The little girls were adorable with their short hair cuts and calico dresses trimmed in lace and rick-rack, a delicate workmanship of their mother's. They wore long dark stockings and leather shoes. The youngest girl was clutching a feather in her tiny hand. Rebekah had given it to her to hold to make her stand still for posing for the photo.

They portrayed happy faces as they stood in front of the Bogart house. Reuben and Rebekah were so very proud of them.

This photograph became the favorite of all those Stella took of the family. It came to be known as their Depression-year photo. It symbolized the health and well being of Reuben's family at the beginning of the Depression years.

During this time, a lot of people in the United States were making big money speculating on the stock market. They believed it was magic, a way to get rich quick.

Then in October 1929, the stock market crashed. This set off a whole chain of events. Stores canceled orders, which meant laid-off workers because the supply was greater than the demand.

People had become accustomed to installment-plan buying. When they lost their job, they also lost the things they had because they couldn't make payments. Banks closed because they had made large loans to stockbrokers, and now they couldn't collect on the loans. So people lost the money they had in the banks. Even big corporations had bought a lot of stock and lost all of their money so they had to shut down their businesses.

It was a devastating time for the country. There were long bread lines and poor shanty towns in the cities. It was estimated that some 15,000,000 people were out of work.

Herbert Clark Hoover was the president of the United States at that time, and most Americans felt he did not do enough to help the local populace. His policy was that the poor should get help from private companies, charities or state and local governments. He said there would be no handouts from the federal government.

Reuben was in town on the Tuesday that word of the collapse of the stock market spread like wildfire. He would never forget the sights of panic that gripped the people. Many years to come he would tell of seeing men beat their heads on walls, while ambulances raced to buildings where reportedly people were killing themselves. On this day, Reuben had not put money in the bank since leaving Sanford, Florida, and he had no investments. He didn't believe in saving money anymore. His plan was to live as well as he could on whatever he made at the time. So far, this had worked well for him and his growing family there in Indiana.

When everyone else was frantically trying to stabilize their lives because of the Depression years, Reuben continued to live well. Bogart kept him working on different jobs.

CHAPTER FOURTEEN

One day in particular Reuben would tell about in later years was painting a large three-story mansion with columns in front. He said when he had finished painting it, the man who owned it walked around saying what a nice job he had done. He asked Reuben how many children he had and when Reuben told him, the man rubbed his chin and said, "You know, I think this house could use another coat of paint. Just start up front and give her another." Reuben was happy to oblige.

It was well known at that time there were men making fortunes in rackets such as bootlegging, gambling and other unlawful acts; in fact, they had opened a chapter in history that made the violence of frontier days look like child's play.

These men could afford to have their houses painted twice. Some people referred to them as Robin Hoods — taking from the rich to give to the poor.

Reuben was well aware of the mosaic of crime throughout the Mid-west. This section of the country was where Reuben found himself at this time, and he tried to take care of his family.

When Reuben read familiar names in the newspaper, he always thought about the old man he had met when he painted a house in Mooresville. That man's name, Dillinger, would become familiar to him.

He could not afford to worry about the times in which he lived; he just knew that when he came home at night, his lovely wife and children were there. They were well clothed, fed and protected.

Rebekah was expecting another child when they received word that her grandparents, John Allen and Rodha Sanderson, had died. They both had been seriously ill and died within a few days of each other. They did not bury John Allen where his mother, Martha, was buried at Old Bunyan Hill, but they buried him at Maxwell Chapel Methodist Church. Rodha, his wife of fifty-four years, was buried beside him.

Rebekah wept as she read the news. It had been only four years since she lost her father. She missed her family, but it was impossible for her to go home at this time because in just one month her baby would be delivered.

As expected in July, another child joined the family. This time it was a boy. Reuben loved the little girls, but the boys gave him special pride. He said that one day they would all be soldiers.

In their Indiana home, the telephone was on the wall. Next to the telephone hung a calendar. At the top of this calendar was a picture. A New York Times photographer had taken that picture of United States General John J. Pershing and some of his troops during World War I. Reuben could remember that day well, standing in front of the Red Cross tent, captured by the camera.

Reuben would boast of his photo being taken with General Pershing and now printed on a calendar. The calendar was kept in the family for years and the children would look close at the photo trying to identify their father.

All of Reuben's boys except one became a soldier in the United States military. His patriotism to his country was the one thing that was consistent throughout his life. At the end of his one hundred years, he saw his youngest grandson wearing a United States Air Force uniform. He shook the young man's hand and said, "Son, I am proud of you."

During these years in Indiana with Rebekah and his children, about the only part of his past Reuben would talk about was the time he spent in the military. It was as though he had never done anything else before he met Rebekah in 1920.

He had succeeded in putting his past behind him. For over ten years, he had felt nurtured, safe and happy, but in the 1930s a patchwork of events would cause his world to crumble.

Under the direction of J. Edgar Hoover, the Federal Bureau of Investigation waged a war against organized crime putting many people in prison. Even the elusive "Scarface" Al Capone was sentenced for tax evasion. The crackdown on crime and the end of prohibition stemmed the flow of money to a lot of people's pockets. Reuben's jobs for painting those big houses were getting to be fewer and fewer.

Franklin Delano Roosevelt was elected president of the United States and his New Deal overhauled the banking system, established aid for farmers and money for roads, dams and other public projects. He brought the country out of the deep depression, but instead of making life better for Reuben and his family, it seemed to have the opposite effect.

In 1933, the doctor arrived at the house for the delivery of another baby. Reuben and Rebekah now had seven children. Many years later one of the older children confessed that he thought the doctor kept bringing those babies in his little black bag.

The baby girl that arrived on this day would be their last child born in Indiana.

In the spring, just before Easter, Marion, Reuben and Rebekah's oldest son, climbed a pole to check out a bird's nest. He jumped from the pole and fell on the ground grabbing his side, crying out in pain. He was rushed to the hospital and the doctor operated on him, removing his appendix.

Some of the children got to visit him in the hospital. His oldest sister had been to an Easter egg hunt at school and she had found the prize golden egg. When she walked into the hospital room to visit, she was clutching an Easter basket in her little hands with the golden egg inside. She handed the basket to her brother. Marion was twelve years old. He would recover from the operation, but he would never be well again.

As the summer months approached, Reuben was desperate for work. Bogart paid him a little extra for taking care of his place and he had free rent, but with seven children, Reuben needed to make more money. The children would need new shoes and clothing when school started in the fall.

Reuben went to see Bogart and told him he would have to get some more work. "Well," said Bogart, "I can get you a few things up in Mooresville."

"You mean at the old man's farm?" Reuben asked, sort of alarmed.

"Yeah, you got something against working up there?" Bogart sounded a little irritated.

"It's just that I have a big family now. One of my boys is not well and I shouldn't be away from home and, George, you know I don't want to get mixed up in anything." Reuben was trying to make excuses. He never knew just what George Bogart was planning.

Bogart laughed. "What's the matter, Reuben? No adventure left in you? You lost your nerve? Gotten soft in your old age?"

"No, it's just that I'm not that naive, Georgia boy anymore. I just need an honest day's work," Reuben said.

"Damn it," Bogart shouted, "honest is hard to come by these days. I'm offering you some work up in Moorseville. Now either you want the job or not. Makes no difference to me."

Reuben was hesitant to accept but he needed the money, so he said, "Okay, I'll do it. When can I get started?"

Bogart slapped him on the back and said, "Tell you what Reuben, at the sound of fights or shooting or noise of bottles shattering or gun fire, you just go to the back of the house." Then Bogart laughed, "Just teasing. Seriously, you get your painting equipment ready and I'll pick you up on Monday morning. You can work up there during the week and I'll see that you get a ride home for the weekend. If you're worried about that Dillinger boy being around, don't be. I think the law is about to catch up with him."

Reuben agreed to Bogart's offer and Rebekah got his clothes ready for the week's stay in Mooresville. She put his white painter's overalls in a big pot of boiling water for a good cleaning, while he went to the paint store and picked up supplies.

Come Monday morning, Bogart was there bright and early to pick Reuben up. When Reuben answered his knock at the door, Bogart told him he needed a few minutes to go to *the* room upstairs. He was referring to the locked room to which Reuben did not have a key. Bogart disappeared up the stairs and Reuben went outside to load his work equipment for the trip to Mooresville.

Reuben had speculated about what was in that locked room that seemed so special to his boss. Every time Bogart came to the house, he would go in there with a little black suitcase and come out a few minutes later with the same black case. Then he would pay Reuben, in cash, the money he owed him for his labor. Today was no different; as soon as Bogart came out of the house, he handed Reuben some money. Seemed to reason that somehow the money was connected to the locked room.

During these Depression years, few people trusted the banks to keep their money, especially questionable cash earnings. Reuben knew that Bogart received a lot of money from unlawful sources and his guess what that he kept it in that room upstairs.

It frightened Reuben to think this could be true since his family was living there and could be at risk for a raid by the police, or worse. But, due to the situation Reuben was in, he had no choice but to ignore his suspicions. He often reminded his wife and children to stay away from that room, and neither he nor his family ever questioned Bogart about it.

Several years later Reuben moved from that home without ever seeing the inside of the locked room. This was proof to those he worked for that he was an honest and trusted man.

It was a hot, sticky August day when they arrived in Mooresville. As they approached the farmhouse, Reuben noticed a large black Studebaker parked in the road and several other cars in the yard, one a sporty Chevrolet coupe.

Standing next to the sports car was a short, stocky man wearing a dark-gray coat, light-gray trousers and a straw hat. As Bogart drove his truck down the drive toward the back of the house, Reuben made eye contact with the man standing by the car. The man tilted his straw hat cockily and acknowledged their presence. When Reuben got out of the truck, he tipped his hat toward the man, who was still looking at him. Bogart said, "Come on Reuben, you just off-load your equipment and work at the back of the house today."

During the day, Reuben noticed cars coming and going and heard the sound of loud laughter coming from the front rooms, but no one bothered him while he painted. About four o'clock he cleaned up his paint brushes, took off his paint overalls and prepared to quit for the day.

Several men came walking up into the backyard out of the nearby woods. They were carrying rifles and a few rabbits they had shot. The man wearing the straw hat came around the house and greeted the hunters. He took one of the rabbits, laid it on a chopping block, and cut off a foot with a knife one of the men had handed to him. He walked over and gave the rabbit's foot to Reuben. "Looks like you do good work. Here, keep this for good luck."

Reuben thanked him, put the rabbit's foot in his pocket and went to the truck to wait for his ride into town for the night's stay. He would be back in the morning to work another day.

That night, as Reuben read the newspaper, he recognized the man in the straw hat. Indeed it was John Herbert Dillinger. Reuben kept the rabbit's

171

foot for many years, but Dillinger's luck ran out a month later when he was captured.

John Dillinger was born in 1903 in the Oak Hill section of Indianapolis, Indiana. As a child he was lonely and sulky and at the age of nine, he was a member of a gang in school called the Dirty Dozen. His father could not control his behavior, and at the age of twenty-one he was imprisoned for a crime he committed. He spent nine years in prison. When he got out, he was more headstrong and rebellious than before.

It was said that no armed robber in history was more industrious than John Dillinger. He robbed banks and stores. In three weeks he robbed ten banks in five different states.

The hunt by lawmen amused Dillinger and for a while he had public opinion on his side because he helped a lot of people financially. To Reuben and others, the capture of John Dillinger was not particularly good news.

Reuben's jobs in Mooresville ended in the fall, but by then he had earned enough money to put his children in school and buy a new car. It was a 1934 Packard, the first car he had ever owned. Reuben was proud, the children were thrilled and Rebekah wanted to learn how to drive!

One day she decided she could drive on her own so she put a couple of the children in the car, started down the road and was doing fine until she stepped on the brake; the car skidded and she almost wrecked it into a ditch. She was trembling as she stopped the car and grabbed her babies. She couldn't explain what had happened to Reuben. She just drove the car back to the house and never again tried to drive.

The cold winter months came and Reuben got a job with the school system, painting school classrooms. He had to work weekends because of the children being in class on weekdays.

It was a February Sunday morning. Reuben cursed as he had to scrap the ice off the car window. "This damn weather. One day I'm going to leave this place. Maybe I'll get me a place in Florida," he grumbled to Rebekah as he left the house for work. Rebekah went about feeding the children their breakfast, but her thoughts were, *that's just a dream, my dear husband.*

Reuben worked inside the school building all day unaware of the snow storm outside. About 3:30 p.m., he decided to start putting his things away in a closet the school had given him for storage. As always, he cleaned his

172

brushes and took off his painter's overalls. Just as he opened the door to go outside he looked at his watch, 4:05 p.m.

The snowfall had stopped, but with nightfall approaching it was bitter cold. Reuben brushed the windows of the car to free them from snow. He started the car, let it run for a couple of minutes then turned onto Portland Avenue heading west. He was thinking of his nice warm home and how Rebekah would have his supper ready.

He gained a little speed, then glancing to the right side of the street, he saw a little girl step down off the curb. Just as he started to put on the brakes, the little girl darted out into the street. He turned the wheel right to miss her, but there was a parked car there and he automatically swerved to the left to miss hitting the car and struck the little girl.

There was a car approaching going eastbound. When this car swerved to miss Reuben's car, which had crowded him to the right, he also hit the little girl. The driver of this car never saw the little girl step off the curb because the parked car obscured his view of her. He did not even know she was in the street until he hit her.

Reuben saw golden curls in the air. He saw the body of a little child dressed in a plain woolen coat. His ears rang with the sound of a pop as though he were pricking a balloon with a pin. His senses left him as his foot pressed the accelerator and he fled from the horrifying scene.

The next hour was lost from Reuben's memory. It was as though his mind, body and soul were all separated and each one was going in a different direction.

It wasn't until Rebekah touched his arm and said, "Reuben, what on earth has happened? You're as white as a sheet," that Reuben realized where he was.

He sat down at the kitchen table, held his head in his hands and wept. Rebekah knew something must be terribly wrong. She knelt down by him and spoke in a soft voice. "Reuben, please let me help you. Tell me what is wrong."

It was several minutes before he could gather his courage and control his speech enough to tell his wife, "I hit a little girl — Oh, God, I hit a little girl. Please, please Rebekah help me. She stepped off the curb. I saw her step off the curb. Golden hair, Rebekah, she had golden hair."

Rebekah gathered her husband in her arms and comforted him. With care she asked, "Did you kill her?"

173

Reuben said, "I don't know. All I remember is she was little, about six years old. She had golden hair. Did I tell you that?"

"Yes, dear, yes, you told me that," Rebekah said as she cradled her husband. "What did the police say?"

Reuben left Rebekah's arms and went to look out the kitchen window. "I don't know, I mean I don't remember. No, I don't know. I didn't stop. There was another car," Reuben rambled as he tried to explain. It was like a nightmare for him. He paced the kitchen floor. "I don't know what to do, Rebekah. What if she's dead? What if they know I did it? What will happen to me? I've got to get out of here. Where will I go? What will I do?" Reuben's voice got louder. Rebekah urged him to speak lower because he would wake the children.

What he and Rebekah didn't know was that two little girls were awake in their beds and overheard everything. They'd heard their mother and father make vows to each other to tell no one of this terrible thing. It would be their secret till their dying day. "No one must ever know," Reuben said to his wife.

Neither of the little girls knew the other one was awake when they heard their parents talking. Both knew it was a secret and they must never tell. Both of Reuben's daughters lived with this secret until their parents died. It was sixty years later before they revealed the secret to someone and to each other.

Neither Reuben nor Rebekah could sleep that night and at the crack of dawn, Reuben went outside to get the newspaper. He read the details of the accident. The little six year old girl was in critical condition. An emergency operation had been done. The police knew the driver of one of the cars that hit the little girl. He had been questioned. The driver of the car going westbound on Portland Avenue had not stopped and the police were looking for him.

Without discussion with Rebekah, Reuben picked up the telephone and called George Bogart. "Hello, George?" Reuben said, "I'm in trouble!"

"What's the matter Reuben, stub your toe?" Bogart jokingly responded.

"No, damnit George, listen to me. Last night I hit a little girl in Jeffersonville. I didn't stop the car till I got home. I think the police are looking for me."

"What the hell, Reuben. I don't need this kinda news so early in the morning. For chrissake, you have got trouble. What the hell you gonna do now?" Bogart was outraged.

"Listen to me, you bastard" Reuben vented his frustrations: "I wouldn't be in this godforsaken place if it weren't for you. Now I got to get the hell out of here and you are going to help me."

"Okay, okay," Bogart said, "Calm down. I know you're upset, but I'll take care of things. Haven't I looked out for you for a long time now? Give me a minute to figure this thing out and I'll call you back."

"George, listen to me, I don't have a minute. You going to help me or not?" Reuben said in a calmer voice. He was scared. His mind was racing over what could happen to him if he got picked up by the police.

Bogart said in a stern voice, "Reuben, you get hold of yourself. We've gotten through rougher times than this and I'll get you through this. Now listen to me. You take that car and park it out back in the barn. Get your wife and children ready and tonight after dark you wait by the phone. When I call, I'll give you the address and directions of a place to go. You just calm yourself down. Everything will be okay. Stella and I will see to it."

Reuben took a deep breath and said, "Okay, George, I trust you. Don't cross me up. I'm countin' on you."

He hung up the phone and turned to Rebekah. "Ole woman," he called her, "you get a few things together. We won't be able to take much, just dress the children and be ready to leave when it gets dark." Without a reply from Rebekah he went outside to hide the car.

Rebekah was washing dishes in the sink. She removed her hands from the water, took a dish towel and stood for several minutes gazing out the kitchen window, rubbing her hands with the towel.

There was no need to question her husband on the action he had chosen. What was done was done, and she couldn't change that. She was not one to feel sorry for herself or to put her needs first.

From the day she married Reuben, his needs came first. Then when her children came along, the emphasis of her needs was lost forever.

Now she must do as her husband said. She must get her things together and prepare the children to leave their home. There was no time to sort her feelings out, no time to look backward or think of the future. She needed to be strong for her husband and children.

The children did not go to school. They helped their mother pack her trunk and they dressed themselves for a trip their daddy said they were going to take.

Inside the trunk, Rebekah placed the knitting needles her father had given her, the photo of herself when she was young, the photos Stella Bogart had taken of the family and a few other treasured possessions. Before the lid of the trunk was closed, Reuben took the calendar hanging on the wall next to the telephone and put it inside the trunk. He closed the lid and his sons helped him carry it to the car.

As the car rolled out of the yard onto the road, Rebekah took her last look at the house. Pain came to her heart and tears came to her eyes. This place had been her happy home for ten years. Five of her babies had been born in that house. She and her husband had shared magical moments and a lifetime of dreams. She was just a farm girl from northern Alabama but here she became a woman fulfilling the needs of her family. Her life in Indiana had been bountiful, filled with all the things she needed to care for her husband and children; now, on this darkest of nights, she was leaving behind all the things she had gathered. She had her children and her husband with her. She must depend on her faith to care for them in the future.

Reuben drove the car slowly and carefully down the street on the river bank. He turned right onto the bridge that crossed the Ohio River. He was headed south, leaving the state of Indiana.

His heart raced wildly, his hands gripped the steering wheel, he had no sentimental thoughts of what he was leaving behind. He was a man on the run. A terrible thing had happened to him and now he was possessed with fear.

His nightmare of golden curls in the air would not soon end. From now on, he must harbor this secret along with the others of his past. The only difference, the secret of the accident on Portland Avenue would be shared with his wife, Rebekah, while all the other secrets of his past would be kept from her.

Bogart had given Reuben the address to a house on the outskirts of Louisville, Kentucky. Reuben had no trouble finding it and he arrived there with his family before dawn. He and Rebekah took the children into the house, and Reuben put the car into the garage.

The house had everything, even beds all made up and dishes ready to use. There was a large kitchen, two large bedrooms, a side room that could be used as a bedroom, a back porch and a front porch that went all the way across the front of the house. The furniture was of fine quality and the inside of the house was decorated beautifully with warm tones of slate, tan and old gold. Materials used for curtain, upholstery and pillows added a splash of pumpkin and aubergine.

Rebekah was puzzled that someone would let them use their well-equipped home, but she asked Reuben no questions. This was what he provided for her and her children, and she was grateful for a warm and comforting bed.

The house was much smaller than the one they had left in Indiana, but there was a place for everyone.

The school bus stopped right in front of the house and the children of school age started to school, all except Marion. He was still too sick to go to school.

Stella and George Bogart came to visit often. Reuben would go off with Bogart on occasion and he started painting houses in that area. Reuben was too afraid to try to find out any news on the accident in Jeffersonville, and when he asked Bogart what he knew, Bogart's reply was always, "I tell you, Reuben. I don't know if the little girl died. Best you just forget about it. I don't think the cops will be wasting time coming after you. They are too busy these days killing off so-called gangsters."

Reuben was able to put the accident out of his mind because his son's sickness was getting worse.

Marion was thirteen years old now. He was of slender build, his hair was like strands of silk and a light golden color that glistened in the sunlight. He had pale blue eyes and fair, delicate skin. He was like a bright light among this family of children. Always smiling and laughing, he would throw his head back and just laugh with the children at play.

In the spring, Rebekah took Marion to the creek that flowed swiftly through the newly blue-green hills and crossed their large backyard. They sat under sycamore, poplar, and elm trees and she would let him take his shoes off and put his feet in the crystal clear stream. With her careful eye on him, Rebekah would watch her son run and play in the field of daises at the side of the house. He was such a joy to her and in her heart she knew she would have so little time with him.

Reuben had kept the Packard and by the summer he felt secure in driving it around. He would take Marion and the other children to town, downtown Louisville, and buy everyone an ice cream cone. He took the older children to the movies to see cartoons. They saw the first Mickey Mouse cartoon, called "Plane Crazy."

Reuben told the children about a man named Walt Disney who at one time drove a Red Cross ambulance, but he had a dream and a talent for drawing. He became a cartoon artist and head of a vast animation studio.

Reuben used Walt Disney as an example to his children. He told them, "Always use your God given talent and follow your dreams. Mark my word, one day this man, along with his Mickey Mouse, will be famous around the world."

The children didn't pay much attention to their daddy's words of wisdom; they only knew that Mickey Mouse was funny.

Reuben would live to see Walt Disney and Mickey Mouse become incredibly famous; twenty-one years later, they would become an important part of Reuben's life.

There was a period of time when Reuben and Rebekah were encouraged that Marion was getting better, then one sweltering hot summer afternoon Marion was riding a bicycle down the driveway and he fell. At first it seemed that only his knuckles were scratched, but then they began to swell. While Rebekah was getting some ice to put on his knuckles, Marion passed out on the kitchen floor. She screamed for Reuben to go get the doctor. By the time Reuben returned with Doctor Brunner, Marion was conscious and Rebekah had put him in bed.

The doctor examined him and said, "I believe he is bleeding internally. I need to do some testing." He asked Reuben and Rebekah about their family medical background. When Reuben realized what the doctor needed to know, if there was any chance of saving his son's life, he confessed to the doctor in front of Rebekah. "My father married a family member. I know there is bad blood running through my veins. This sickness my son has is my fault, isn't it, Doc?"

The doctor answered him, "Let's not put the blame on anyone, there is no time for that. It is true when people of close relation have children, it is an unpure bloodline. A hemophiliac can be produced, but we haven't determind if that is Marion's problem. Now that I know the family history, it will help me with the testing. Whatever it is we will do the best we can for Marion."

After the doctor left, Reuben and Rebekah went into Marion's room and stood by his bed. Reuben looked at the frail little boy lying on snow-white sheets and said softly to him, "I'm sorry, son."

Marion looked up at his daddy, and with a big smile, said, "Don't worry, Daddy; I'll be all right."

The other children all helped in caring for Marion. Everyone who knew him loved him. He had a special girl friend named Anna Mae. She would bring him little gifts and stand by him and talk to him for hours. Marion's brothers would tease him about having a girl friend. Marion would just laugh and tell them they were jealous.

The first Christmas in the house in Kentucky came quickly, and by the time the next Christmas came, there was a new baby in the house. This little girl was only about a month old when Santa Claus put her name on a sack under the tree. Now there were eight sacks of treasures left beneath the Christmas tree.

This year Santa brought a special gift to the eldest girl: a China tea set. It was of toy size, but to the little girl it was the real thing. All of the girls of the family at one time got to play with the tea set, but it became a cherished possession of the little girl whose name was on the Christmas toy.

Although the little girl and her family's life was about to be changed forever, this little tea set would not be left behind.

It was the morning of April 4, 1936. Rebekah fixed Reuben's breakfast, and he left the house to meet Mr. Bogart. She got the older children off to school except for Marion. About ten o'clock she turned the radio on in the living room and sat down with her six-month-old daughter in her lap. Marion was sitting close to her reading a book. The news came on the radio about the killer of the Lindbergh baby. The man had been electrocuted at 8:44 the night before. Some people believed this man did not commit the crime. He was convicted on circumstantial evidence, but the execution put a closure to a tragedy that struck the Lindbergh family five years before when their young son was kidnapped and killed. The whole world had mourned with Charles Lindbergh. He had become a hero to the people of the United States and to the world when he made his solo nonstop flight across the Atlantic Ocean. When his child was kidnapped it affected everyone.

It had been the topic of many discussions between Reuben and Rebekah. That morning, hearing the news, Rebekah held her baby close to her bosom. How could anyone bear to lose a child? She looked at Marion seated beside her and touched his golden hair. Tears streamed down her cheeks. The burden of her son's sickness was too heavy for her to carry, and she knew in her heart that Marion would not be with her long.

Marion got up from his seat and wrapped his small arms around his mother's shoulders. "Don't worry, Mother," he said, "Everything will be okay."

That night after everyone had gone to bed, Marion got up, went into the kitchen, got a pencil and a piece of paper and wrote down these words: Everyone that wants to move to Alabama, please sign. . .

He left the pencil and piece of paper on the kitchen table and slipped back into bed.

Marion had seen the pain on his mother's face and he knew the reason for it. He wanted to take her home. She would need the arms of her mother and the love of her sisters and brothers.

Just before Marion went to sleep, he murmured softly to himself, "I'll feel better when we get to Grandma's house."

The next morning by the time everyone left for school, all the children's names were on the piece of paper. Each had signed their name. They even had the baby hold a pencil in her hand while another child guided it along to write her name.

Without a word, Rebekah signed her name beneath the children's.

Reuben had seen the note that morning, but he ignored it and made no mention of it to Rebekah. As Reuben worked painting a house that day, the words of the note kept going through his mind. He was distraught over his son's illness, and he knew that Marion was the one who wrote the note. His work had slowed down. He couldn't find much here in Louisville, and he couldn't go back to Indiana. Bogart was finished with him. He had advised Reuben that a Chicago agency had rented him a house on the beach in Florida and he was going down there. If things worked out, he might buy a place down there.

Reuben knew that his buddy, George Bogart, was telling him that the good life was over. Just about everyone he ever worked for was locked up or dead. That Dillinger fellow had been gunned down by the FBI in front of the Biograph Theater in Chicago. Ratted on by a girl friend. His name, along with Al Capone, Baby Face Nelson, Big Jim Colosino, Johnny Torreco, Pretty Boy Floyd and many others, would one day be found in history books that Reuben's children and grandchildren would read.

Reuben had the feeling he was in for some rough years ahead. Perhaps the best thing for him to do was to take Rebekah back to her family in northern Alabama. When he got home that night, he took the piece of paper and signed his name.

One month later, when school let out for the summer, Reuben and Rebekah prepared for the trip to Alabama. Rebekah packed her trunk with her prized possessions. She wrapped the tiny little tea set carefully for her daughter and placed in it the trunk, and she didn't forget the calendar.

Stella and George Bogart came over to tell them goodbye. Stella hugged Rebekah and said how much she would miss her best friend. Rebekah thanked Stella for all she had done for her and the children. She would always cherish their friendship.

George Bogart shook Reuben's hand and said, "Well, ole boy, it's been a good race. Good luck with your family. Hope the boy will get better. You need work in the future, look me up. I'll be in Florida."

After saying their goodbyes, the children settled themselves in the big Packard. Everyone including Reuben and Rebekah seemed excited and happy. It was only Marion who looked back. He knew that never again would he run free in the field of daisies.

CHAPTER FIFTEEN

*T*welve years ago when Reuben had taken his young bride and two baby boys north, he had dared to leave his past behind. His dreams were of a better future and for ten of these years, he lived his dream. Every two years Reuben and Rebekah shared the birth of a new baby. Their children were all healthy except for the oldest boy, Marion. Reuben had been a wonderful father, providing his children with all their needs, and he protected and loved the mother of these children. He planned for this life in Indiana to continue for all their life together.

The winds of the era swept upon this family, and circumstances eroded the life Reuben had built. That tragic accident on Portland Avenue had turned his dreams into nightmares. He became a man on the run from the consequences of that, but he tried to hold his family together under the protection of those he worked for. After relocating into Kentucky, the prospect of work for him deteriorated, and the illness of his son made the future look bleak.

Today Reuben found himself turning back. The purpose of his future in the North had been defeated. It would be a long, long road south. There had been no packing or shipping of household goods. The car he was driving, and Rebekah's trunk filled with a few possessions, were the total sum of his assets. He had no bank account or investments. He had borrowed money from Bogart for the trip. All the children sat quietly in the car. By night, they had left the state of Kentucky and were now in northern Tennessee.

Reuben pulled off the road and parked under a big oak tree. Rebekah had prepared food for the trip, and the older girls helped her with making sure everyone had something to eat. Reuben spread some quilts on the ground, and everyone slept on the pallets except for Rebekah, Marion and the baby girl. Rebekah cradled the baby in her arms and sat in the front seat of the car. A place was prepared for Marion in the back seat of the car because he was sickly.

It was 1936 and there were no motels along the highways in this part of the country, and Reuben did not have the money to put his family in a hotel in a city. The children enjoyed the adventure of being outside at night, lying on blankets, gazing at the stars. To them it was fun; to Reuben and Rebekah it was a hardship. The next day, they crossed the Tennessee River going into Decatur, Alabama. Reuben and Rebekah had returned to the place where they began their life together. Rebekah was anxious to see her mother and the children kept asking, "When are we going to get to Grandma's house?"

Out of Decatur, they took a new road because Rebekah's mother had moved her family. When John Sanderson, Rebekah's grandfather, died in 1931, he left his daughter, Lousinda, Rebekah's mother, five hundred dollars. Lousinda took the five hundred dollars and bought one hundred thirty-seven acres of land. This land was in the Tennessee Valley at the base of Caddo Mountain. Caddo Mountain is a part of the mountain range overlooking the forest where Rebekah grew up.

At one time, this entire region was occupied by tribes of Indians. Rebekah's grandmother, Martha, was a Cherokee Indian and they stayed mainly in the forest where the Sipsey Wilderness is located. Caddo Mountain was named after the Caddo Confederacy, which included the Arikaua and Pawnee and related tribes of the southeastern plains. Most Caddos were hunters and farmers. This region was good for them because they could find wild game in the forest of the mountain and grow crops in the rich soil of the flat land.

The Caddo Indians were forced to join the Trail of Tears and relocate in Oklahoma in 1838-1839. The only thing they could leave behind was their name for this mountain. Today, some 1,200 Caddos live on a reservation in Oklahoma.

Reuben had no trouble driving the car to the top of Caddo Mountain because the road had been recently paved. Once he got to a crossroad at the top, he noticed a little white church sitting off the road nestled in a thicket of trees. There was a man standing at the door of the church, so Reuben decided to stop and ask him directions to the farm owned by Lousinda McCormick.

The man was the pastor of the church and he was very friendly, quite talkative and helpful. He did not let Reuben walk away without following him to the car and meeting Rebekah and all the children. He shook Rebekah's hand and invited them to attend church services. As the car pulled away, Marion looked out the back window. He thought the church looked so beautiful with its pure white color surrounded by the deep green shade of the trees. Beyond the church Marion could see a small cemetery illuminated by the sun.

Reuben maneuvered the car along the winding dirt road down the other side of the mountain. It was late afternoon and nothing disturbed the sweet peace of the countryside. Sweet williams had awoken to blossom and colored the landscape with a cascade of velvet pink. The entire family discovered the pleasure of coming home as they approached the hewn log house sitting in the valley below the foothills of Caddo Mountain.

When they pulled into the yard, there stood Lousinda with open arms. After a joyous greeting, the children scampered off to different areas of the farm. Lousinda put her arms around her daughter, and Rebekah felt a warm sense of comfort. It had been a long journey. Lousinda told Reuben to make himself at home, that she had his coffee on the stove and supper would be ready soon. Arm in arm, Rebekah and her mother walked into the house. They had a lot to talk about.

After several days of visiting with Lousinda and her five sons — her four daughters had gotten married and lived in their own homes near by — Rebekah and Reuben moved their children into a little house by the railroad tracks. The railroad tracks ran through the farm land about a half mile from Lousinda's house, which quickly became known as "Grandma's Place." Reuben's family had crossed the railroad track on the dirt road, when they descended the mountain. The little house sat within a few yards of the tracks. It had been used by sharecroppers.

Rebekah's mother helped out, and Reuben sold his car for money to live on. When that money ran out, he went to Decatur to find work. He began painting large homes located on Sherman Street and Gordon Drive. These homes varied in styles from the French influenced Empire period to the Edwardian cottage and beyond. They were elaborate with corner turrets, large encircling verandahs and numerous characteristics of late-Victorian houses. Much of the interior woodwork and wainscoting was made of the red gum wood native to Alabama.

Reuben had perfected his painting skills while working for people who owned such elaborate houses in Indiana and Kentucky. Now he was painting the houses of the Southern rich. In contrast to the lifestyle of the people who lived in the homes, Reuben got up every morning before daylight, walked the railroad track from the little house into Decatur. He walked these ten miles, did a day's work of painting, then at the end of the day he took off his white overalls, stored his working materials and walked the ten-mile railroad track home.

There was no way he could afford to move his family into the city. Rebekah and all the children were doing well except for Marion. He was never well enough to go to school. Rebekah would spend as much time as she could with him. On cold winter days, they would sit by the fireplace and Marion would comb her hair for long periods of time. He remained sickly throughout the winter, then in the spring, it hit him in his right arm. He was in excruciating pain one night and Reuben went to Lousinda's house and asked one of her boys to go for the doctor. Dr. Parker came to the house and examined Marion. There wasn't much he could do because there was internal bleeding in the arm. He told Reuben to give him a mixture using whiskey.

Reuben and Rebekah did not keep liquor in the house because Rebekah was very much opposed to people drinking. She would not allow it around her. Reuben had not touched alcoholic drinks after he married Rebekah. Also, even though the prohibition law had been rescinded, the county they lived in remained what is called a dry county. That is, there was no legal selling of alcohol there.

Dr. Parker told Reuben about a man in Decatur whom he could buy whiskey from. The man was a drugstore owner and he was authorized to sell it for medical purposes. On this darkest of nights, Reuben began the ten mile walk down the railroad track to get the whiskey for his son. On his way into Decatur the sounds of an approaching storm began to brew. He had no trouble finding the druggist and buying the whiskey. He gripped the paper sack around the neck of the bottle and tucked it inside his coat. Hastily, he found the railroad track out of town.

By this time, the storm had grown violent. The wind whipped at his hat

185

as he held it in place with his left hand. His right hand never let go of the bottle of whiskey inside his coat. The rain fell in sheets and slithered over his clothing and beat at his face. He walked the middle of the track because he could not see in the darkness. He knew there was a crossing sign near the little house where his family was waiting. He hoped he would be able to find it. The roar of the storm drowned out the noise of the approaching train. Had it not been for the beam of light coming from behind him, he would not have escaped the track before the train rolled past. He leaned to the ground inches away from the track and crouched until the train passed. Only then did he stand up and curse aloud at the train. He was still clutching the bottle. He had protected it with his life.

The storm never let up as he returned to the middle of the track and continued cautiously over slippery railroad ties. He had walked this ten-mile track many times before, but tonight it seemed like an endless journey. He began to think he had gone too far and missed the crossing. He was about to turn back when ahead he saw a faint light. The light seemed to float about. The rain was pouring down, and he wiped at his glasses. His vision was blurred, but he was drawn to the light. He stumbled away from the railroad track following the light. Then all of a sudden the light disappeared behind a large object. It was the little house with Reuben's family inside.

He found the door and pushed it open with his shoulder because one hand was holding his hat on his head and the other was still clinging to the whiskey bottle. Rebekah was kneeling beside Marion's bed. The other children were still asleep. The house was dark inside, and the fire had gone out in the wood burning stove in the kitchen. When Reuben opened the door, the wind and rain came rushing in. Rebekah jumped up to close the door behind him. She said, "Thank God, you're back. I was so worried. It's a terrible storm and I was afraid something would happen to you. You're soaking wet; here, let me take your hat and coat. You need to get out of these wet clothes."

Rebekah continued to take clothing off Reuben, but he didn't seem to notice her as he walked over to Marion's bedside.

Marion reached up with his left hand and said, "Hi, Dad, I've been waiting for you."

Reuben took his hand and replied, "I brought you some medicine. Your mother will fix it for you. It will make you feel better."

Rebekah took the whiskey bottle from the wet paper sack and prepared the mixture for Marion. She handed the bottle back to Reuben. A strong urge came over him to take the top off the bottle and have a good long drink. He was wet and cold and it would have done him a lot of good, but instead he walked over to the fireplace and set the bottle on the mantel. That was for his son and he would do whatever it took to make him better.

Days went by and Marion didn't get any better. He had to stay in bed most of the time. The children could play around him, but Reuben demanded they be very quiet while they were in the house in case Marion was sleeping. The children all loved Marion very much and would do anything to see that big smile on his face.

One day, one of his sisters who always enjoyed being outside rather than in the house, went down to the pond back behind the barn at Grandma's Place. She got a corn stalk and made a fishing pole. She took ragweed and made a line. Then she got a safety pin and used it for a hook. She dug up a live worm and put it on the hook. When she was all ready, she sat down at the edge of the pond and cast the line into the water. Almost immediately a fish grabbed the worm on the hook and jerked the pole. It scared her and she started screaming! An older sister came running out of the corn field to see what was wrong. Together they got the fish to the bank of the pond and stared at it as it was flopping around on the grass. Neither one of them had ever caught a fish before! The older girl ran to the house and got a dish pan. She came back and they put the fish in the pan. Of course the hook was still in the fish, and they didn't know what to do. Marion had always helped them with any problem they had, so into the house they went with fishing pole, dish pan and fish, to Marion's bedside.

He was delighted! He laughed and teased his sisters as he removed the hook from the fish. Rebekah heard all the commotion from the kitchen. When she came into the room, Marion held up the fish and said, "Look, mama, they caught my supper!"

That night Rebekah cooked the one and one-half pound catfish, and everyone enjoyed watching Marion eat better than he had in months. Late in the afternoon on the third of May, the right side of Marion's chest started swelling and he was in terrible pain. Reuben broke into a run to the nearest telephone, which was in a little place called Fish Pond. He would call for an ambulance, which had to come from Decatur.

The nearest main road was at Fish Pond also, so Rebekah got one of her brothers to hitch up the wagon to the horses. They would take Marion to meet the ambulance at Fish Pond. They made a bed in the back of the wagon, laid Marion on the bed, put pillows around him, and Rebekah got in and sat down beside him. His oldest sister reached over the side of the wagon and patted his hand. He looked up at her and smiled.

The ambulance took him to the hospital in Decatur. When they laid him in the bed in the hospital, his skin was like soft cotton, his hair was white and his blue eyes still had a bright light in them. Rebekah stood on one side of the bed holding his hand, and Reuben stood holding his hand on the other side of the bed. Their son looked up at them and said, "Don't cry, you did everything you could."

The nurse came into the room, lifted his head, and gave him a drink of water. Marion said, "Thank you." When his head rested back on the pillow, the bright light in his eyes went out.

Rebekah's sisters gathered about her and after some time, they took her to one of their homes that was nearest to the hospital. It was decided Brown's Funeral Home would pick Marion up and prepare everything for viewing at this sister's home. Reuben would go home to tell the children. One of Rebekah's brothers went with him. As they came to the gate of the fence surrounding the yard, Reuben slumped down by the gate. "I can't do this thing. God help me, I can't do this thing."

The brother-in-law lifted Reuben up and said, "Lean on me, Reuben, I will help you."

When they got to the porch, Reuben sat down on the steps and with his head in his hands he wept. The children all gathered around him. They had never seen their daddy cry before. They knew their brother was dead.

The next day, the children were taken to the aunt's house to see their brother. The casket was gray with a white satin cover inside. Marion was wearing a light-gray suit, white shirt and a tie. When a friend saw Marion, he said he was looking at an angel and when he died he wanted to be buried close to him. The next summer this young boy was struck by lightning while plowing a field. He was buried next to Marion. He was the same age as Marion, only fifteen years old.

On the third day after Marion died, a hearse took him to the cemetery he had seen behind the little white church on Caddo Mountain. The children gathered fresh flowers from the country side, and they asked neighbors for flowers from their yards. Most of the flowers were sweet williams and roses. The sun shown brightly over the family and friends as they gathered for the graveside service. After everyone had left, Reuben and Rebekah remained until they lowered the casket into the grave. Rebekah walked up to the edge of the grave with a rose in her hand. She lifted her arms as high as they would go to the heavens and spoke to her God. She then let go of the rose and it fell onto the coffin below. She stood on the edge of the grave for a moment, then she turned to her husband and softly said, "Whoever goes first don't forget the rose." She then turned and walked off down the path and into her mother's arms.

Reuben stayed until the grave site was complete and everyone had left the cemetery. He knelt beside the grave and took some of the red soil and rubbed it through his hands. How could it be that he must leave his son here? He felt weak and alone and his heart was empty. The shadow of late evening covered him when he finally stood. It was then that he felt the strength from the earth flow from the ground into his legs and through his body. He remembered this feeling the rest of his life. He knew that Marion would always be with him.

When Rebekah returned home from the cemetery, she took the bottle of whiskey off the mantel and took it outside and poured every drop into the ground. Later she got out a photo of Marion taken the last year he went to school. He looked handsome, wearing a white shirt with the collar buttoned. His light colored hair was well groomed. He had a tender look in his eyes and his lips revealed a warm smile. Rebekah sat the photo on the mantel. It gave her comfort to look at it and it reminded all the children that Marion would remain a part of their family.

After Marion's death, Reuben and Rebekah did not take time to nurture themselves. Reuben felt responsible for his son's death because of his family's blood disorder. A distance came between Reuben and Rebekah. Reuben began to isolate himself from his family. He moved them out of the little house by the railroad track into a farm house up the mountain about twenty miles from Grandma's Place. He tried to isolate them from the rest of the world.

The misery of the times was evident in his eyes, and the idea of his wife and seven children surviving on a farm in the South was hopeless. He was not alone in this respect. The South waited for relief when the country's president, Franklin Delano Roosevelt, took office in 1933 and promised a "New Deal." The New Deal had provided jobs for a lot of people and it had built new roads, dams and bridges such as the Golden Gate Bridge in San Francisco, but it had not ended the Depression in the South. No one had suffered more than the farmers.

Over half of the South's farmers were tenants or sharecroppers. The South had twenty-one percent of America's population, yet earned only nine percent of the national income. The South had the nation's top economic problems, which put the entire nation at risk. The winds of war had begun to stir in Europe, beginning when a man called Adolf Hitler became Germany's chancellor and declared himself, *Der Furher*. This man had drawn attention to himself from the people of Alabama when he snubbed their star athlete, Jessie Owens, when he won four gold medals during the 1936 Olympic Games.

The games were held in Berlin, Germany, that year and Hitler attended. He was infuriated when he observed that ten members of the American team were of the Negro race. He called them the alien race. When Jessie Owens, a black man from America, emerged as the world's fastest athlete it was an embarrassment for Hitler, but it was a proud moment in time for the American people, especially the people of the South because Jessie Owens was born in Oakville, Alabama.

After this, the conflicts in Europe escalated, and it looked as though the United States was going to be drawn into the situation. The people, remembering World War I, did not want to return to war. Southerners strongly opposed it, saying they had enough to deal with and they were persuaded that the only way to avoid war was to eschew any foreign involvement. The American people were fighting to save the American dream at home, but by September 1, 1939, they realized they must fight to save the world for democracy. Everyone was opposed to entering the war, but they agreed to build and furnish supplies to allied countries.

Also the country began to stock its arsenals because Americans did not want to get caught unprepared for battle.

Because of the turn of events, the Great Depression came to an end. The war in Europe gave an enormous boost to heavy industry and because of the roaring steel mills and hustling ports, Alabama lived up to its Indian name, which means "I clear the thicket."

Where Reuben lived with his family, employment increased because of the projects built on the Tennessee River. The government had formed the Tennessee Valley Authority (TVA) to build major flood-control and hydroelectric projects on the river, and they also built the Redstone Arsenal at Huntsville, Alabama, which is just across the river from Decatur. The government bought forty acres of land from Lousinda to use as a practice airstrip, and now the children wanted to go to Grandma's Place for another reason — to watch the airplanes land and take off.

All of this improved the living standards for some of the people who lived in the Tennessee Valley area, but it was not a cure for Reuben.
He had continued to paint houses in Decatur when he could find someone to hire him. Days he was not working, he spent in Decatur at the Princess Theater watching movies, or he was known to visit the local brothel. His family remained out in the country working on the farm.

The first Christmas after Marion died was the hardest time for Reuben, Rebekah and the children. They missed him terribly. By the next Christmas, time had healed some of the pain, and Reuben and Rebekah began to come closer together. It would never be the same, but for the first time in four years, they became intimate again. Together they attended Decoration Day at Caddo Cemetery. For many years, it had been a tradition in that area of the South for cemeteries to have decoration days. That is a day set aside for putting wreaths and flowers on the graves, and family and friends would gather in remembrance of their loved ones. At the Caddo Cemetery, this day is always on the second Sunday in May.

Rebekah and her sisters had made flowers out of crepe paper, and they decorated Marion's grave. The year that Marion died, Rebekah had gone to the forest and taken a cutting from the rose bush of her great-grandmother, Martha. Each year on Decoration day the vibrant rose bloom graced Marion's tombstone like arms of his ancestors.

Reuben and Rebekah stood next to their son's grave so that someone could take a photo. They had worn the best clothing that they had. Reuben had on a long-sleeve white shirt and a tie, dress pants and new shoes. On his head was a new hat and he wore his pocket watch. Rebekah had on a print cotton dress with a big bow at the neckline. She had made the dress herself. She had new shoes and a small round hat, which sat at the back of her head nestled in her beautiful chestnut brown hair. Each one stood separate from the other. They had both borne their own pain. Reuben had one hand in his pocket jingling his change; Rebekah held a rose.

Like the change in the seasons of the year, time has a way of changing feelings in the heart. Rebekah was pregnant with her ninth child. It was late fall. The trees of autumn lit up the land with shades of claret, amber and gold. Leaves of scarlet were like wings in the wind, showering the earth like rain in the summer. Birthing time was near, so Reuben took Rebekah to Grandma's Place so her mother could be with her.

In the early morning, inside this farmhouse in the middle of a cotton field, a baby's cry returned joy to their hearts. The midwife wrapped the baby girl in a blanket and placed her in Reuben's arms. He looked at her and called her his golden girl. He laid her beside Rebekah, then reached for his hat and walked away. He would not name this child. The midwife filled out the birth paper. She would be named Martha, after Rebekah's great-grandmother and Lou after Rebekah's mother, Lousinda.

Fifteen years later, Reuben would file an affidavit to amend this record of birth.

The winter that followed this beautiful season when Martha was born was harsh. Rebekah kept her wrapped in quilts to keep her from freezing. The old house they lived in was drafty and cold. The children played around the fireplace, and Reuben would sit with them. Sometimes when Martha would cry, Reuben would pick her up, take his pocket watch out and put it to her ear. Her eyes would sparkle, and she would be still and quiet as she listened to the tick of the watch. All through her childhood years, Martha would ask her daddy to let her listen to his pocket watch. It was like magic to her.

Reuben and Rebekah could have used some magic to help them out of their meager living condition. The Depression years were fading away for the rest of the country, but for this family there was no glitter like Hollywood was depicting in their movies. A writer from Atlanta, Margaret Mitchell, had written a novel called *Gone With the Wind*, and Hollywood had made a movie out of it. It was a Southern melodrama taking place during the Civil War. Reuben's only reaction when he heard about this book and movie was, "Hell, my whole damn life has been a war. If people want to read about someone's life and a war, then someone should write a book about me!"

Because of the bad weather, there were no painting jobs in Decatur. Reuben was having to depend on Rebekah's family for food to feed the children. Lousinda was very good to them. The children were always wanting to be at Grandma's Place.

It was right after a terrible snow storm in January that Lousinda fell on icy steps and broke her hip. Six months later, she died. Rebekah said she couldn't get her mother to eat. It was just like she gave up on life. The morning she died, Rebekah was sitting by the bed holding her hand. One of the children walked into the room holding the baby in her arms. Lousinda looked up from her deathbed and said, "Take care of my little Martha Lou." Those were her last words. They buried her at Caddo Cemetery beside Rebekah's papa and only a few feet from Marion.

Because of the escalation of the war in Europe, the United States commitment grew more and more. The government was calling for a draft registration of men ages 21 — 36. Reuben and Rebekah's son was only seventeen, but he volunteered for the service. Several of Rebekah's brothers were already in the military. As Reuben watched his son go off to join the military, he knew he had to do something to get his family out of the conditions they were living in. After a lot of soul searching, he made a phone call to a farmhouse in Mooresville, Indiana.

To the man who answered the phone, Reuben gave his condolences on the death of his son although it had been seven years ago. The man's response was receptive and he was pleased to hear from Reuben. He told Reuben he had heard about the unfortunate accident in Jeffersonville and had often wondered what had happened to Reuben after that. After renewing their acquaintance, Reuben told the man the purpose of his call.

He needed work and he figured since big businesses in the North were making money now that the Depression was over, maybe people could afford to have their houses painted again.

The man told Reuben that a lot of the guys had moved to Florida.

"Yes," Reuben said, "that is what my friend, George Bogart said he was going to do, but I don't know how to get in touch with him."

"Well," the man said, "I am not sure about George, but I do know a man in Jacksonville who needs some work done for him. I will call him and set you up. If you are sure that is what you want to do."

Reuben said without hesitation, "Yes, I need a job."

"Okay," was the response, "it's settled. Call me in a couple of days and I will give you the man's name and instructions on what to do. I assume you will want to take your family there."

Reuben said, "Yes, Rebekah, my wife, and I now have eight children. My oldest boy passed away in May of '37."

"Oh, I am so sorry to hear that. Terrible thing to lose a son. I know

193

how it feels," the man said with sympathy in his voice. "Well, I guess you do need work with all those children. Okay, let me see what I can do; I don't mind fixing you up because I know what a hard worker you are, and I know you are an excellent painter. Talk to you soon."

The man hung up before Reuben could say thanks. As Reuben walked away from the phone, his heart raced at the thought of returning to Florida. But, that is exactly what he did. He took Rebekah and the seven children — one boy was in the service — and they moved into a nice house in Jacksonville, Florida. The place was located in the country. There was a good house, fine furniture and plenty of space for a garden, chickens, and a cow.

It was a good place for Reuben because he was getting worse about isolating his family, especially Rebekah. He didn't like it that the older children went to school, but they all did.

CHAPTER SIXTEEN

On December 7, 1941, after the Japanese bombed Pearl Harbor, the United States entered the war on two fronts. Rebekah was afraid for their son, that he would have to go to the war since he was already in the military. Reuben refused to show any fear and made the remark to his wife, "A man has got to do what a man has to do, and the boy is now a man. I believe in fighting for your country and I will join the war if I'm needed. I did it once before, I can do it again."

Every once in awhile, Reuben would take the old calendar out of the trunk. He would remind the children that there he was in the picture with General Pershing during World War I.

When Rebekah left Alabama, she was pregnant with another child. This was her tenth pregnancy; she was thirty-nine years old. She was sick during the whole time and when she delivered, she almost died. The doctor told Reuben and Rebekah that her body would not do this again. They were lucky to have a fine healthy boy this time. Reuben and Rebekah now had nine living children. For Rebekah this meant a lifetime of commitment to her children and her husband. For Reuben, he would always love his children, and Rebekah, but he would seek solace from other women.

All in all, Reuben's life was good in Jacksonville, Florida. He was making a good living for his family, a remarkable feat during those wartimes. Everyday the newspaper was delivered to his home about four o'clock in the afternoon. The children were allowed to bring it inside the house, but no one was allowed to open it up and read any part of it until after Reuben had read it, which was the first thing he did after supper.

Rebekah had to have supper on the table when he came into the house at 5:00 p.m. Reuben believed in eating three meals a day, right on time everyday. He never snacked in between meals. Rebekah always prepared the foods Reuben would eat, and of course the table was always set with two saucers for his coffee.

On a hot afternoon in June, Reuben settled in his chair to read the newspaper. All the news was of the war. He began to read an article about the United States invasion on one of Japan's islands in the Pacific called Okinawa. They had begun the preliminary bombardment in April and at first got little resistance, leading some to hope the Japanese were giving in, but Japan had set up their lines of defense inland and sent out kamikaze aircraft attacks against American ships that were supplying the invasion. What the Americans first thought would be a walkover turned into a bloody battle.

Both sides were suffering heavy casualties and it was not until June when American units spearheaded by flame throwing tanks overran Japanese positions, that the island was declared secure.

Okinawa had been a costly battle for American forces. The ground forces suffered nearly 8,000 dead and more than 30,000 wounded and, in addition, 10,000 Navy casualties. After reading about these losses, it was no surprise to Reuben when the United States military sent out the message that all able bodied men should register for the draft. Reuben, feeling it his patriotic duty, went to the Selective Service Office in downtown Jacksonville and received his draft card.

Holding this card in his hand, he remembered another day, twenty-five years prior that he held another draft card in his hand. That one was for the First World War and he had been at the Selective Service Office in Sanford, Florida. For many years to come, Reuben often wondered what made him do what he did next. He walked over to a bulletin board where the names of men from Florida that been killed in action were posted. His eyes glanced down the alphabetical list till they stopped on a familiar name, Kincaide. He ran his finger over the name, as he read it out loud, "Felix Lucky Kincaide — Sanford, Florida."

The sweat ran from his hand onto the bulletin board. He was trembling and couldn't seem to remove his finger from the name. A clerk in the office came over to him and asked, "Is anything wrong, sir? May I help you?"

196

Reuben looked at the clerk without moving his finger from the board and said, "Do you know this man?"

The man looked at the name and replied, "Oh, no sir, but if you need information on him, you can go to the military base and get assistance there. Here, let me give you the address of the place to go and name of the person to talk to."

Reuben returned to the counter as the clerk explained to him what to do. After that he never remembered how or why he got there, but before his eyes was a piece of paper and he was reading every word. A man in a military uniform said to him, "You the boy's father? Reuben Oliver Kincaide?"

Reuben folded the record and handed it back to the officer. He looked him in the eyes and said, "Yes, I am."

The record gave Reuben reason to give that answer. He had read, "Felix Lucky Kincaide, Born January 16, 1918, Sanford, Florida. Trained at Sanford Training Station in 1941. Killed in battle at Kakazu Ridge, Okinawa, April 1942. Cause of death — Seventeen machine gun bullets. His mother was named Tasha Ann Benson, Sanford, Florida, deceased. His father was named Reuben Oliver Kincaide, Tallapoosa, Georgia. Did not state living or dead."

Reuben turned from the officer, put his hat on his head and walked out the door. He walked down the steps and onto the street. The hot summer sun beat down on the pavement causing stifling waves of heat to rise, engulfing Reuben. He walked down the street on a road to nowhere. The curtain of time had been frayed, and the remembrance of his past drove all other thoughts from his mind.

There is a river that flows north from Sanford, Florida, into the city of Jacksonville in Florida. Bridges of the city allow one to pass over it by car, train or on foot. On this day, Reuben would walk to the top of one of these bridges that rises two hundred feet above the St. John's River. Fate had returned him to this river once again. In 1915, Reuben had been summoned to the shores of this same river; only then he was a hundred miles south of where it flows past Sanford. He remembered it well.

He had been seeking solace from an intolerable life. Fleeing in haste, he had caught a train out of his hometown of Tallapoosa, Georgia. He had deserted his wife and child and his beloved mother. He had also left behind another woman he loved and a daughter this woman had given birth to. For

197

him there could be no choices here, no right or wrong, no confessions of guilt because he loved each of them. Also accusations of criminal activity had shrouded him so that his only option was to run.

He rode the train as far south as it would take him — Sanford, Florida. When he got off the train, he made his way to the banks of the river. There he sat under an old cypress tree sorting the ripples of the water. Somehow the river had helped him clear his mind and to the old cypress tree he had made a commitment. He would make his life better, make it account for something, and he and the tree would keep his past a secret.

In Sanford, he made a life for himself as the manager of a celery farm and there he found a passionate woman who tantalized his senses. Tasha, his beautiful young paramour. Tasha, who, with her desires, filled his needs. Their love brought them unimaginable pleasure. Tasha gave her total self to Reuben and she became to him an unforgettable treasure. When he left Sanford to go to war, he carried with him the memory of her standing on the platform of the train station, waving her little hand in the rain.

He knew that he was leaving part of his heart, but he did not know that with her he was also leaving his son. When Reuben returned to Georgia from the war, he was told Tasha had died. Without her in Sanford, he had no reason to return there. He was not told about his son. Lucky had been taken in by a family who lived on the farm, and he had grown up working in the celery fields in Sanford. He had a loving family and they always told him about his mother and daddy, Reuben Oliver Kincaide.

When Lucky got older, he did try to find his daddy once or twice. All his letters were returned unopened or with replies that no one knew anything about Reuben. He never had enough money to go anywhere to search for him. When World War II started and he was drafted into the military, Lucky filled out the papers needed for records. On these documents he wrote the name of his father, Reuben Oliver Kincaide, Tallapoosa, Georgia. By writing this, Lucky found his father, but for Lucky and Reuben it was too late.

Standing on the bridge, Reuben felt alone and angry. Flooded with all the memories, he seethed inside. How much could a man take? He cursed the heavens and the earth. There must be no God. Why would he take his two sons — one that he had nurtured and cared for and one that he had never known. The clouds had gathered energy from the hot earth and they burst with the roar of thunder as lightning streaked the sky. Reuben reached his arms upward and shouted, "Why don't you kill me? Damn you!"

A gust of wind blew his hat off; he watched it as it fell into the river. He stepped up on the railing of the bridge and looked down into the deep blue water. When the ripples from the falling hat had disappeared and the waters smoothed again, there he saw the face of a little boy: one he did not know. Tears flooded his eyes and joined the rain drops as they fell from the bridge onto the face in the water. Reuben, a broken hearted man, spoke in the wind. "The only thing I can do now, my son, is say, I'm sorry."

He stepped down from the railing and stood on the bridge. The rain washed his body and as it did so, brought him a sense of peace. When finally he walked across the bridge to the other shore, he somehow knew that his two sons were together now and they would take care of each other.

Reuben walked home in the rain. It was late when he opened the door to the kitchen and stepped inside. Rebekah was worried. "Reuben, you're soaking wet and where is your hat?"

"Well, ole woman, I guess someone stole it. You don't see me wearing it, do you? Is supper ready?" Reuben tried to act as if nothing was wrong.

Rebekah tied the strings to her apron and quietly said, "Yes, Reuben, supper is ready." The evening was spent without conversation.

When Reuben first met Rebekah, he had blocked out seven years of his life when he lied to her about his age. His life spent in Sanford, Florida, was part of those seven years so how could he tell her about what happened to him today? She just wouldn't understand. Reuben did not go to Rebekah's bed that night and when she got up the next morning, he was gone. He did not return for three days. This was the beginning of his leaving Rebekah and the children for periods of time and not telling them where he was going or when he would be back. This was also the beginning of his return to his past.

The following year brought another dramatic change in Reuben's life. After the day on the bridge, he became more and more withdrawn from Rebekah and the children. None of the children knew what was wrong with Daddy, just that Daddy had changed. The older ones remembered him playing with them when they lived in Indiana. They remembered the little sacks of candy he brought them every day after work. They no longer heard the laughter and giggles coming from their mother as Daddy teased her. The death of their brother, Marion, had left a hole in their hearts, but the absence of their daddy left a hole in their family.

The war still raged in the Pacific and in Europe. Rebekah and Reuben feared their son who had joined the military would have to go overseas. All five of Rebekah's brothers had been drafted into the war. Before the last one left their home, "Grandma's Place," he wrote to Rebekah asking her to come back to the farm, live there and take care of everything. When Rebekah asked Reuben what he thought about doing this, Reuben's reply was, "Hell, I don't know why not. We need to get out of this Godforsaken place." Since the man Reuben had been working for took sick, there seemed to be no one around asking him to do jobs for them. So their decision to return to north Alabama seemed to be the best thing to do.

Reuben sold everything he could get his hands on: his car, tools, furniture, everything but Rebekah's trunk and their clothes. This time there was no one to give them money to move. Rebekah packed her trunk once again and prepared her children. They caught the train out of Jacksonville going back to Decatur, Alabama. On the train, Reuben sat apart from his family, reading the newspaper from cover to cover. He returned to one page several times, reading an article over again.

The headline of the article was, "Dillinger, Buried next to Son"; sub-headline, "John Dillinger, Sr. dies. Buried Crown Point Cemetery, Chicago, Illinois." Once Reuben got Rebekah and the children back to Grandma's Place he had no intention of staying there himself. He was not going to farm! Reuben told his wife, "I'm going to look for a job, maybe in Birmingham."

Rebekah stood in the doorway to her mother's farmhouse watching Reuben as he walked off down the road. He was wearing a new hat.

If you travel out of Trinity to the top of Caddo Mountain, you can find a country dirt road meandering down the hillside. Take the journey slow, smell the honeysuckle vine and stop for a drink from the sweet spring water that runs from the forest. Listen for the call of the whippoorwill from the trees and the clatter of the crickets from the thicket nearby. Take heed to the wind for the sound of the train. Cross the track cautiously and revel in the sight of the bounty of wild flowers along the way. Notice the trees on the right side of the road, a field of white cotton on the other. Turn onto the short path that leads to the clean swept yard of a weather-beaten farmhouse with clapboard siding and a rusty tin roof. Rebekah stands on the porch.

Her body is slim and her apron is clean. Her hair pinned back reveals the face of a gracious, but lonely woman. She is fourty-one years old with eight children at home and one son in the war. One son is buried in the cemetery atop Caddo Mountain. She looks out across the valley and beyond into the forest of the mountains from where she came. She would need the strength of her ancestors to sustain her to care for her children at the farm they called "Grandma's Place."

When Rebekah's brother asked her to move back there, he did not tell her that he had mortgaged the house and property and it was now in foreclosure because the payments had not been made. Rebekah tried to get the woman holding the mortgage to let her pay for the place, but she refused and it was sold on the steps of the courthouse to a man called Mr. Smith, who agreed to let Rebekah remain on the farm as a tenant farmer.

She would be a sharecropper — working the land for a share of the crop and to pay the rent. There were turbulent years ahead for Rebekah and her children. The older children worked in the fields. They planted cotton in the spring and picked it in the fall. After the last harvest picking in the fall, Rebekah would put on her cotton sack and drag it through the fields, picking any leftover cotton. She used the money from this to buy the children's Christmas presents. Rebekah was certainly no stranger to farm life, although for most of her married life to Reuben they had lived differently.

Now that Reuben was gone for months at a time, and she could not depend on him, she used her knowledge of farm life, her strength and courage. All these she relied upon to scratch out an existence for her family. Using a wood-burning stove, she cooked all their meals. She drew water from the well in the yard and caught rainwater to wash the clothes. The older girls would iron the clothes they wore to school and church. They used an iron that had to be heated on the stove. It was molded from one piece of iron and the handle remained hot, so you had to use a cloth to hold it. They used the top of Rebekah's trunk for an ironing board.

When the girls were doing this, they had no idea that one day they would all own an electric iron and that someone would invent Perm-a-Press clothing! Having no electricity, the older children who went to school had to use a kerosene lamp to do their homework at night. Rebekah always encouraged them to study. She was very smart and often delighted the children when she would rapidly say the alphabet backwards. Perhaps it was her Cherokee heritage that made her such a quick study.

It was the Cherokee scholar and leader, Sequoyah (1760-1843), who created the Cherokee syllabary. Rebekah's grandfather, John Allen, had told her about the Cherokee nation. Rebekah went through the eighth grade in school, which at that time was the highest grade offered in rural areas. All the children would get a higher level of education in school, but from her they would learn how to live their life. For it was during these years together, they learned the necessity of hard work, the sharing and caring for one another and the importance of a strong faith in God.

Between farm work and school, there were not many idle hours for this family. Their hours of leisure were on Sunday afternoons. On hot summer Sundays, the children would spread a quilt out on the ground under a big shade tree in the front yard. They would play games and tell stories. Often times, cousins would come by with their guitars and would play them while the children sang songs. Rebekah would sit on the porch and pull the threads from flour sacks to save for her oldest daughter to knit with.

On cold winter Sundays, the children would gather round the fireplace and read and play games. Their mother would prepare fried fruit pies for them as a treat.

Rebekah depended on the older children to look after the younger ones. Martha Lou was then four years old, and her favorite thing to do was to go to visit her Aunt Ronda. Aunt Ronda always treated her special. She would make popcorn and make balls by rolling popcorn with molasses. She would show Martha Lou the pretty cloth for making dresses she had put away in her trunk under her bed. When Martha Lou was allowed to sleep overnight at her Aunt Ronda's, she was always tucked into bed with pretty warm quilts to keep her warm.

It was about a mile down the dirt road, across the railroad track from "Grandma's Place" to Aunt Ronda's. Martha Lou was allowed to walk over there only when one of her older sisters or her brother would go with her. Rebekah lived in fear of one of her children getting hit by the train, because it was only a country road crossing with no signal to warn of an oncoming train. Most of the time train conductors would sound the whistle before they got to the crossing. Rebekah knew the times for the trains by heart.

On a warm day in late spring, Martha Lou was outside playing in the yard. She had on a little cotton dress her mother had made and she was barefoot. Her long golden hair hung down her back to her waist and she squinted her eyes when she looked toward the sun. After several attempts to get her sister to go with her over to Aunt Ronda's, she decided to go by herself. She left the yard, went down the path to the dirt road and walked toward the railroad track. She skipped along playfully as she stopped to pick up little sticks, rocks or objects of interest. Unaware of any danger ahead, she looked across the little ditch of the road to a patch of wildflowers. Mixed with the bright and dark shades of springtime green were colors of orange, yellow, red, blue and white scattered about like pepper. She was about to step into the flowers when her eyes caught the folds of a skirt brushing the blooms. She raised her eyes to see the most beautiful lady standing there in the middle of the wildflower patch.

Her long dress was sheer organdy, pale blue like the sky and frail to see. She wore a wide brim hat with a band of ribbon streamers that tossed in the breeze. Resting on her arm was a basket laden with gathered flowers. She held out her hand and said in a soft spoken voice, "Come little girl. Will you help me with my task?"

Martha Lou was not afraid as she came close to question, "Are you lonely out here all by yourself? Are these your flowers? Do you live here? Who are you picking them for?"

The lady sat her basket down and answered with a smile, "No, I'm not lonely. I've been waiting for you and gathering all the while. Come, pick me some clover and we will make a necklace for you to wear."

Martha Lou picked the flowers and the beautiful lady gracefully tied the stems. She took the strand and placed it around Martha Lou's neck. It hung like a necklace as a trim on her dress. Then the lady said, "You are a beautiful little girl."

Martha Lou asked, "Am I as pretty as you?"

She looked into her twinkling green eyes and stroked her hair of gold. "Someday you will be me. Now you must go to Aunt Ronda's, she's looking for you."

Martha Lou said goodbye to the lady and walked back out onto the road. When she turned to look back, she saw only a field of wildflowers glowing brightly in the sun.

Rebekah was taking clothes off the clothesline when she heard the whistle of the 2:00 p.m. train. She looked around to notice that Martha Lou was missing. She panicked and screamed, "Children, children come quick; your sister is gone!" Everyone came running.

The two oldest sisters came out of the house; a brother and sister stopped their work in the corn field. Another sister picked up the baby boy and ran toward the railroad track. The little girl next in age to Martha Lou began to sob and cry as she said, "It's all my fault. She asked me to take her to Aunt Ronda's, but I didn't want to go."

Rebekah took her hand and said, "Don't cry, honey, we'll find her." She kept talking as they hurried down the road, "Everything will be all right. You'll see!" She called out, "Martha Lou!" But Martha Lou did not answer. The older children reached Aunt Ronda's house before Rebekah did. There they immediately saw little Martha Lou standing beside Aunt Ronda holding on to her apron.

They all began to talk at once, one saying, "You're going to get a whipping!"

Another one said, "You are in big, big, trouble little girl!"

Aunt Ronda stood between Martha Lou and her brothers and sisters. Martha Lou held on to her apron and tears rolled down her face. The oldest girl bent down, took the little hand away from the apron and picked Martha Lou up in her arms. Sobbing on her sister's shoulder, Martha Lou said, "I didn't do anything wrong. We just picked flowers and the pretty lady made me a necklace."

Her sister hugged her close and comforting her, she said, "No you didn't do anything wrong. No one is mad at you. We all were afraid you had gotten lost."

When Rebekah reached Martha Lou, she placed her hands first on her chubby little feet, brushing the sand from between her toes. Then she felt her arms as though she was a new born baby and she wanted to make sure she was all right. Martha Lou turned in her sister's arms and reached for her mother. Rebekah took her and let her stand on the ground. In a calm, soft voice, she said, "You must never do this again. Don't leave the yard without someone with you. You could get lost and be all alone. It frightened me when I couldn't find you."

Martha Lou looked up at her mother and said, "Don't be afraid Mama. The pretty lady was with me. Do you know her? Look, she made me this necklace." All the way back home, down the dirt road and across the railroad track, Martha Lou chatted about seeing the pretty lady in the field of wildflowers.

Rebekah tried to tell Martha Lou that there was no lady like that living near them. She dismissed the idea of a lady as a child's fantasy, but often she did wonder where the clover necklace came from.

All of Martha Lou's life, she remembered the beautiful lady she had seen that day. Fifty years later, she and her two older sisters returned to "Grandma'a Place." The old house was gone and the entire field was covered with new growth of a cotton crop. Martha Lou walked down the dirt road; she heard the whippoorwill call from the trees from the other side. She gazed in the bright sun and saw the railroad tracks ahead. Nothing had changed. Her memories were untouched. She was beckoned to the field where wildflowers grew. She stood in the patch with many blossoms at her knees. She smiled to herself as the breeze whispered in her ear, "Someday you will be me."

While Reuben's family lived at "Grandma's Place" Reuben stayed in Birmingham. He had been successful in getting work there and he would ride the bus back and forth to see Rebekah and the children. The bus had replaced having to take the train and it came closer to the farm. It was about an eighty-mile trip, so he didn't come home very often. When he did come home, he wouldn't eat the corn pone and vegetables from the garden that Rebekah cooked. He would bring flour, sugar and meats from Birmingham he had gotten with his ration stamps. Things were rationed because of the war, and Reuben got a lot of stamps because they issued the amount according to how many children you had. Even shoes were rationed, but Reuben always managed to have enough stamps to keep him wearing new shoes.

Thanksgiving came and Rebekah and the children were excited because Rebekah had seen a wild turkey on the fence around her garden and she, with the help of her oldest boy that was at home, killed it. They would have turkey for Thanksgiving! They all hoped that Daddy would come home. Reuben did not disappoint them. He came home, but he did not eat any turkey. Reuben's outlook on life was that it was hopeless. He could not make enough money to take his family to Birmingham to live in the city with him, and his living on the farm was out of the question.

He was fighting against memories of his past. He was distant with Rebekah because he couldn't bring himself to share everything with her. Rebekah was always kind and understanding because she was aware of the heartache he had with just the parts of his past she knew about. When Reuben looked at little Martha Lou, he began to long for the two little girls he had left behind — one he had never seen and the other only for a brief time. Also, he remembered another little girl with golden curls he had seen on that fatal day in Indiana.

Every time Martha Lou saw her daddy, she wanted to hear his watch tick. He would place it to her ear and observe her as she listened to it. One day Martha Lou asked him if he saw the beautiful lady who lives in the flower patch.

"No," he said, "but I did see a blind lady on the bus today."

"Really, Daddy, how could she see to climb the steps to get on the bus?" Martha Lou asked.

"She had a big walking cane," he said.

"What did she do on the bus, if she can't look out the window?" Martha Lou was full of questions.

"Well, she takes out a book and reads it by using her fingers to trace over raised lettering on the paper. They call it Braille," Reuben explained.

"Is she pretty?" Martha Lou asked.

With a little smile, Reuben answered, "She is a nice looking woman, about sixty years old I would say. The bus driver said she lives down in Tuscumbia and her name is Helen Keller."

Martha Lou put the watch back in her daddy's pocket and just before she skipped off, she said, "She's not my lady, because my lady is pretty and she lives in the wildflower patch."

It was a beautiful Sunday morning in the spring of 1944. Reuben had not been to the farm to see Rebekah and the children for several months. As he usually did on Sunday mornings, he bought a newspaper and went to the Vanderbilt Hotel for breakfast. It was an expensive hotel, but Reuben went there because it reminded him of the Lithia Hotel in his hometown, Tallapoosa, Georgia. He sat in the dining room alone. When he had finished eating and reading his paper, the waiter came and he took care of the check. He picked his hat up from the holder nearby and walked toward the door with it in his hand.

Seated near a large window on the side of the dining room was a lovely lady. Reuben caught sight of her out of the corner of his eye. Sunlight came through the window illuminating her beautiful face. Reuben, realizing she was looking at him, tipped his hat just before placing it on his head. He always did have an eye for a pretty face. The lady smiled graciously and turned her head to gaze out the window. Reuben walked through the dining room door and through the lobby of the hotel. He stepped outside into the cool, brisk air of a lovely spring day. Glancing toward the sun, he noticed there was not a cloud in the sky.

A warm feeling spread throughout his body and a tender ache entered his heart. The winds of time blew across his face and in that brief moment his mind raced through the years. He remembered her. He remembered the first time he saw her standing on the balcony of the house with the white columns. He had tipped his hat then, just as now. Like a prayer he whispered, "My God, my God, could it be her?" His little body wanted to move, but he stood perfectly still.

The sounds of the city fell on deaf ears and as though from a distance far away, he heard a soft, sweet voice say, "Reuben, is that you?" He turned to stare at the lady he had just tipped his hat to. She was the most beautiful woman he had ever seen. Her stature was elegant, her dress of high fashion. Her dark black hair was pulled away from her face with a few ringlets straying here and there. On the top of her head was a tiny little hat, nestled in the soft black curls. A small piece of delicate netting came from the hat barely touching the top of her forehead. When she came closer, he could see her fair skin had a few fine wrinkles. There was a blush to her cheeks and her lips were soft rose in color.

Reuben looked into eyes full of tears. He beheld the woman he had last seen thirty years ago. He had hidden her name in the depths of his heart. He reached out as though to a child and said to her, "Victoria. Yes, it's me." She stepped forward slowly into his arms. He gathered her gently and time disappeared for their hearts that had remained one throughout the many years.

She sobbed as she spoke his name again and again. He held her close and cried as he said, "I'm sorry, Victoria, I'm sorry." She leaned away and with her delicate hand she touched the tears on his face. She traced his lips with her fingers then kissed him softly. It was not a dream. The moment was real. Victoria had found her husband and Reuben had returned to his past. So much needed to be said. So many questions needed to be answered. But, today they would spend walking in the park, sitting under dogwood trees and strolling through a rose garden.

The trees and roses had their buds of early spring, and Victoria and Reuben vowed to return when their full blossom was on display. Although Victoria was now forty-nine years old and Reuben was fifty-six, they were instantly young again. Their feelings for each other had not changed. Today, they were like two lovers who had met for the first time. They refused to think about yesterday. They agreed to talk about that tomorrow. For now they had a need for each other.

At the end of the day, Reuben escorted Victoria to her room at the Vanderbilt Hotel. She was only in Birmingham for a few days and would be returning to Atlanta tomorrow. How could they say goodbye? They could not. She invited him into her room. They laughed and teased, remembering their honeymoon night at the Lithia Hotel in Tallapoosa thirty-one years ago.

CHAPTER SEVENTEEN

*R*euben could not take his eyes off her. He stood behind her, lifting her long dark curls, touching and kissing her neck and her delicate shoulders. She responded to his touch and their desire for each other could not be denied. He had deflowered her when she was eighteen, but to him, her nectar was still virginal. No other man had touched her. They were not strangers. They remembered every part of each other as they tangled in their rapture. She succumbed to his movements of joy and they lay in a bed of passion. On this night, the heartbreak was mended. Victoria and Reuben pledged their tryst for days and nights to come.

Early in the hours of dawn, as they lay in each others arms, Victoria told Reuben what had happened to her after he left her. "When I realized you were not coming back," she said, "I thought I was going to die. I kept wondering what I had done wrong to make you leave me like that."

Reuben kissed her on the forehead as he said, "It wasn't you, my love, it was me; you did nothing wrong."

"That is what Father said. He said you had gotten into some trouble with the law. Said you stole some money from Jessie's dad, Mr. Bailey. He said you were a patsy and couldn't face up to your responsibilities. I tell you Reuben, I couldn't bear all the mean things he would say about you, and Jessie said he would beat you up if he ever saw you again." Victoria continued to explain what it was like when Reuben disappeared from her life in 1915. She said, "So, when Father suggested I go to Atlanta to school, I didn't argue with him because I needed to get out of that town. Everyone would stare at me. Of course no one ever said anything, because

Jessie threatened everyone never to say a word to me. He was really a good friend and from the beginning he adored little Vanessa and she him. It was no surprise to me or anyone when they got married."

Reuben jumped up. "What did you say?" he questioned.

"I was telling you that your daughter married your dear friend Jessie," Victoria spoke lovingly.

"That bastard ain't no friend of mine." Reuben cursed as he grabbed for his clothes and started getting dressed. He was shouting as he said, "Damn it, Victoria, I didn't do any of those things your father said. I was being accused of all kinds of things; that's why I had to run away from that place and that low life Jessie Bailey is a lying son-of-a." Reuben was so mad he couldn't finish the curse. He was pacing the floor jingling the change in his pockets and after a few moments shouted out again, "I can't believe you let our daughter marry that low-life. Have you no sense?" Then he kinda chuckled as he said, "Oh, I get it, you believed all the bull that was said about me. That's why you ran off and left our daughter with your mama. Guess you were in on it to tell her that I was dead. That right? That right, Victoria? You told Vanessa that I died?"

Victoria was curled up in the sheets whimpering like a child. "Yes, my father told us you were dead. Yes, yes, I believed him. I believed Jessie. I had to believe something. You left me, Reuben; you left me and our baby." Victoria sobbed into her pillow.

Reuben's temper had flared and he was over it. He walked over to the bed, sat on the edge and reached over and took Victoria in his arms. "Victoria, please sweetheart, don't cry. I've waited so long to ask you to forgive me for leaving you like I did. Now that I have found you, I don't know what to say to make you understand. There is so much, sweetheart, please listen to me. When I left you, I went to Florida and worked for a while before I went off to the war; then when I came back, I went back to Tallapoosa to see you and my daughter, but I was too late. Your father had told Vanessa, you, everyone that I had died during the flu epidemic. You were already a success with your career in Atlanta, and also you had filed papers for a divorce. I knew your parents were taking good care of little Vanessa, and I knew you would have no trouble getting a divorce if I just stayed out of the picture. So, I left Tallapoosa again. I haven't been back there since 1919."

Victoria clung to him as she said, "I'm not a strong person, Reuben."

"I know, sweetheart. I know and I'm sorry I hurt you. God knows, you didn't ask to get mixed up with a person like me. You deserved better," he spoke to her as he cradled her close.

"From the first day I saw you I loved you," Victoria said, "Against all odds, I've only loved you. No matter what, I will love you all my life."

When she said these words to Reuben, he knew he had said enough. Why should he risk hurting her anymore? She must not know about his affair with Mary and she must not know about the baby, Reuben thought to himself. She had been protected from that scandal and, like it or not, Jessie had protected both Victoria and Vanessa from the truth. Victoria's innocence made it easy for Reuben to tell her untruths.

She believed in him, and when he asked her not to tell Vanessa and Jessie that he was living in Birmingham, she agreed to do what he thought was best. Working with the designing firm, she spent a lot of time in Birmingham, so they would get an apartment there. Reuben told her he had a good job in Birmingham and assured her that they would be together as much as possible. He made no long-term commitment to her, however, she began to plan for their future together.

Reuben let Victoria return to Atlanta that day without ever telling her about Rebekah and the children or Tasha and his son, Lucky. He hid his secrets well as he kissed her goodbye and thrilled at the thought of knowing they would be together next weekend. On Thursday, Reuben telephoned Victoria at her office with the designing firm in Atlanta. He wanted to know just when she would arrive in Birmingham. Victoria explained to him that she would not be coming to Birmingham this week because it was the weekend of Easter Sunday and she was expected to be at Vanessa's home there in Atlanta. "Oh, Reuben, I wish you could come. Vanessa and Jessie have a beautiful home here in Atlanta and they have a precious little girl, your granddaughter. Her name is Beth and she has your sparkling blue eyes. My mother lives with them, since Father passed away and she takes care of Beth just like she did our Vanessa."

Reuben said sarcastically, "Oh, I bet she does," remembering Mrs. Sherwood's manipulative ways. He was not going to upset Victoria, so he explained, "Victoria, you know I can't come with Jessie there. Remember we promised not to tell him that I am in Birmingham. As long as that man's alive, I can't be a part of that family."

Victoria protested, "But, Reuben..."

211

"Just leave it be, Victoria, just do as I say," Reuben continued, "if Vanessa is as happy as you say then it is best if she never knows about me. I've done some things I am not proud of and I don't want her to ever be hurt by what I've done. You go to her, Victoria, enjoy your Easter day with our granddaughter and for God's sake, Victoria, don't tell anyone about me. You promise?"

"I promise, Reuben, I promise," she answered, sounding depressed. "I love you. I will see you the weekend after Easter."

"I love you too. Goodbye, Victoria," he said, then he hung up the phone and as he walked away, his thoughts were of a little girl, his granddaughter, Beth. That night as he lay in his bed in the boarding house on 24th Street, he decided tomorrow he would go to see his family. The next morning he got up early and walked to the bus station. But the ticket he bought was not to Decatur, Alabama, where his wife Rebekah and the children were; it was a round-trip ticket to Tallapoosa, Georgia.

In Reuben's mind, the gate to his past had been opened when he found out that after he left Sanford, Florida, in 1918 his beloved Tasha had died in childbirth. She had given him a son and this son had been killed in the war. Reuben walked through the opened gate when he saw Victoria, the girl he had married in 1913 in Tallapoosa, Georgia. Although they were now divorced, they renewed their love for each other. Reuben had returned to Victoria's bed; now he felt the need to return to other loved ones. He had to go home. It had been twenty-five years since Reuben was in Tallapoosa.

The town never returned to being the boomtown it was when Reuben was young. In fact, it had remained about the same since the Northerners left and took their businesses with them before World War I. About the only visible difference was the once elegant Lithia Springs Hotel was gone. The structure was dismantled when World War II began and builders purchased the wooden timbers to incorporate into other structures in the Tallapoosa area.

When Reuben left this town in 1919, he left behind two little girls. One would grow up having plenty of ribbons for her hair; the other would grow up having none. His daughter, Vanessa, was raised by her grandparents in the big house with the large white columns. Everyone doted on her, perhaps because she had no father and her mother came to see her only on holidays. Even so, she grew up a happy child. She was a beautiful young girl like her mother. She was slim and petite, and her blue eyes twinkled when she talked. She was very popular in school and just before graduation, she was dubbed a debutante.

The ceremony was held at the Lithia Hotel ballroom just as it had been with her mother coming out in 1913. Only this time, Reuben was not there. Vanessa was escorted by her protector and the man that would become her husband only weeks after her graduation. This man was Jessie Bailey. Jessie attended Emory College in Atlanta and had remained close to the Sherwood family after his last encounter with Reuben. He went along with the story Doc. Sherwood told everybody about Reuben being dead. Jessie hoped he was. Anyway he had patiently waited for Vanessa, and in 1932 he married Reuben's daughter.

After they were married, they moved to Atlanta where Jessie became successful with his own retail business. Reuben had been right when he decided that Vanessa would always be well cared for.

The other little girl, the one with the soft blonde curls, Reuben never saw before he left Tallapoosa. When he heard that her mother, his sweetheart and lover, had married, he somehow felt betrayed, so he quit sending her any money for their daughter. Annie Mae had grown up not having material things, but she was a hard worker and had a heart of gold. She was always doing things for others.

As she grew older, her hair turned dark, but she never seemed to age. She had a beautiful figure and all the boys were after her, but she waited till she fell in love to share her bed. In 1935, when she was twenty-one, she married. She never left Tallapoosa. After they were married, she and her husband bought a house in town and lived there with their two children.

The bus ride from Birmingham to Tallapoosa took only three hours. Why had it taken Reuben so long to make this trip? He was asking himself this question as the bus traveled east on Highway 78. The bus transportation had taken over a lot of the train passenger business. Reuben preferred to take the bus because it could take him closer to where he wanted to go.

The first thing Reuben noticed as the bus pulled into town was the dogwood trees in full bloom. The whole town looked like a place in a child's storybook. The trees looked like cotton candy. Some trees blossomed with different shades of pink, while others displayed their snow-white flower. Reuben had always loved this time of the year. It was spring, April 11, 1888, when he was born here in Tallapoosa. He had spent his young life on his family's farm, but he moved into town and learned the ways of city life.

After that, he tried to return to farm life several times, but he just couldn't. He often recalled the words of his father, "Son, you need to get out there in the world to be somebody." His brother, Frank, had correctly labeled him a "city slicker."

The bus stopped next to the train depot. There was no actual bus station in Tallapoosa. Reuben stepped down off the bus and looked at his pocket watch. It was almost noon. There was no hesitation as he started walking down the street that ran beside the railroad track. The track still ran through the middle of town, but now the street that ran along either side of the track was paved. Headed west toward the Kincaide farm, Reuben paid no attention to anyone. As he walked past the spot by the railroad track where he and Jessie had fought the day he left Tallapoosa, he barely glanced in that direction. He only noticed that the kudzu still grew there covering the banks of the railroad tracks.

Had he taken the time to look closer, he may have found something more than just a memory hidden in the thick, green kudzu: the knife Jessie Bailey had attacked him with. Before the pavement ran out, Reuben turned onto a dirt road that led down a small hill to farmland. He took a familiar path through an open field. The springtime growth of wild flowers billowed in the breeze that came across the field. Some grass and flowers came to his knees and brushed his pant legs. He slowed his pace and kept his head bent down until he got to the little dirt road that ran by the barn and up to the house.

The barn looked old with its rusty tin roof and its weather-beaten boards. It seemed to lean to one side. Across the road from the barn was a new little house sitting about fifty feet back from the embankment of the road. Reuben looked closely, but he didn't see anyone around the house or the barn. He looked up the hill to the family farmhouse, expecting to see Felix sitting on the porch and Old Shep near by. What he saw was unbelievable to him.

First of all there were fences that seemed to block off sections, leaving the big house almost fenced completely in with a big yard leading down into a pie shape to meet the road. As Reuben got closer, he could see the house was all boarded up. The paint was just about all peeled off the sides of the house and the porch had rotten boards with one of the two steps missing.

Reuben walked around to the back through tall weeds. He came back to the front of the house and stared across the flat land into the trees. What had happened here? Where was his family? The picture of home in his mind faded like rain on watercolors. When he left his mother here with Felix, he tucked the memories away, so recently when he took the memories out, they remained the same. But those memories were no longer real, for time had changed everything. After leaving Decatur, Alabama in 1924 to move to Indiana, Reuben stopped writing to Felix and his mother. That was twenty years ago. If ever a thought of them crossed his mind during these past years, it was of open arms welcoming him back home.

Now those thoughts were just a dream. He walked away from the broken-down house, past the old barn, toward the cemetery. He stepped out of the trees onto the sacred ground. He went straight to his papa's grave. He took his hat off and stood next to the time worn stone with F. M. Kincaide, D. 1913 crudely carved on it. Tears came to his eyes as memories of his father raced through his mind. After a few minutes he took out his handkerchief and wiped his glasses off. Looking around, he noticed there was no new grave next to Papa's. Only the one that was there when they buried Papa. This must mean that his mother was still living.

The cemetery had grown in size. Reuben began to walk around looking at the names on graves that were not there when he last visited. As he read the names out loud, he remembered each one. All these people buried here were family members. Even Edmond Kincaide and Isaac Windom were considered part of the Kincaide family. These two men had been slaves owned by Reuben's grandfather. Their stone markers did not have their names on them, but Reuben remembered them well. He remembered that his papa told him that one of them did not have a name when they got him, so he took the Kincaide name. This was a common practice during those times.

When the two black men died, the family buried them side by side. The two stones looked like miniature boulders pointing toward the sky. They had come here as slaves. When they died, they had been free men.

Just as Reuben was about to leave the cemetery, his eyes caught a name on one of the newer stones: Elijah Felix Kincaide. He dropped to one knee and touched the date, Died 1928. "Felix," he said, "I came too late, I know

215

you are mad at me now." Reuben then found himself saying, "I'm sorry," to another person of his past. This time he could only hope that the words would be heard. Felix was his cousin, but he had been like a brother and after Papa died, he treated Reuben more like a son. If Reuben had come home seeking words of wisdom from Felix as he had done so many times in the past, then on this day Reuben must face the fact that Felix was no longer there to give him advice. All Reuben could do now was look toward the heavens and say, "Thanks, Felix, thanks for being my best friend."

Searching the cemetery one more time, Reuben wondered where his mother was.

It was getting late in the afternoon, but Reuben was not hungry because he had eaten a big breakfast when the bus stopped in Heflin, about twenty miles before they got to Tallapoosa. He was tired though and felt like he needed to rest before walking over to his brother Frank's place. It was about ten miles over there and he had no idea what to expect after seeing the family farm and knowing that Felix had died. He left the cemetery.

The walk through the woods was easy because the fall of the leaves over a period of time had snuffed out any undergrowth. He seemed beckoned to a clearing on the banks of the river that ran behind the Kincaide farm. As a child he was frightened by the size and the noise of the river, but now when he thought of the river, he remembered only a girl and her expression of love. He stood in the middle of a place where time had made little change. A tree had fallen at the edge of the clearing and lay stretched out away from the bank of the river. Its branches dipped down into the water.

Reuben found a clean spot at the base of the tree trunk and sat down. He took his hat off and placed it beside him. He leaned back and closed his eyes. He felt caressed by the stillness and his mind drifted. His senses could smell her sweet scent, and he remembered how she gave her soft body to him. She came to him here on a crisp autumn day and released him from his bondage of loneliness and desire.

As he lingered in his thoughts, a figure was emerging from the trees. It walked through the woods like a deer and when it stepped into the clearing, it saw a man with his eyes closed, sitting on the fallen tree trunk. A soft touch on the arm opened Reuben's eyes and in one swoop he grabbed his hat and leaped to his feet. She giggled a little as she said, "Did, I scare you?"

216

Reuben standing tall by the stump said, "No, you did not. I heard you coming."

"Did, huh?" she said.

As she walked over and placed her foot on the tree trunk, Reuben looked at her and said, "What are you doing here? Don't you know you shouldn't come up to a stranger that way?"

"Is that what you are? A stranger? You look familiar to me." She was certainly fearless. She wore jean pants and a loose fitting cotton shirt that hung loosely over her well-endowed figure.

Reuben said to her, "I used to live here, but you are too young to remember me. I left this place twenty-five years ago. How come you're out here anyway? You live around here?"

The girl had climbed out onto the fallen tree limb that stretched out across the river. She dangled her legs down toward the water, careful not to get her shoes wet. She continued the conversation. "I live in town, but I used to come here with my mother when I was a little girl. Then when I got older, Mother quit coming out here, but I find when I am troubled about something, there seems to be someone here I can talk to."

"That why you came today? You got troubles?" Reuben asked.

"No," she said, "I don't know. I just seemed to want to come here today. Guess I'm weird." She tossed her hair about to let the breeze catch it and she laughed as she looked at Reuben with her bright blue eyes.

A slight chill went through Reuben's body. Hearing her laugh, it was kinda like a giggle, one that used to delight him so. She was such a friendly young woman, so much like — no, no, he shut out the thought. "Well," Reuben said, "I better be going. I was intending to walk over to my brother's place but I think I will find a place in town to stay for the night and go over there tomorrow. I see the big Lithia Hotel is gone. Any good place to stay for one night?"

She got up from the tree limb and climbed back onto the riverbank saying to Reuben, "A couple of places right on the main street, you can't miss them. Boy, you have been gone a long time."

Reuben said, "It's been nice talking to you." He started to walk away.

She stuck out her hand and said, "Yes, sir, same to you; my name is Annie Mae, Annie Mae Brown."

"Annie Mae," Reuben repeated softly like a murmur. The name burst through his mind like thunder. It was the name of a child conceived here thirty-one years ago. Reuben did not shake her hand. He turned and took steps toward the woods. The young woman had looked into his eyes and she refused to believe he was a stranger.

She called out to him, "Are you my daddy?"

Reuben did not turn around; he continued to walk into the shade of the trees. Annie Mae stared at his back until he disappeared. Then she turned to the river. Wind began to rustle the trees and small twigs, leaves and moss fell into the water. She watched the debris as it floated downstream. Reuben had left her standing alone and wondering.

The faster he walked, the longer it was taking him to get out of the woods. He wasn't even sure he was going in the right direction. His mind raced. Is that my daughter? Is that Mary's child? Reuben had done many wrong things during his lifetime, but the one thing that was most hurtful and that he regretted the most was that he had left his little girls in Tallapoosa without a father. Was he going to walk away from Annie Mae again? He had been given a second chance to make that decision. Would it be possible for him to right a wrong?

He realized he must turn around and go back to her if these questions were to be answered. He walked up behind her, spoke her name, "Annie Mae." She turned and looked at him. Then he said, "I am Reuben Oliver Kincaide. I am your daddy." The lateness of the day brought a coolness to the air and the setting sun made the river glitter. Reuben embraced his daughter. Annie Mae was six years old when her mother had promised her that one day her daddy would come. She had waited twenty-four years to realize this promise.

Annie Mae took her daddy home with her and on the way they talked. They decided to tell her two children, Nellie and Billy, that Reuben was their uncle. It would be decided later whether or not to tell them he was their grandfather because they wanted to ask Mary about that decision. Reuben told Annie Mae that he wanted to see Mary, but tomorrow he had to go to his brother's place, then he would have to return to Birmingham to work on Monday morning. He gave Annie Mae a post office box address in Birmingham where she could send him letters.

Annie Mae told her daddy that her mother had married Robert Wilson in 1920, and he had been a good husband and a good step-father. She said her mother tried to be happy, but that she always got misty eyed when she talked about him. Everyone knew the truth was that she would always love

Reuben. Mary had never revealed to Annie Mae or anyone the true facts about the night Jessie Bailey came to her house looking for Reuben. Mary had kept that a secret.

Nellie and Billy were delighted to fix a room up for Uncle Reuben. They thought he was a nice man and he promised to bring them presents from Birmingham the next time he came to see them. The next morning Reuben got up early and said goodbye to Annie Mae and her family. He walked off down the road and Annie Mae turned to her husband. She had tears in her eyes. Her husband said to her as he put his arms around her, "He is your daddy."

She replied, "Yes, he is."

It was Easter Sunday morning and Reuben felt good about himself after leaving Annie Mae's house. He had finally met his daughter after all the lost years. He hastened his walk as he anticipated finding his mother living with his brother Frank. Reuben knew the road to Frank's place well. Frank had not moved since he bought his place in 1912. Back in those days, Reuben would go there mostly to get liquor or to drink with his brother. Frank had always been the rowdy one, getting into trouble when he went into town, and he never did learn how to read or write. He just wasn't interested in the ways of the world like Reuben was.

He had chosen a perfect spot to build his log house. The terrain was densely wooded. There were steep hills and deep hollows. Miles from anyone else's place, you had to follow a passage that was like a shaft dipping down into the bowels of the earth to find it. Frank favored solitude and even though it was now the year 1944, Frank had no electricity or plumbing in his house. A creek ran through the basin about fifty yards from his house and supplied him with fresh spring water. Reuben walked the path that crossed the creek, and now he could see the log house almost hidden by the shadows of the trees.

As he approached the yard, he could smell coffee brewing and his heart leaped. He just knew in a few minutes his mother would be pouring him a cup of her coffee. Inside the house a woman stood at the kitchen stove. As she turned to sit a plate on the table, she glanced out through the opened door. She saw a man with a hat on walking up into the yard. She said to Frank, "Who is that man coming yonder?"

Frank got up out of his chair at the table, looked out the door and said, "Why, it's my brother!" Frank had not been well, so by the time he got out the door, Reuben had stepped onto the porch. Frank said, "You lost, city slicker?"

Reuben replied, "No, I came to see you," The two men shook hands and embraced each other. They had not seen each other in almost thirty years. The woman in the kitchen stepped behind Frank. Reuben looked at her. She was a stranger, not his mother. Frank turned and said to her, "Come here, daughter, I want you to meet my brother."

He introduced her as Molly and explained to Reuben that she was not actually his daughter, but she was the woman his nephew Dan was intending to marry. Molly had come to help Frank out because he had been sick and there was no one living with him. The first words out of Reuben's mouth were, "Where is Mama?"

There was no good way for Frank to say it, so he just said, "Well, little brother, your mother has passed on."

Reuben sank to the edge of the porch. He took off his hat and sat with his arms on his knees, his hands holding the hat, rubbing its brim. After a few minutes he said aloud, "I'm too late."

Frank sat down in a rocker on the porch and began to talk to Reuben. "I'm sorry we had to bury Mother without you here, but I didn't know where you were. She passed on in '36 and I had word sent to you at an address in Jeffersonville, Indiana, but they said it couldn't be delivered because you no longer were there. I did the best I could. Miss Lizzie Dobbs washed her and laid her out, then old man Miller at the funeral home gave me a casket for her."

Reuben broke in and said, "She's not buried by Papa. I was there yesterday. She's not there."

"I know," Frank said, "she didn't want to be buried out there on the family farm. She wanted to be buried up here by that little old church on Providence Road. She said she always liked that church and wanted to rest in peace there."

With few interruptions from Reuben, Frank continued to tell him what had happened. "When Felix died in 1928, Mary Ann came here to live with me. She said she didn't know where you were because you had left Alabama. Felix told me before he died that you, or that is I believe he said your four oldest children were to get the property that the farm is on. I don't know what ever happened over there. I just know that Mary Ann came over here to live.

"No one ever said anything to me about what went on with the property. Guess they all know I don't read or write and think I am stupid. Lots of folks thought Mary Ann shouldn't be living down here with me. But she did and I'm glad she did. She spent eight years here and I know she thought you would never come back to Tallapoosa. She used to spend a lot time down there by the creek. She would gather the watercress that grows down there."

Frank left Reuben with his thoughts of his mother and went into the kitchen to tell Molly to fix Reuben a cup of coffee. After a while, Reuben came in and sat down at the table. The first thing he did was ask Molly for another saucer. He always had to have an extra saucer to pour his coffee into to drink. Molly thought this a little strange, but from then on whenever he came to visit, she always put the two saucers out for him.

Reuben was curious, so he asked Frank how he knew he was in Indiana and how did he get an address there. Frank told him that Felix knew about a man named Bogart over in Birmingham at a hat store, and that he might know where Reuben was if they ever needed him. "So," Frank said, "In 1934, I come upon some hard times. I was about to lose my place here. Didn't have the money to pay taxes and they were going to take everything away from me. That meant Mary Ann wouldn't have a home either. I looked up the hat store in Birmingham and they told me there that this Mr. Bogart was in Indiana and they gave me the address. I got on a train and went up there because the fellow told me that you lived up there at the Bogart place. Had the darnedest time finding the Bogart place.

"Finally when I got there I saw two little girls playing under a tree in the yard. I asked them if they were Kincaide girls. One little girl said 'I'm not,' but she pointed to the other little girl, saying 'she is.' I shook the hand of the little Kincaide girl and told her I was her Uncle Frank and asked if her daddy was home. She said she didn't know, to go up to the house and find out. Looked to me like you were living good up there, little brother." Frank paused for a response from Reuben, but Reuben just got up and walked toward the door. He stood there looking out, jingling the change in his pockets.

Frank continued, "Anyway, when I got to the house, you weren't there, but this fellow Bogart was. Strange man. Anyway, he says you were gone off someplace and asked me what I wanted you for. Well, I just plain told him that I needed some money and from the looks of things figured you could make me a loan. Don't know what you were doing for this fellow, but he sure must have liked you, cause he pulled out a wad of money and asked me how much I needed. He said best thing I could do was take the money and leave. I didn't see any signs of you or a woman around, thinking you had a wife, and I did need the money. So, I just took the money and came home.

"I never told Mary Ann where I got the money or anything cause I just didn't know what to think. I always figured when you got ready you would let her know where you were. What did you think Reuben? Did you think your mother would live forever?"

When Frank asked that question, it was too much for Reuben. He had been standing there at the door barely hearing what Frank was telling him. He certainly was not going to explain to Frank about his life in Indiana. It came as no surprise to him that Bogart never mentioned to him that Frank had been there to see him. His little nine year old daughter never said anything to him about meeting her uncle. This daughter never asked about her Uncle Frank's visit, but she always wondered what happened to the man who told her he was her Uncle Frank.

Throughout the years, she told her brothers and sisters about meeting their Uncle Frank. Some of them believed her, others did not. Reuben said something to Frank about going outside to take a look at his chickens. He walked out the door, put his hat on, stood in the yard a few minutes, then walked down toward the creek. He noticed a path, a winding dent in the grass and he thought, someone has been this way.

The grass, sprinkled with dew, sparkled in the sunshine, and water glided over pebbles in the stream. A breeze stirred the leaves, and birds sang from the trees. Nature had created here a magical setting like a garden that had been freshly painted.

Reuben could only imagine his beloved mother here by this running stream, gathering watercress. He could only wonder if she was lonely. He asked himself, *why did it take me so long to come home?*

He walked along the stream where his mother last walked. He tried to breathe life into his forgotten past, but on this day his mind was like a mist in a forest. He walked out of the hollow without saying goodbye to his brother and took the bus back to Birmingham.

CHAPTER EIGHTEEN

$\mathcal{P}$lans had been made to spend the following weekend with Victoria, but after finding out about his mother's death, Reuben felt the need to be with Rebekah. He felt guilty because he had not been home to see Rebekah and the children in about six months. He had not been there for Easter or to help with the planting of the crops. He knew he needed to come up with an excuse for his absence so they would be sympathetic toward him because he desperately needed their comfort and care.

He was certain of one thing — Rebekah and the children must never find out the truth about his past before he married Rebekah. Rebekah was a fine Christian woman and he was sure she would not understand his wrongdoing. The children were getting older now and he feared they would start questioning him about his family, even try to go to Tallapoosa to see them. He had told them he was from Tallapoosa, Georgia. This was a mistake because they must never go there. He could tell them his family all died, but he didn't want them to go searching for graves. He definitely didn't want anyone to find his brother, Frank, so he could perhaps tell them that Frank moved away — far away, like to Hawaii.

These were his thoughts as he made his way to Decatur, Alabama. When he got there, he missed the bus out to the countryside so he found the familiar railroad track and walked the ten miles. Two of the older children were in the field plowing when they saw their daddy coming down the train tracks. One said to the other, "I wonder what he will tell Mother? Why he has been gone so long?"

The reply was, "He will lie to her, that's what; he will tell her a big fat lie!"

When Reuben came near the field, he called out, "Children, put your tools down and come on to the house. I have just come from Georgia and I have some bad news, so come on to the house."

He walked on to the house with the two children following a short distance behind him. When he reached the steps to the house he fell onto the porch and bent himself over weeping with grief. All of the children came running, some calling out, "Mama come quickly; it's Daddy!"

Rebekah wiped the flour dough from her hands onto her apron as she ran through the house from the kitchen. Seeing Reuben at the edge of the porch, she rushed over and leaned to help him sit up. "Reuben," she said, "whatever is wrong?" She could see tears streaming from his eyes and pain on his face. She embraced him with both arms and called to the children, "Help me with your daddy." After they got him up and into a chair, Rebekah asked him, "Are you sick, Reuben? Are you hurt anywhere?"

Reuben looked straight into Rebekah's eyes and said, "I've got some bad news, ole woman. Give me a minute and I will tell you and the children." Rebekah stood beside him and the children gathered round. After a few minutes, this is the story he told: "There has been a terrible accident in Georgia. On Easter Sunday, my brother, Felix, took Mother, my sister, Vanessa and two young children for a drive while his wife Ann stayed home to fix dinner. The word is the car skidded and went into the river. They all drowned."

He put his head in his hands and wept again. Rebekah and the children had lingered on every word. They felt sorry for him and even though some of them thought he was probably lying, no one questioned him. They had been taught strict obedience to him, and Reuben used this for complete control over this family. Reuben had constructed the story carefully. The drowning was so there would be no bodies recovered from the waters of the Tallapoosa River, therefore no graves to find. He left the sister-in-law alive just in case anyone ever saw him in Birmingham with Victoria, he could say she was Ann, his sister-in law.

He dealt with anyone ever finding his brother, Frank, in this manner. He said that Frank had moved to Hawaii and was killed in World War II on the island of Okinawa. He also said that Frank owned a pineapple farm in Hawaii and there would be an inheritance coming to them. He had told Rebekah before that their four older children would get money out of the

Kincaide farm in Tallapoosa. After their son, Marion, died, Rebekah asked him about the farm inheritance, what would happen to Marion's share, and Reuben told her then it would be split three ways — that is between the three oldest children.

Then after he told the story about Felix and Mother drowning, he never mentioned any money from the farm again.

Reuben had been a master at twisting his story with part truths. He had combined his grief of losing his mother and Felix and finding out about the son he never knew being killed in the war with other facts he wanted to cover up such as where his brother, Frank, was and that he had other children. He had obtained the basic element, the drowning, probably from a newspaper story, but the only part of this story that was the truth was that he had been to Tallapoosa, Georgia.

Reuben had started out his life with Rebekah by lying to her about his age. Then, he had looked into her eyes and blocked out seven years of his life, but those seven years had now come back into his life, so once again he lied to her. For the better part of his life, Reuben told the story about his family drowning in the river. He told it to his grandchildren and always the story remained the same.

The story would shield Reuben's secrets of the past from Rebekah and their children. This lie would allow him to continue a relationship with Victoria, his first wife, and at the same time he felt free to go to Tallapoosa to spend time with Annie Mae, his daughter, his grandchildren, his brother, Frank and even Mary, his mistress. Reuben had been successful in telling a story that would make Rebekah and the children feel sorry for him.

That night Rebekah put on her ankle length cotton nightgown and went to bed with her husband. Her soothing spirit caressed the man she loved. Through an open window a summer breeze was invited indoors, sweeping the room with a fragrant meadow scent. Reuben was inspired to recapture the roles reserved just for them. There had been happy days and a lifetime of shared love. He made promises to his wife that he would make her life better. She believed him. The next day they went to the Caddo Cemetery. There they stood before the grave of their first born child. The roses that Rebekah had planted billowed from their bed and formed a canopy over the stone.

Rebekah stood there remembering her dear little Marion. Reuben had thoughts of two lost sons. Reuben and Rebekah's son, who had joined the military, was now in Europe. World War II continued to rage on both fronts in Europe and the Pacific. On Friday, June 6, 1944, allied troops stormed the beaches at Normandy. It was a turbulent crossing for the American troops across the English Channel en route to Normandy.

General Eisenhower's orders were, "Full victory, nothing else!" Their landing took the Germans by surprise. The plan for D-Day was called "Operation Overload" and was the biggest secret ever kept during war. As soon as the beaches were secure, Hitler's Atlantic Wall was breached and the allied command began unloading tons of equipment and soldiers. Now all roads led to the long-awaited liberation of Paris.

D-Day was a fateful day for Germany, but it had cost the Americans 2,000 casualties. Reuben could only pray this son would survive the war. He did not know exactly where his son was, but he did have an address to send him mail. When he returned to Birmingham from seeing Rebekah and the children, he wrote his son a letter. In the letter, he told him the same story he told Rebekah and the other children about his family in Georgia being drowned on Easter Sunday.

Before he went to Decatur to see Rebekah and the children, he had called Victoria in Atlanta and told her he would be away for a couple of weeks working a painting job he had outside of Birmingham. When he returned to Birmingham, he went to the Vanderbilt Hotel to see if Victoria was there. She was not. He called her in Atlanta and they made plans to meet at the Vanderbilt the next weekend. Perhaps Reuben had honorable intentions of telling Victoria about Rebekah and the children, but when he saw her standing there in her chiffon dress revealing her graceful curves beneath its delicate folds, he could not resist her out of sheer pleasure. This feeling of passion for her kept him from telling her the the truth about his life.

He loved Victoria, loved her when he took her as his teenage bride and he loved her still. He longed for her when she would leave him and return to Atlanta. At first he thought of it as a simple, whimsical affair, but Victoria's thoughts were different. She was making plans for her future, but she had agreed with Reuben that for right now she would keep staying at the Vanderbilt when she was in Birmingham. Reuben told her he was living in a boardinghouse near his job and that she wouldn't feel comfortable there. He said he had been missing some things from his room. One thing missing was his wedding ring that Victoria had given him when they got married.

He said someone stole it from him at the boardinghouse. This lie Reuben told had a two-fold purpose: one being it would keep Victoria from staying or even visiting the boarding house, and it would be a cover up for him having given the ring to Rebekah on the day he married her. Victoria believed everything Reuben said. This made it easy for him to schedule the time he could be with her, and meanwhile he was setting things up to try to make life easier for Rebekah and the children.

Mrs. Adams, the feisty little lady who ran the boardinghouse, let Reuben rent an apartment attached to the house. Before school started in the fall, Reuben went to Decatur and brought the four oldest girls to Birmingham to live with him and go to school. He was really good to them. He bought them clothes and school supplies. He even bought one of the girls a violin.

The daughter who received the violin remembers it well. She had a boyfriend in school, who she thought was beautiful. He had beautiful blue eyes and blonde hair and he played the violin. She wanted to take lessons, so Reuben went to a pawn shop and paid $23.00 for a violin, case and all. This violin was a genuine Stradivarius. The daughter took lessons for awhile and did well. She was in a recital held at the Music Hall in Birmingham. Reuben gave her money to buy a dress and she and her sisters picked out a beautiful white organdy with lace appliquéd. One sister said she looked like an angel standing there all alone, playing her violin. She played a beautiful melody to her audience as her eyes searched the room, but she did not find her daddy there. Without Reuben's continued encouragement, she became disinterested. When she was sixteen years old she pawned the violin for $5.00. At the time neither she nor Reuben realized the value of this violin.

Reuben brought his little daughter, Martha Lou, to Birmingham to visit her sisters. While she was there, the girls fixed her up and took her to a studio to have her photograph taken. The oldest girl had curled her hair making ringlets of golden curls, then she put a ribbon on top. Martha Lou wore a little cotton dress her mother had made of red dotted Swiss fabric with white trim at the sleeves, neckline and around the waist. The girls adored their little sister. They told her she was as pretty as Shirley Temple, who was a famous child movie star.

This photo of Martha Lou became one of the family's favorites, perhaps because it reminded the girls of a good time in their lives or, most likely, because they loved their baby sister. In 1983, Martha Lou's oldest sister made a large 8 X 10 copy of this photo and wrote a poem expressing her feelings toward this little girl:

Guess Who?

I will give you a clue.
The most beautiful little girl I have ever known.
Adorned in a dress that her mother had sewn.
Her hair was brushed by a sister with love,
Now can you guess from the clues above?
Another clue to guess who ...
A beloved sister, a pleasure to all
Sent to us late in the Fall.
She is a sister who cares for her family with love,
Now can you guess from the clues above?
The last clue, the easiest of all ...
She came to my aid when I started to fall.
Her love and care meant so much to me,
So I give you this picture, I want you to see,
The most beautiful little girl I have ever known,
Remains to be beautiful although she is grown.

Martha Lou was taken back to Rebekah to live on the farm. Reuben seemed to have everything under control when a man from his past got in touch with him. The man's name was George Bogart. Reuben was not surprised that George found him, and he was not surprised that George wanted him to do something for him. George had only to remind him that he knew all about his past and boasted when he told Reuben, "At anytime I could have you locked up or worse!"

"Anyway," George said, "all I need for you to do is work with this paint contractor on some jobs here around Birmingham."

Reuben agreed and he was pleased when he met the paint contractor. He seemed like a nice man and he was very generous to Reuben with sharing the profits from their jobs. Reuben did not have a car, so this man would let him borrow his. It was a 1941 black Plymouth. Sometimes on Sunday he would take the girls for a ride. Of course, if Victoria was in town, he made excuses to the girls as to why he didn't come home on Saturday night. He knew the girls would never go near the Vanderbilt Hotel. It was in a completely different part of town and a part of the world of which they could only dream.

In later years, Reuben's daughters remembered that their daddy would sometimes stay away for long periods of time. He would not explain to them where he was and they never asked him. Easter vacation in school came for the girls. Reuben put them on a bus to spend the holiday with their mother on the farm. He then borrowed the big black car and drove to Tallapoosa. It had been a year since he was there. His daughter, Annie Mae, had sent him letters to the P.O. box number he gave her.

They were always nice friendly letters asking him when he was coming back to see her. When Reuben pulled the car up in front of Annie Mae's house in Tallapoosa, he noticed a lady sitting in a rocking chair on the verandah. It was late in the afternoon and the verandah seemed to be a perfect spot to sit and enjoy the cool breeze of a spring day. As Reuben approached the steps, the lady got up and stood by the railing of the verandah. Reaching the top step, Reuben removed his hat and looked at her.

Reuben had remembered her the way she was the last time he saw her sitting on the sofa in her mother's house. She was such a pretty little thing, wearing a gingham dress with vintage lace collar and her golden hair in ringlets about her face. He had been thinking of her often during the past year. He vividly recalled her firm, young body and his delight in just being near her. She could always make him laugh, but it was not laughter in his heart thirty years ago when he had to send her away. He had taken advantage of her affection and she was pregnant with his child. Last year when he returned to the riverbank, he had met his daughter, Annie Mae. Today he was looking at the face of her mother.

When Mary stepped toward him, he could tell that her high-spirited feistiness as a youth had been stolen away by time. There were no tears in her eyes and little emotion in her facial expression. She reached for his hat as she said, "Here, let me take your hat. Have you been driving all day? You look tired, Reuben."

She acted as though she had just seen him yesterday. Only the little break in her voice when she said Reuben, let him know that she was not acting. He didn't know just what he had expected her to say to him, but he

229

couldn't believe how distant she was. He walked over to a small table next to a chair on the verandah, laid his hat down and said to her, "That's all right, I will just put it here."

In silence they stood before each other for what seemed like a lifetime to Reuben. Finally Mary spoke. "Annie Mae told me about seeing you when you were here last year."

"Did she tell you where we were when we met each other?" Reuben asked.

"Yes, she said you were out at the Kincaide farm, down by the river. I understand everyone is gone from the farm now. I heard that your mother passed away. I'm sorry, Reuben." Mary talked without emotion.

"I'm sorry too," Reuben said. "I went to see my brother, Frank, and he told me all that went on with the family."

Reuben couldn't stand all this polite talk any longer. He reached over and took both her little hands in his. She did not pull away. "I didn't think you would recognize me, Mary," he said.

With a quiver in her voice, she said, "We only age, Reuben, we never really change."

Still holding her hands he said, "You have not aged, you are still as pretty as a picture. The color of your hair has changed, but you still have these." He let go of her hands and played with the tiny hair ringlets about her forehead.

She tossed her head slightly and smiled for the first time.

"There," he said, "you still have that same smile, too." He then took her by the shoulders and turned her around.

Teasingly he said, "Yep you still got..." He didn't finish the sentence. Mary gave out a little giggle and Reuben finished his sentence, "still got that same little giggle."

Mary stepped away from him and said, "No, that's not what you were going to say, Reuben Kincaide, you were going to say something else."

"No, I was not, unless I was going to say *same laugh*. That's it. I was going to say you have the same...," and again he didn't finish the sentence.

They both laughed together. The ice had been broken. The tension was gone. Reuben put his arms around Mary and she put her arms around him. He said to her, "I'm here, Mary. What do you want me to do?"

Mary replied, "I waited for you Reuben. Then Felix told me you had gotten married in Alabama. I knew that Victoria divorced you and I hoped you would come and get Annie Mae and me. When I understood that you were not coming back, I married Robert Wilson. Do you know him?"

"Yes," Reuben said, "I know who he is. He is a good man."

"Yes, he is," Mary answered.

"What happened to us, Mary? Why was it never right between us? God knows I've always loved you. You were always so special, such a sweetheart. My life got all messed up and I know I hurt you. Can you forgive me?" Reuben said these things and he held her a little tighter.

"Let's not talk about forgiveness, Reuben," Mary said, "it's been too long. The only thing I want you to do is be a father to Annie Mae. No matter where you go or what you do, just promise me you will always keep in touch with her. She needs you." After saying this, Mary pulled away from Reuben. "Once I needed you more than you will ever know," she said as she looked away with a mist in her eyes.

At that time, a pickup truck pulled into the yard. Annie Mae and her two children came bounding out of the truck and hurried across the lawn. They had seen the big black car parked on the street in front of their house, and now they could see Mary and Reuben standing on the verandah with her. The children were delighted to see Uncle Reuben. He had brought them a gift and it was in the car. He went with them to the car to get it.

Annie Mae said to her mother, "Is everything all right? Did you and Daddy talk things over? What all did he say?"

Mary said to her daughter, "Annie Mae, I think the best thing to do is for you to take me home. Let Reuben enjoy his visit with you and the children. I will answer all your questions later."

Annie Mae made no argument; she called out to the children that she would return in a few minutes and for them to show Uncle Reuben to his room. Reuben spent the night with this little family and when he left the next morning, the children still were calling him Uncle Reuben.

The car would not make it down the dirt path leading into the hollow where Reuben's brother lived. So Reuben parked the car on the hill just off the main road. As he walked down the road, he gazed at the wild flowers all abloom alongside the road and filtering through the trees of the hollow below. He walked over the little bridge above the flowing stream. He stopped for only a minute to glance at the clean, clear water and the fresh spring growth of the watercress. He knew if he should tarry, the memories of his mother would forbid him to pass this way in such haste.

In his heart he understood it would do him no good to linger here. When he arrived at the door of Frank's log house, he was welcomed by Molly. She treated him like an old friend and immediately fixed the coffee, not forgetting the two saucers at Reuben's place. Frank came in the back door. He had been feeding the chickens out back. When he saw his brother, he asked no questions and just said, "Hey, city slicker, good to see you."

Reuben shook his hand and settled down in a chair for his visit. Frank talked him into a game of cards. Molly brought in some ears of dried corn and the men used the kernels of corn for money for their bets. Molly had no idea at the time that one day what they were doing now would be used to identify Frank and Reuben. Reuben's visits with his brother never lasted long. Each time he would go and come without deep discussion of the past or the future. As Molly would say, "Just simple visits."

Reuben turned the car onto Highway 78 and headed west out of Tallapoosa. When he got to the bridge that crosses the Tallapoosa River, he stopped the car. The setting sun was gold in the water and the rocks at the river's edge held the land encroachment steadfast. Branches of trees protruded over the banks of the river, allowing the shadows of leaves to play in the water. Reuben thought of the meaning of the word "Tallapoosa."

He had been taught in school that the correct interpretation was "Tali" meaning "rock," which came from the Choctaw Indians, but some say the name Tallapoosa means "Golden Water." As Reuben stood by the bridge railing looking down the river, both meanings came to him. He used his thoughts of the river to clear his mind. Perhaps in some way, his connection with the river had drawn him back into his past. Now that he had been connected with his past and the people he loved, he was not willing to let go again.

From now on, he would embark upon being a part of all these people's lives. He felt he could do this without hurting anyone. He had a wife, Rebekah, and their children in northern Alabama. He had a daughter, her children and his mistress, Mary, also his brother living here in Tallapoosa. Then there was his relationship with his first wife, Victoria. Reuben got back into the car and drove toward Birmingham. He was fifty-seven years old and he felt confident that he could live in three different worlds.

The events of the forthcoming months were governed by the ending of

World War II. On April 12, 1945, the United States suffered the death of their president, Franklin Delano Roosevelt. The country was still engaged in the war when they buried their president in his hometown of Warm Springs, Georgia. The vice president, Harry S. Truman, was sworn in as the thirty-second President of the United States. He took up the gauntlet to lead the country to victory in the war. On May 7, 1945, the war was ended in Germany and on August 14, 1945, it was over with Japan.

Reuben was with his wife Rebekah the day their son came home from the war. There were great excitement and happiness in the family on this day. One of the children rang the dinner bell that their grandfather had put in the yard of the farmhouse. None of the children ever touched the bell, because they had been taught that you rang the bell only for something that was really important. They knew their grandfather, James McCormick, rang the bell when the house burned down and all the neighbors came to help the family rebuild.

The bell had been rung once since Rebekah and the children moved into the farmhouse. This was when the two youngest children were in the house alone one day and they were playing with matches. They were sitting between two beds, and one of the bed sheets caught on fire. The daughter who was looking after the two smelled the smoke, jumped across one of the beds and tried to put the fire out; when she couldn't, she ran outside and rang the dinner bell. Everyone came running out of the fields, and the fire was put out before it did too much damage.

James McCormick had rung the dinner bell at the end of World War I in 1918, now here it was only twenty-seven years later and the ringing of the bell would declare another world war ending. Reuben's life was good. He did not know it, but he was at the peak of his happiness. His son was home safe from the war. He was continuing his relationships with the three women he loved and he was getting no interference from anyone. He was sure he was successful in keeping everything separated and under control. The daughters that lived with him in Birmingham did see some things they thought were odd, and many years later, when asked to recall some of these things, one of the daughters said she once saw her daddy having dinner with a young woman about thirty years old and a little girl about eight or nine.

She said it was on a weekend and her sisters had gone to the farm and she was alone with her dad. He had taken her to the movie, then afterward just left her in town. She was fourteen years old and didn't know quite what to do alone, so she just followed her dad. She saw him go into a real nice restaurant. She started to go inside when she looked through the window and saw Reuben sitting down at a table with this dark-haired lady and a little red-headed girl. She was shocked and didn't know what to think. Why was he having dinner with these strangers and why had he not asked her to go with him?

She waited across the street outside. When Reuben came out of the restaurant, he was alone. He walked across the street and saw his daughter standing there. The only thing he said was, "Let's go home."

Had she gone inside the restaurant, perhaps this fourteen-year-old daughter would have met her half-sister, Annie Mae, and her niece, Nellie. They had come to Birmingham from Tallapoosa to visit Reuben. He gave them money to go Christmas shopping. The daughters living with Reuben later discussed the fact that they had seen their dad with an older dark-haired woman. She was maybe fifty years old and she was always dressed really nice. They had seen Reuben with her on several occasions, but really didn't think much about it because the places where they were seen together were so public. Many times a big black limousine would pick Reuben up at the boardinghouse.

The daughters had no idea what was going on and they dared not ask Reuben. They did not want to get him mad. Reuben never gave them an explanation when he borrowed his friend's car, and would be gone for the weekend. They had no clue that on these weekends, he was driving to Tallapoosa.

It was the week before Christmas when Reuben decided to take one of these trips to Tallapoosa. He had promised Annie Mae that he would come and bring the children some gifts for Christmas, but he didn't know just when he would be able to get his friend's car so a definite date was not set for his visit. It was a cold winter day in Georgia. The snows of the North had come south, turning into a freezing rain. Reuben absolutely hated cold weather. He cursed as he drove the highway, "Damn it, some day I'm moving to Florida!"

He was relieved to reach Annie Mae's house. He pulled the car up into the yard as near the front door as possible. He gathered the packages in his arms and ran for the door, trying to keep himself and the packages dry. A knock on the door summoned a lady inside. When she opened the door she exclaimed, "My, my Reuben, you look like a drowned rat!"

"Freezing rat, is more like it," he said as he hastily entered the front room. He took off his hat and laid hat and packages on a table near the door. Seeing a roaring fire in the fireplace, he walked directly to it and stood warming his hands. After a few minutes, he turned around and said, "House is awfully quiet. Where are Annie Mae and the children?"

Mary had positioned herself near the sofa, but she was still standing just looking at him. She seemed in no hurry to answer him. Finally she said, "We weren't expecting you, Reuben. Annie Mae and her husband have taken the children to visit Aunt Mae down in Albany. You remember Aunt Mae don't you, Reuben? She was the one I stayed with when..." She didn't finish the sentence.

"Yes, I remember, Mary," Reuben said, then continued, "I had told Annie Mae that I would come sometime before Christmas. Will she be back today or tomorrow?"

"Probably late tomorrow afternoon because she will have to go to work Monday morning. She got herself a job in the dime store downtown. She is a hard worker, that girl," Mary said, answering Reuben's question, then continued the conversation. "Dry yourself off there by the fire and I will go make some coffee."

Mary disappeared into the kitchen and Reuben stood by the fire feeling the warm heat on his arms and face. He had watched Mary walk through the room. Since he first saw her as a teenager, Mary had been the sexiest woman he had ever known. She still reminded Reuben of a fresh Georgia peach when it was ripe, first picked from the tree. She had a sense of affection about her that always aroused a fervent desire within Reuben.

After several minutes, Reuben walked into the kitchen. Mary was standing at the stove with her back toward him. He said, "So, is the coffee ready yet?"

Mary jumped and turned to say, "Reuben, you startled me. Coffee will be ready in a minute."

Reuben sat down at a small kitchen table watching her, "You still jump when I come up behind you; remember how I used to sneak up on you and scare you? You would jump and make that shrieking noise. Remember that, Mary?" he laughingly asked.

"I remember," Mary said as she turned her head and gave a little giggle. "You were mean to me, Reuben."

"And you loved every minute of it," Reuben said. They both laughed as they remembered their past. It was no surprise to Reuben or Mary that this afternoon turned into a time for them to share and revisit those special feelings they had for each other. Their daughter's house became a cozy winter's nest. They drank coffee in the kitchen then returned to the living room where he sat in a large chair near the fireplace.

CHAPTER NINETEEN

$\mathcal{M}$ary put a couple of pillows on the floor close to the fire. When she sat down on the pillows, her dress draped around her legs and feet. She drew her knees to her face, rested her chin on her knees, then gazed into the crackling flames of the fire as she talked. Reuben could not take his eyes off her. When the fire needed more wood, Reuben got up, took a few pieces of wood from the hearth, placed them on the fire and stirred them into place with the poker.

As if in slow motion, he reached down and lifted Mary to stand with him. He first kissed her on the forehead and placed his hands about her waist. When she did not pull away, he drew her close and slightly touched her lips with his. Mary absorbed his touch and responded by putting her arms around his neck and returning his kiss. They looked into each other's eyes and rekindled the spark of passion they once had for each other. They kissed softly and longingly. He found the sweetness of her neck, the warm inviting crevice of her breast.

She whispered, "Reuben, I still love you."

He picked her up like a little doll in his arms. She clung to her lover. Once inside the little room that was reserved just for him, he laid her gently on the bed. He closed and locked the door, then returned to her extended arms. There was no breeze to stir the pole curtains, but she shivered as he undressed her. Without clothes to inhibit them, he pulled the covers over and around them.

They wrapped each other in a pleasure that placed them in a world of their own. Their kisses ignited torrid movements. Their bodies entwined, he slid his hands beneath her to hold her tight as their desire searched for rhythm. He vowed his love for her and called her name as once again Mary declared her love for him.

They lay close to each other and drifted into deep sleep. Hours passed before Reuben released himself from her and cradled her in his arms for an intimate night together. When he woke, he eased out of bed. Only a pleasing murmur came from Mary as he covered her and left her there. He dressed and went out into the front of the house. He was surprised to see the sun shining bright as on a summer day. The fire had gone out in the fireplace, but Reuben gave it no thought as he picked up his hat and walked out the door. He did not go to visit his brother. He drove the car back to Birmingham.

That afternoon when Annie Mae came home, her mother was still there. She took one look at Mary and knew there was something different about her. She noticed the packages on the table and asked, "Was Daddy here?"

Mary answered, "Yes, Reuben was here." Annie Mae walked over and hugged her mother. There were no more questions asked.

It was Sunday night and Robert, Mary's husband, had gone to church when she returned home. When he came in, he never mentioned the fact that Mary was gone the night before. If he knew the reason why, he never said.

When Reuben went to be with Rebekah and the children for Christmas, he learned from Rebekah that Mr. Smith had asked her to move out of the house and off the farm. Since the war ended things were changing and the sharecropping system had collapsed. Mr. Smith wanted his land free to sell, so Rebekah had no choice but to leave the farm. The day she had to walk away her heart ached, for this had been her home. When she was a young girl, she had gone into the nearby forest and roamed where her ancestors were. She had met Reuben in the cotton field and she fell in love with him. Twice Reuben had taken her out of this Tennessee Valley, to make their life in another place; both times he brought her back.

Once again, she packed her trunk and gathered her children to prepare to leave their home. Going down the road, she looked back at the old farmhouse. It wasn't much to look at but the memories of her life there would never be forgotten. In that old shack, she had given birth to her little baby girl and named her Martha Lou. On that land, she had eked out a living for her children when times were hard.

There had been many times when her sisters and brothers came to visit and all the children sang songs and laughed and played. All her children would carry the memories of this place and their early years here with them as they scattered around the world. When the house was lost from her view, Rebekah looked toward the mountain beyond. There on top of Caddo Mountain was a little white chapel shaded by dark green trees. A path behind the chapel led to a bright sunny place. There Rebekah and Reuben had buried their son. The hardest thing Rebekah ever had to do was to leave her first born son atop Caddo Mountain.

Rebekah's brothers and sisters never understood the circumstances under which Rebekah left the farm. Some of them believed she had sold the place and never gave them their inheritance. The fact was she left their home with only her trunk and the clothes on her back.

Once they left the Tennessee Valley area of northern Alabama, neither Rebekah nor Reuben, nor any of their children ever returned to live there. The old farmhouse, "Grandma's Place," was torn down, but in later years, some of the children came to gaze across the cotton field and remember when. For Rebekah, it remained only a memory.

Reuben got a house in Pinson, which is much closer to Birmingham. The girls staying with him in the apartment in Birmingham moved in with Rebekah and the other children. They were all together again. Even the son who had been in the military was there when a family photo was taken. It was 1946 and there stood Reuben with Rebekah and their nine children. All the children looked healthy and happy. Rebekah was lovely in her flower print dress with a large white collar trimmed in lace. She held a pleased look on her face. She was very proud of her children. Reuben stood with an attitude of complete confidence.

He had this family under his control, while he continued his secretive relationships with others. The only member of the family missing from this photograph was the family dog. Ironically, the dog's name was "Old Shep." Old Shep was the same name of the dog that lived on the Kincaide farm in Tallapoosa. This Old Shep was Felix's dog. Reuben was told that in 1928 when Felix died and was buried in the family cemetery, Old Shep never left the site of his grave. Three days after they buried Felix, Old Shep died. When Rebekah and the children got a little shepherd dog to live with them in Pinson, Reuben named the dog Old Shep.

While the family was still living in Pinson, an unknown person poisoned Old Shep. The children were heartbroken.

Reuben did not stay at this Pinson house with Rebekah and the children. He got a small apartment near his work in Birmingham. "It was just too far to go back and forth from Pinson to work," he explained to Rebekah. On the weekends that he went to Tallapoosa or stayed with Victoria at the Vanderbilt Hotel, his explanation was, "I have extra work to do."

It was several months after his blissful night with Mary — and Reuben had not gone back to Tallapoosa — that he received a letter from Annie Mae. He packed his little brown suitcase, laying the letter on the bottom. He was going to Tallapoosa, but at the last minute he found out his son would be home on a military leave, so he went to the Pinson house. Rebekah was checking Reuben's suitcase to see if he had any dirty laundry for her to wash. When she took everything out, she saw the letter. Three of her oldest daughters were in the room with her when she picked it up.

"Children, " she said, "does your father have a P.0. box in Birmingham?"

The girls told her that they didn't think so, but they didn't know for sure. They were curious as to why she asked and noticed the letter she was holding.

"What is the letter, Mama? Is it to Daddy?" one of the girls asked.

"Here, give it to me. I'll open it!" another daughter exclaimed.

Rebekah said, "No, if there is any opening to do, I'll do it."

"Well, do it Mama. Open the letter!" the third girl said.

Rebekah turned the letter over and over in her hand. The envelope did not have a return address on it and it was postmarked from Albany, Georgia. Rebekah opened the unsealed envelope and took the one piece of paper out. She unfolded it and they all read the message written there. The paragraph the daughters would never forget read: "The children are keeping your room aired out. Waiting for when you return."

Almost fifty years later, the daughters told their baby sister, Martha Lou, about the letter. When she asked if they remembered who signed it, they all agreed. There was three signatures, Nellie, Billy, and Annie Mae.

Rebekah calmly folded the letter, put it back in the envelope and placed it back inside the little brown suitcase. She told the girls they must not say anything to their father about seeing the letter. The girls never said anything to Reuben about the letter; neither did Rebekah. When Reuben started to get ready to go back to Birmingham to his apartment, he opened his suitcase. There, lying right on top of his clothes, was the envelope with the letter inside. A dreadful fear streaked through his body. He was shocked to see the letter there on top of his clothes. He knew he had laid it on the bottom. His little body quivered as he thought she must have seen it. Did she read it? Why had she not said anything? Did anyone else see it? All these questions came to his panic-stricken mind.

It was not fear, but madness that motivated his immediate actions. His suspicion was that Rebekah had found the key to one of his secrets. His reaction to this possibility was violent. He slammed the top of the suitcase shut. He shouted obscenities as he gathered his things feverishly to escape any possible confrontation. He said goodbye to no one as he practically ran across the yard and into the woods to take the shortcut to the bus stop. The letter would not be discussed today, nor would it ever be the topic of discussion in Reuben's presence. Rebekah never mentioned the letter to Reuben. He could never be sure that she read it.

Over the next few years, all but three of Reuben and Rebekah's children left home, one by one. The four oldest daughters got married and moved away. Another son joined the military. Rebekah took the three children left at home and moved to a small town north of Birmingham called Hartselle. One of the girls and her husband lived there. More and more, Rebekah became dependent on her older children, because Reuben gave so little of his time or money to her. The longer Reuben was involved with the separate families of his life, the deeper his commitments became. His secrets were in constant danger of being discovered and with all his children getting older and relocating, all his deceptions were increasingly difficult.

When he was with Victoria, she made him feel rich and important. She had bought a place in North Carolina and was planning for them to move there and live together for the rest of their life.

In Tallapoosa, his visits with his brother, Frank, were becoming unpleasant because the girl staying with him had married Frank's nephew and now Molly and the boy lived with Frank. Frank told Reuben he made out a will and was leaving all his property to his nephew because he and Molly were taking care of him. This didn't set well with Reuben, perhaps because he felt that in some way, he had a right to some property around

Tallapoosa.

After all it was his grandfather who owned over five hundred acres here. Reuben's father never got his share and that share had been promised to Reuben. What actually happened to all the Kincaide property was not known. Reuben did not have the money to hire a lawyer to figure things out, so any inheritance he might have had a claim to slipped through his fingers. Reuben grew resentful and quit going to visit his brother, Frank.

Reuben's stolen moments with Mary were blissful, but he was tired of never knowing if he could be with her when he made the trip to Tallapoosa. He did know that if he asked Mary she would come away with him, but he didn't know if that was what he wanted. A problem had come up with Annie Mae and once again, Reuben's heart was torn with guilt.

Annie Mae and her husband had another boy. He was a beautiful child, but from the start, Annie Mae knew that something was wrong with him. The doctors told her it was a problem with his blood, and that if they were very careful with him, he could possibly live to be fifteen or so. When Annie Mae told Reuben about the baby boy, they cried together. Reuben knew he carried an impure blood line, and he cursed the sins of others. He told his daughter that the boy would need a lot of medical care and that he would help pay for it.

Remembering that the only thing he was able to do for his dying son was get a bottle of whiskey for his medicine, Reuben told his daughter Annie Mae, about his son, Marion. She said to him, "Daddy, it was not the whiskey that was so good for your son, it was the fact that his daddy got it for him."

Joseph, Reuben's grandson, was born in 1949. He died seventeen years later.

Reuben was sixty-two years old when the man he was working with in Birmingham, Alabama, came to him and said, "Reuben, I heard from some people I know that live in Orlando, Florida. They have a lot of work down there and they asked if I would consider moving. I told them on one condition, that is I bring my side-kick, Reuben Kincaide, with me."

Reuben said, "That right? And what did they say?"

"Say? They had only one question. When can you get here? So, what is your pleasure, Reuben? Coming to Florida with me?" the man asked, slapping Reuben on the back.

Without hesitation, Reuben's reply was, "Sure, why not, I'll go to

Orlando, Florida."

* * *

The ten years of the 1940s had been turbulent for Reuben. There had been many times of great joy and happiness, but there had also been times of fear, pain, and having to say I'm sorry. He had worked hard painting buildings and houses for the rich people of Birmingham, but there had never been enough money to put him in a better economic situation.

The United States had emerged from World War II, not just victorious, but supreme. They had brought the use of nuclear weapons into the world, and this created their dominance of international affairs. World War II had ended, but another type of war began with their new rival, the Soviet Union. This war became known as the Cold War. These wages of war brought massive public spending and economic growth to America. Although there was the constant threat of war with the Soviet Union, the United States, because of its prosperity and leadership in the world, entered into a period of tranquility during the 1950s. The prosperity of the country made it possible for a new level of affluence.

Poor people became middle class, and middle class people found themselves rich.

Reuben was hoping that if he went to Orlando, Florida, he could make his life better. He had great expectations of making good money, and he was willing to overcome any demands that this move would have on his life with the people he loved. Reuben was embarking on a new crossing in this life. What parts of his past would he take with him, which would he leave behind?

The one thing he had learned is there is no such thing as starting over again. Your present is always just a continuation of your past. The weekend before Reuben was leaving for Florida, he went to see Rebekah and the children. He said to Rebekah, "I'm going to Florida to look for work. The man I work with is taking me with him. He says there are plenty of jobs down there and with the good weather in Florida, we can get year round work." He added to this statement, "I don't know when I will be back."

Sunday afternoon before Reuben left, his daughter asked him to let her take a photo of him and Rebekah together in her front yard. Reuben stood erect, holding his hat in his right hand down by his side. He wore a white dress shirt and a tie. The sleeves of the shirt were rolled up just to his elbows. His pocket watch was in the pocket of his dress pants. You couldn't see his shoes because they were covered in the grass. Rebekah had on a summer cotton dress with diagonal stripes The dress had a large bow at the neckline and she wore a leather belt. She had a really nice figure for a woman forty-seven years old who'd given birth to ten children. Her long chestnut brown hair was parted in the middle and tightly pulled back away from her face. Rebekah never wore any jewelry.

Standing there waiting for the photo to be taken, their arms barely touched each other. Reuben was smiling at his daughter as she took the photo. Rebekah had a faint smile on her face. She held her hands behind her back and wondered, is this the last photo I will ever have taken with my husband? After he leaves me today, will I ever see him again? These were her thoughts, well-hidden from Reuben and her children.

The photo taken on this day was made into large paintings, and several of the children have copies hanging in their homes at present.

When Reuben left Birmingham on Monday morning, he made no effort to contact Victoria. He did not leave a message at the Vanderbilt Hotel for her, nor did he call her in Atlanta. Traveling south, he made no mention of going through Tallapoosa or contacting anyone there. In fact, he traveled a route he had never taken before. This time the river he crossed would not be the St. John's, but a Southern river made famous by the great songwriter, Stephen Foster. The name of the river is the Suwanee.

It flows from the north down through the northwest section of Florida and into the Gulf of Mexico. Stephen Foster wrote the song "Suwanee River" when he was twenty-five years old. It was in 1851 and he drew his tunes from the Negro sounds he heard when he attended church meetings with a servant and from Negro laborers at the Pittsburgh warehouse where he worked. When Reuben reached the Suwanee River, he got out of the car to read the sign posted there in tribute to Mr. Foster. As Reuben stood there on the banks of this wonderful old river that laced the Southland, and as he gazed through the moss laden trees, he reflected on his life.

The words to the song that a man had written before Reuben was born, struck a chord in Reuben's heart and when he drove on down the road, he was humming the tune.

He approached Orlando from the northwest on Highway 441. Thirty-three years ago, he had caught a ride in Sanford, Florida, and rode over the twenty-five mile new brick road to Orlando. This road became Highway 17 and came into Orlando from the northeast. Today, Reuben was not on the same road as he had been on in 1917 and he had no intention of even thinking about Sanford and his time spent there. It could be a thousand miles away instead of only twenty-five; he was not going there, and he would not allow his mind to wander there either.

He had remembered Orlando as "Just a wide place in the road," and he never had thoughts of returning there, but now here he was. He didn't know just what he expected to find, but driving into town, he couldn't believe his eyes. It was the most beautiful place he had ever seen. The countryside slopes were covered with bright-green trees bearing golden colored oranges. Small blue watered lakes dotted the landscape every few miles. The streets were clean of any debris and the delightful warmth of the sun made Reuben's body feel good.

He gazed at the tall palm trees reaching high to the sky, and driving around a small lake in the middle of the city, he marveled at all the beautiful bright flowers growing there. "No wonder they call it, `The City Beautiful,'" Reuben exclaimed, "I believe I have found God's country!"

It was 1950 and Orlando, Florida, was a small town. It was not yet experiencing the burgeoning commercial and population it was destined to have in the near future. Reuben was sixty-two years old and believed he had found the perfect place in which to live out the rest of his life. Surely, he thought, the rain has stopped and I will finally he blessed with a life of sunshine.

Adjacent to Orlando was an area called Winter Park. Its streets were lined with stately old mansions and moss draped oak trees. There was a college there with magnificent ornate buildings and a quiet atmosphere for higher learning. Reuben and his companion found ample work there at Rollins College and for the rich people of Winter Park.

Rather quickly, Reuben found a place to live and set about the task of deciding whom he wanted to share his life with in his newfound paradise. When he thought of Victoria, he pictured in his mind a fragile flower. He had loved her so dearly and he never meant to hurt her. Would it be possible to have her again to cherish and to love? Somehow, some way, could he meet his daughter Vanessa and be a part of her life?

When he left Birmingham without contacting Victoria, she was again devastated. She had no way of knowing where Reuben was. She never questioned him about his life away from her. She loved him unconditionally and believed in his love for her. She never allowed herself to believe there could be other women in Reuben's life. If there were, she didn't want to know about them.

She never discussed Reuben with their daughter, Vanessa. She had promised Reuben she would not tell Vanessa or Jessie that he was in Birmingham. She did not understand Reuben's hatred of Jessie, but she knew he must have good reason to hate him so much. Soon after Reuben left Birmingham, Victoria's mother died. She had been living with Vanessa and Jessie in Atlanta, but when she died, they returned to Tallapoosa to bury her beside her husband.

Doctor Sherwood and his wife had kept their granddaughter, Vanessa, from knowing the truth about her daddy, Reuben Oliver Kincaide. Mrs. Sherwood and Mrs. Nicholson had guarded their secret that Reuben was the father of both their granddaughters. Mrs. Nicholson's granddaughter, Annie Mae, had found out the truth Vanessa had not.

After her mother's death, realizing that Reuben was gone from Birmingham, Victoria moved to her place in North Carolina. If Reuben ever wanted to find her, he would be able to, because she gave him the North Carolina address.

The last time Reuben was in Tallapoosa, he had said nothing to his mistress, Mary, about making a change in his life. He could not remember a time when Mary did not occupy a place in his heart. On several occasions, it was Mary's love that lifted Reuben out of depths of depression. If a man was lucky, a love like Mary's would happen to him once during a lifetime.

When Mary and Reuben were together, they had a way of shutting out the world and experiencing total bliss. Mary knew that Reuben was married to another woman. She had known he was married to Victoria when she went to him on the river-bank, but in her heart she felt that Reuben would leave Victoria and come to her. When finally Reuben and Victoria were divorced, Mary had waited only to find out that he had married someone else.

Out of spite and hopelessness, Mary also married another. Her husband had compassion for her and she was a care giver to him, but Mary's love belonged to Reuben. When Reuben came back into her life after thirty years, Mary felt like she had been born again. The years had passed, but the feelings between them remained the same. Reuben was truthful with Mary and told her about Rebekah and the children. He made promises to Mary that he would always look after their daughter, Annie Mae, and be a part of her life. Could it be possible to make things right with Mary? Would Annie Mae leave Tallapoosa and move to Florida so they could all be a family?

Now that Annie Mae had a son who was not healthy, Reuben would not desert them. This was one responsibility he could not walk away from. Reuben had told his wife, Rebekah, that he was going to Florida to look for work. All but three of their children were now out on their own making a life for themselves. Rebekah would always love Reuben because he was the father of her children. She understood the secrets he must hide because of things he had been involved in during their life together. She would never betray his trust in her to keep those secrets.

Rebekah could only guess that her husband had another family somewhere. She thought this could be true because of the letter she found in his suitcase and the long periods of his absence from her. She had no idea of the great lengths Reuben had gone to keep her from finding out about his life before he met her. Reuben and Rebekah's early years together had been so happy and fulfilling with the birth of their ten children. Reuben loved his children. He blamed himself for the death of Marion, and no way was he going to give up being a part of his children's life.

CHAPTER TWENTY

*M*any of Reuben's children began to question in their minds the actions of their father as they grew older. They could not understand his moods. They respected him and were obedient, but many times it was out of fear. He held control over them and no matter how old they got, or what their life styles became, these children never broke away from Reuben's autocracy.

Reuben's youngest son was thirty years old before any of the children tried to uncover the secrets of their father's life. As the children grew older, Rebekah began to be dependent on them. Rebekah had bonded her children together and taught them the importance of each other. The bounty of their love for her could not be measured. Although some of them had left her nest, they carried her comforting spirit and knowledge of her constant caring. Till this day, when the children gather, they can feel their mother's loving arms around them, and they know that their circle of love will never be broken.

Reuben had married Rebekah in 1920. She became a wonderful mother, lover and his best friend. She was nurturing and always forgiving. Reuben needed Rebekah.

Reuben went to the post office in Orlando and made arrangements for a post office box where he could receive his mail. He sat down and wrote two letters. The first one was to Annie Mae, his daughter. He wanted her to know he was in Orlando, had a job and would send money for the boy. She could write to him using the Orlando post office box number.

The other letter read: I am in Orlando, Florida, and have found plenty of work here. It is a beautiful place and I have rented an apartment. We can get a house later. I am enclosing a bus ticket. There is a bus leaving there every Saturday evening at 4:00. Next Sunday morning, I will be at the bus station here at 8:00 a.m. when that bus arrives in Orlando. Reuben signed his name. He addressed both envelopes, enclosed the letters, and dropped them in the mail.

Sunday morning came and Reuben went to meet the bus. He was early so he paced the waiting area, jingling the change in his pockets and looking at his pocket watch every few minutes. When the bus pulled in and stopped, Reuben walked over and stood by the luggage that was rapidly being unloaded from the baggage compartment. There was a beautiful lady on the bus. She stayed seated until all the other passengers got off. Then she stood up and gracefully made her way toward the door.

The bus driver assisted her down the steps, and she thanked him for a comforting ride. She glanced over the waiting crowd for a familiar face, then she heard him call her name, "Rebekah." She hurriedly walked toward him and as she grew near, he reached down and picked up a little brown suitcase and said to her, "Is this all you brought with you?"

"Yes, Reuben," she said, "that is all I brought with me."

Barely looking at her, he said, "Let's go. I'll get a taxi."

After a couple of weeks, Reuben and Rebekah sent for their three children. Rebekah had left them in her daughter's care. She had packed up all her special possessions in boxes. She told her daughter that when Reuben sent for the children to see to it they had what they needed for the bus trip and to send her packed boxes on the bus with their luggage.

Before she left Decatur, Rebekah had checked with the bus company about her luggage. They would not carry her trunk, everything had to be in a small suitcase or boxes. She cried as she emptied her trunk and told her sister to keep it for her. Among her special keepsakes that she put in the boxes was the calendar with the World War I photo on it, the oldest daughter's little tea set and favorite Christmas ornaments. The ornate little Santa Claus was not left behind. It was a miracle that Santa didn't get broken, or was it? After all, these things had been wrapped with Rebekah's love.

Reuben, Rebekah and their three youngest children settled down to live the life of a middle class family in Orlando, Florida. Reuben had chosen his wife, Rebekah to live with him the rest of his life. What he didn't know

249

that although he was now sixty-two years old, he would live thirty-nine more years. His courage would be tested and also his endurance to hide his fears and keep his secrets from Rebekah and the children. If he could be successful in keeping a low profile, he had faith that his life in Orlando was going to be good.

He was making good money and it wasn't long before he bought his dream house in Florida. When he was young in Tallapoosa, he had dreamed of owning a house like this someday and on the cold days in Indiana, he had placed his dream house in Florida. As he went about giving the house a fresh coat of paint, he thought to himself, I guess dreams do come true, even for Reuben.

The house was on Amelia Street in the city, but at that time it was not a busy street. The pavement was of bricks and beautiful old oak trees lined the sidewalks. In places tree branches grew over the street and formed a canopy. A short drive led to the Victorian-design house. A porch on the front with large white columns gave the house an inviting quality. The shaded porch provided an inviting and comfortable sitting area where the family spent more time than inside the house.

The side yard had an abundance of azalea bushes that burst with vibrant blooms every February denying any coolness of winter. At the back of the house a path was worn in the grass from the side street to the back door. This path reached out to family and others like a warm embrace and was used more often than the front entrance. Rebekah could usually be found in the kitchen where she could see anyone approaching on the path. She always had a warm greeting for family and friends. Reuben usually sat passively in his chair in the living room. Most of the time he would acknowledge his family, however he had no friends.

His friend and protector of many years, George Bogart, had died, and Reuben had no idea where his wife was or if she was still living. Once, when asked by the man who worked with him, did he know what happened to Bogart, Reuben's reply was, "I guess his past finally caught up with him." When he said this, he was wondering if the same thing would happen to him one day.

Reuben moved into this house on Amelia Street with Rebekah and his two youngest children. The older daughter who came to Florida had married before Reuben bought the house. These two youngest children would grow up here experiencing life in the 1950s. Dwight Eisenhower had followed Harry Truman as the president of the United States and when he took office, the United States was involved in the war in Korea. This war was called "a police action" but by the time it ended in 1953, there were 55,000 men dead and over 102,000 wounded. Reuben had lost a son in World War II and he was relieved when his two boys, who were in the military at this time, escaped this Korean "conflict" unharmed.

He always gave praise to President Eisenhower because Eisenhower had been a military man and led the Americans in war and now he would lead the country in peace. It was true that during Eisenhower's term in office there were no declared wars but he warned the country about the threat of spreading communistic expansion. He said we must rely on atomic weapons and on strike forces to meet the threat wherever it might erupt.

During the '50s, a time of change began to take place inside the country. The question of segregation came to the forefront and a man named Rev. Martin Luther King, Jr. became a symbol of this change. Reuben's two young children attended an all-white school and they were embracing styles such as cool crew cuts, neat flat tops and ducktails for the boys, and felt skirts with poodle appliqués and crinolines for the girls.

It was the days of the hoola hoops and for entertainment there was the sex queen of the screen, Marilyn Monroe, and the biggest hit of all, Elvis Presley, the king of rock n' roll. Surprisingly, Reuben and Rebekah were tolerant of the young people's ways. Some parents labeled the rock n' roll as medieval types of lunacy, even prehistoric rhythmic trances.

It was 1955 when Reuben's young son bought a television and Reuben welcomed it into the living room, that he became a fan of a program called "Gunsmoke." Reuben had known about the invention of television since 1923 when Russian born engineer Vladimir Zworykin invented the iconoscope, which made possible the transmission of pictures. Then in 1927 the Scottish inventor, John L. Baird, improved the clarity and the TV became a household appliance, but it was not until 1955 before it was introduced to Reuben's family.

While Reuben's two youngest children were busy with their teenage life, they paid little attention to Reuben. They mostly thought he was just old and old-fashioned with his hat always on his head and his habit of jingling the change in his pockets. By the mid-fifties, several of Reuben's older children moved their families to Orlando. Reuben was delighted.

Usually on Sundays, Reuben would sit in his chair reading the newspaper and watching the parade of his children coming in and out. He had several grandchildren by now and it seemed like every visit from his children brought another baby to him. He would always look them over and question if they were healthy. He was relieved when the answer was always yes.

Reuben took pride in his children and their accomplishments. He didn't have many words to express his feelings to them, but the children continuously felt the need to make their daddy proud of them.

Reuben bought himself a car, a 1955 Packard. He did not have a driver's license and his eyesight prevented him from getting one. One of the older married daughters drove him every place he wanted to go. He never missed a day's work, Monday through Friday. On Saturdays he would walk downtown and spend the whole day away from home. No one ever knew exactly just what he did on Saturdays, and they never questioned him.

Reuben was living the good life, but still there was no escaping his past. One thing he would do on these Saturdays in town was get his mail out of the post office box, which remained a secret from Rebekah and the children.

Annie Mae sent him news from Tallapoosa and Reuben continued to send her money. Eight years after Reuben had settled his life in Orlando, he received a letter from his daughter, Annie Mae, telling him that she was told his brother, Frank, had died. This was in February, 1958. Reuben barely acknowledged the news, and he didn't say anything about it to Rebekah.

Shortly after he received the news about his brother's death, he received a letter from Annie Mae saying her mother, Mary, was ill. Was there any way he could come to Tallapoosa to see her?

The man Mary was married to had died in 1953, but Mary went on living in their home and never mentioned to Annie Mae that she wanted to see Reuben again. It was only now when she knew she didn't have long to live that she wanted to see him one last time.

Reuben tried to ignore the request, but after three months, Annie Mae's plea was desperate. Reuben readied himself to return to Tallapoosa. He told Rebekah that his brother had died and he had to go see about his estate. Rebekah knew that he must not be telling the truth because he had told her that Frank died during the war. Rebekah didn't know why her husband was going to Tallapoosa, but at this point in time, she had her children and they were her whole life.

Reuben took the bus. When he arrived in Tallapoosa he did not know what the situation would be at Annie Mae's house, so he checked into a hotel. He picked up a newspaper and once he was settled in his room, he began reading it. On the third page there was an article about a local woman who had died two days ago and today her funeral was held at the Mount Zion Cemetery. Reuben put the paper down and sat staring into space. He was too late. Late in the afternoon Reuben knelt at the foot of Mary's grave. He took his hat off and held it with both hands. He knelt with dignity when all he wanted to do was fall on the grave and tear at the fresh dug earth. It was Mary under there, his sweet, sweet Mary. She always looked like a little doll to him and he had loved her from the start. He loved her still.

As he was remembering all they had shared, a little boy touched him on the shoulder. "Hey, mister," the little boy said, "Do you know my grandmother?"

Reuben stood up and asked, "Is this your grandmother's grave?"

"Yes," said the little boy "Her name is Mary; did you know her?"

"Yes," said Reuben, "Yes, I knew her." Reuben looked around at the vacant cemetery and asked, "Where did you come from? Anyone with you?"

Fumbling with something in his hand, the little boy explained, "My mother and dad were here, but they left. I'll walk home by myself. I'm allowed; I'm nine years old, and I walk everywhere. I saw you come up from the road. I was over there in those trees. I was trying to open this knife so I could carve my name in a tree. Can you get it open, mister?"

Reaching for the knife, Reuben said, "Here, let me see."

He took the knife and was shocked to see the initials J.B. on the pearl handle of the knife. Even though the knife was old and rusty he could still see the initials clearly. Jessie Bailey — the name raced through his mind. The image of a railroad track, Jessie Bailey with a knife stuck in his gut, flashed at him like slides of a movie show. Just a passing thought, no way could this be the knife. That memory was almost forty years old. Reuben turned the knife over and over in his hands saying, "Don't think we will get this blade out again. It is too old and rusty. Where did you get this?"

Without hesitation the little boy said, "It's mine. I found it. Yes, I did. I found it yesterday when I was walking into town along the railroad tracks. I saw the sun shining on something over in the kudzu and when I fetched it, it was this knife. Only the blade was sticking out. I used a rock to knock it back in and now I can't get it out. Guess it's too old. Huh, mister? I might have known I couldn't cut into a tree with a rusty old blade like that."

Refusing to put thought to what the little boy just said, Reuben handed him back the knife. Still he thought, it couldn't be!

Next to Mary's grave was a vacant place; then there were several graves. They were of children, one woman, and a man named Robert Wilson was at the far end. The little boy walked over and stood by Robert Wilson's grave. "You know Robert, too, mister?" he asked. "I called him grandfather, but Mama says he wasn't my real grandfather. She says my real grandfather lives in Florida. Where do you live, mister?"

Reuben's heart knocked at his chest. No longer could he dismiss the little boy's chatter. He was staring at the white-headed, blue-eyed, fair-skinned little nine year old boy.

"I live in Florida," he said.

The boy's interest in Reuben grew as he said, "Wow, I sure would like to go to Florida someday! Is it nice and warm all the time there? Can you stay outside all year round there? Gets cold here sometimes and a lot of the time I'm sick and Mama is always telling me, `No running Joseph, you hear me, Joseph. I don't want you falling down.'"

Reuben couldn't take his eyes off the boy. "That your name, Joseph?" he asked.

"Yes, sir," he said, "and since you are from Florida, maybe I will just call you grandfather. You're old enough to be my grandfather, right?"

Reuben smiled as he said, "I am at that young man. Yes indeed, I am at that."

Joseph took Reuben's left hand and said, "That's a mighty pretty ring you have. Is that a blue diamond in the middle? Are you married? Did your wife give you the ring?"

"My, my, so many questions from such a little boy," Reuben said, "but no, no my wife didn't give me this ring... It's getting late," Reuben continued, "shouldn't you be getting home?"

"Guess so," said the little boy, "Say, you want to go home with me for supper? Mama won't mind. She's always feeding strangers. Besides you're not a stranger. You know my grandmother and you come from Florida. You could talk to my mama about Florida. She says someday, we may go there."

"Maybe another time, Joseph. Maybe another time, I will see your mother. Right now it will soon be dark; you better hurry on home," Reuben said as he followed Joseph away from the graves.

Walking together down the hill from the cemetery, Reuben took his ring off. When they reached the main road, they paused. Reuben handed Joseph the ring. "Here," he said, "I'll trade you my ring for that knife of yours."

Joseph took the ring and tried it on his finger. "It's too big," he said, "it won't fit any of my fingers."

"Keep it," Reuben said, "you can wear it when you get older."

Joseph took the knife out of his pocket and handed it to Reuben. "Thanks mister," he said grinning, the ring in the palm of his hand.

"Thank you, Joseph," was Reuben's reply.

Joseph was thrilled with the great swap, so before the man could change his mind, Joseph took off running down the road toward home. Reuben wanted to call out to the little boy, you shouldn't run, Joseph, but he couldn't say a word. He watched him until he was out of sight, then he turned toward town. He slipped the knife into his pants pocket. He wondered what Jessie Bailey would say if he knew that Reuben Oliver Kincaide was still alive, here in Tallapoosa on this day and had his knife in his pocket.

Reuben smiled to himself at having the knife, but his regret was that the knife had not killed Jessie. He hated the fact that Jessie was now married to his daughter. There is no telling what Reuben would have done if he had know that it was Jessie who attacked Mary thirty-nine years ago.

That night, as Reuben lay in bed and just before he went to sleep, his thoughts were of the beautiful little boy he had met that day. He would miss Mary always, but he knew she must have smiled today when Reuben was talking to their grandson.

The next morning, Reuben got up early, dressed, had breakfast then went downtown to the dime store. He knew that his daughter, Annie Mae, would be coming to work today. When Annie Mae arrived at the store, she saw her daddy standing near the door. It had been eight years since she saw him last, but she ran and hugged him. He hugged her back saying, "I couldn't come till now. Do you understand?"

"Yes, Daddy," Annie Mae said. "I knew you were here because Joseph told me about seeing a man at Mother's grave late yesterday. He said you gave him that ring."

"I did," Reuben said, "I want him to have it. I didn't tell him that I am his grandfather, did you?"

Annie Mae dropped her head as she said, "No, none of the children know. Mother never wanted me to tell them. At the end she made me promise that I wouldn't. She said you never made her your wife, so you shouldn't be called the children's grandfather."

"Then do as your mother said. I can never be much of a part of their life anyway. I've never been able to tell Rebekah and our children the truth about my life in Tallapoosa. I don't think I could ever make them understand."

Reuben was jingling the change in his pockets as he talked to Annie Mae. She knew he was anxious to get out of town, but she asked him anyway, "Daddy, I do understand everything. Do you want to stay a few days at my house while you visit any of your family? Did you look up Frank's grave? Mother never wanted me to go around your brother, Frank, or to say anything to anybody about you. So I never did. I don't know where any of your family are buried except the ones out at the old Kincaide cemetery."

Reuben took his hands out of his pockets and placed them on Annie Mae's shoulders. Looking her straight in the face he said, "Your mother was right. Don't you go near any of that family. They would mean nothing but trouble for you. Stay away from them. As far as me looking up Frank's grave, I don't intend to. I think that nephew, Dan, got all his property so I don't have nothing for that bunch. I'm catching the bus this morning back to Orlando. I'll have to work the rest of the week."

"Okay, Daddy," Annie Mae said, "Just write me once in awhile and I'll write you too." She kissed him on the cheek and said, "I wish things were different, but like Mother said, they never will be."

Reuben barely spoke the words, but they were loud enough for his daughter to hear, "I loved your mother."

"I know, Daddy, and she loved you."

With having said that, they parted. Reuben walked away and got on the bus for Orlando, Florida.

The day after Reuben left Orlando going to Tallapoosa, Rebekah and one of her daughters decided to do some heavy-duty house cleaning. The daughter was to clean out closets and straighten up dresser drawers. She opened one of her daddy's dresser drawers and was sorting papers and other things when she noticed a paper that looked like a legal document. The letter head read, "Department of Commerce, Bureau of the Census, Washington DC." It was addressed to Reuben Oliver Kincaide, Amelia Street, Orlando, Florida, and dated April 6, 1955.

The information given was that Reuben was the son of Francis M. and Mary A. Kincaide, born April 1888. When the daughter read the birthdate, she thought that was odd, because she was told all her life that her daddy was born in 1895. She took the piece of paper and showed it to her mother. "Look at this," Reuben's daughter said, "a census document stating Daddy was born in 1888. According to this, Daddy is seven years older than he says he is. Do you think he hasn't been telling the truth about his age?"

Rebekah read over the paper, then said, "That figures, he lied to me about a lot of things." She continued to talk to her daughter. "I do believe that was his first lie to me when he told me he was seven years younger than he actually was. I had no reason to ever question his age. I've lived with him almost forty years and I am just now finding out the truth about this first lie he told me. I don't know why he would do such a thing. Maybe someday he will tell me what it is about those seven years that made him want to take them out of his life. I'm sure there are many things about Reuben's life that I don't know about."

Rebekah's daughter said, "Well, I would sure ask him about this paper. When and why did he need this information anyway?"

"I'm sure it was sent for when he applied for his social security benefits," Rebekah said. "That was in 1955, same date as on the paper. I do remember asking him why he was applying for social security because he was not old enough. He said something about getting early benefits because of his service in World War I. I had no reason not to believe him."

The daughter Rebekah was speaking to was the one who always drove her daddy anyplace he wanted to go. She remembered that when he was talking about applying for his social security, he said he would have to go to Sanford, Florida, but he never asked her to take him there. She did not know where, when, or how he had made the social security transaction;

neither did Rebekah.

As to the remark the daughter made to Rebekah about confronting Reuben with this document they had read, Rebekah's reply was, "Just put it back where you found it."

A few years after Reuben's death, the remark that he made to his daughter about having to go to Sanford, Florida, to see about his social security benefits would be recalled to her mind, and it would be the clue to finding out about Reuben's life in Sanford from 1915-1918 and a connection to his military service. Reuben never revealed to anyone his life in Sanford, Florida, even though when he moved to Orlando, he was only twenty-five miles away.

In 1963, Sanford would be brought to the forefront of Reuben's mind when he had a grandson born at the hospital there. The night Richard was born, the winds stirred a breeze across the St. John's River. On the banks of its riverside shore stood a grand old cypress tree. Through the branches of the tree the sound of a baby's cry rang the birth of Reuben's grandson. Forty-eight years before, Reuben sat beneath this grand old tree, swearing his past to secrecy and contemplating a better future.

Reuben was seventy-five years old when Richard was born. He did not go to the hospital in Sanford to see his daughter or her son. The memories of his years spent living in Sanford were still vivid in his mind and hidden in his heart. It was in Sanford where his body had triumphed over the flu epidemic. It was there he had found a great love, only to suffer the pain of losing her. He never knew his son who grew up in the celery fields of Sanford. When he found his name, he had to endure the knowledge that he had been killed in World War II.

Reuben's daughter Martha Lou wondered why he never came to visit her in Sanford. The only thing he ever said to her about Sanford was that he knew they grew a lot of celery there and he knew there was a big cemetery in Sanford near where she lived. Martha Lou couldn't understand her daddy's mood when she mentioned Sanford. She was not aware of the connection.

It was after Reuben died that Martha Lou stood in absolute amazement when her sister showed her a photograph she had found when she was reviewing old newspaper reels in the Sanford Library. The picture was printed in the Sanford newspaper in 1917, and it showed Reuben standing in the middle of a celery field.

Martha Lou was also shown a copy of the registration card for Reuben Oliver Kincaide when he registered for military service in World War I. The card showed that Reuben had been born April 11, 1888, in Tallapoosa, Georgia. His present job was manager of a celery farm in Sanford, Florida, and where it asked married or single, Reuben had marked married. This was dated 1917, and Reuben did not marry Martha Lou's mother until 1920.

With her curiosity piqued after seeing her sister's findings, Martha Lou searched for more information. She was astonished when her search led her to the door of the Lundstorm family, who live in Sanford today. They told her that their relative, "Old Doc Lundstorm," had come to Sanford in 1917, and had treated Reuben when he was sick during the flu epidemic. Reuben had made mention of "Old Doc Lundstorm" all of Martha Lou's life, but he never said the doctor was in Sanford, Florida.

It was not the grand old cypress tree that revealed the secrets of Reuben's past. Even the presence of Reuben's daughter and his youngest grandson would not make the tree bend. The culprit who would reveal the truths was the passage of time as measured by the big street clock that still stands on First Street, downtown Sanford.

Reuben had set his pocket watch by the time on this street clock when he arrived in Sanford in 1915, and, for the rest of his life, he had an obsession with checking the time of day. When he left Sanford in 1918, he had added more secrets, and from then on, his life was mangled with lies and truths. As long as he lived, the time never came when he had to confront the truths, but after his death, it was a matter of time that betrayed him.

Rebekah's desire was to know the truth about her husband's age and his past life, but after she read the census document and Reuben returned from Tallapoosa, she never confronted him.

Reuben had nightmares and would pace the yard in the middle of the night when he could not sleep. When he closed his eyes, he could see images of a little girl with golden curls lying in the street, a man's body hanging from a tree, and he could clearly see the faces of lost loves. At night he had his dreams, but during the day, he lived a normal life. It was the 1960s and Reuben and all Americans were entering into the space age.

Living in Orlando, Florida, just fifty miles from Cape Canaveral, Reuben was intrigued with the space launches. He had lived from the time he could hear the first automobiles coming miles away until now when he was experiencing the sights and sounds of space vehicles.

John Fitzgerald Kennedy had taken office as president of the United States in 1961. He actively supported the space program and had a vision of man going to the moon. The moon landing happened in 1969, but the president did not live to see it. He was assassinated on November 22, 1963. The day when astronaut Neil Armstrong said, "That's one small step for man, one giant leap for mankind," as he walked the face of the moon, Reuben was eighty-one years old.

He smiled as he thought of the jokes he had made about man going to the moon. He never imagined it really happening. Although the space program had brought economical growth to the central Florida area in which Reuben lived, the people were being confronted with other turbulence which they shared with the entire country. The traumatic event of Kennedy's assassination began a profound change in the nation's future. Lyndon Johnson became president and the United States was drawn into the Vietnam War. Once again, Reuben had a son involved in a war.

His youngest son had joined the military after he graduated from high school. All three of his living sons were serving in the United States Air Force. It was Reuben's youngest son who would serve two tours in Vietnam.. Reuben was fearful for his son, but Rebekah had faith that their son would return to them safely. God answered her prayers.

Reuben always blamed President Johnson and the Democratic Party for the Vietnam War. The only thing he ever was grateful to President Johnson for was establishing the Medicare program. By the 1970s, Reuben and Rebekah's nine children lived in places all over the world and the family was growing in number with more grandchildren. Reuben and Rebekah themselves had moved out of the big house on Amelia Street in 1965.

Reuben had made one final attempt at being recognized for some claim to Kincaide property in Georgia. When he learned that the nephew whom his brother, Frank, had willed his land to had died, and also other eligible members of the family, Reuben had his daughter drove him to Warm Springs, Georgia, for a reading of the wills. Finding out that everything the nephew had was willed to his wife, Molly, Reuben was satisfied about his not having any claims to Frank's property.

As long as Reuben lived, it remained a mystery as to just what happened to the old homestead out where the family cemetery was. But Reuben was seventy-six years old when he read the wills and he was tired of hoping that someday he would own a part of his ancestor's land. He knew the one right he would always have was to visit the family cemetery where his loved ones lay.

Reuben encouraged Rebekah that they should move out of the city so they could have a little garden and some chickens. They found a place west of Orlando. The house was small, but very nice and, of course, Reuben would give it a fresh coat of paint. In back of the house was a small orange grove, with a few grapefruit trees. Reuben and Rebekah planted a vegetable garden and Reuben bought himself some chickens.

When Reuben's daughter, Martha Lou, came to visit them for the first time after they had their new place, she asked her dad, "Daddy, why would you want to move out of town like this?"

Reuben's reply was, "It's not that far out; one day it will be all built up out this way. It's only about five miles to that new place they're building called Disney World."

Reuben was absolutely right. Walt Disney had come to Orlando in 1955 and told the people he was going to build a theme park and a future world there. He had a vision that not even the land owners had: a vision of tomorrow. When the construction began on the Disney World project, Reuben said, "It will change this city forever. I always said that Walt Disney was a man of dreams, like any other man, but he worked to make his dreams come true."

Walt Disney did not live to see the gates of Disney World in Orlando, Florida, open on October 1, 1971, but Reuben did. Reuben never visited the theme park.

After Reuben and Rebekah moved out of the city, Reuben continued to go into town on Saturdays. He never gave Rebekah an explanation, he would just call a taxi. He had kept his post office box open and received letters from Georgia. His daughter, Annie Mae, was busy with her family in Tallapoosa, but she wrote as often as she could. Her letters were mostly filled with news about her son, Joseph. She knew her daddy worried about his health, and Reuben continued to send money for her to use for medical bills. Annie Mae had not told Joseph that the man he met at the cemetery the day they buried his grandmother was his grandfather.

She told him it was Uncle Reuben as she had told her other two children.

Joseph was nine years old when "Uncle" Reuben swapped his ring for the old rusty knife. The ring was Joseph's favorite possession. The next favorite was a baseball he had that was signed by Ty Cobb. Joseph had inherited his love of baseball from his grandfather Reuben.

Reuben had followed Ty Cobb's career and remembered well when his name was put into the baseball hall of fame in 1936. Since 1928 Ty Cobb held the record of batting .300 or more for twenty-three consecutive seasons. This Detroit outfielder had an aggressive style that intimidated his rivals, but to Reuben that was showing his true grit. After all Ty Cobb was from Georgia. He was born in 1886, two years before Reuben. He died in 1960. Reuben had outlived him, but he never forgot him. When Cobb died, Reuben cut the news of his death out of the newspaper and kept the clipping with his special things.

When Annie Mae wrote to Reuben telling him about Joseph's love of baseball and that his hero was Ty Cobb, Reuben felt a special kindred with that little boy he had seen only once. The inevitable finally came when Reuben reached into his post office box, took out the letter from Annie Mae and read the words: "Dear Daddy, I am so sorry to tell you this, but our Joseph passed away. It was always a worry, but it happened quickly. I thought it best that I wait to let you know. He had the best care we could give him and you did all you could."

"I do want you to know that before he died in the hospital, he asked me to bring him the ring you had given him. He said it was in a little box in his dresser drawer. I took it to him and just before he died, I told him that you were his grandfather and I was sorry he never got to go to Florida. He looked up at me and said, "That's all right, Mama. I'll see Grandfather when he comes to heaven." He took the ring and put it on his finger and said to let you know it fit. We never took the ring off his finger. Daddy, if you can send me a phone number where I can call you if I need to, I promise never to bother your family there."

Reuben took the letter, folded it and put it in his pocket without reading all of it. He was standing in the doorway to the post office. After stepping outside he thought at first it was only tears that stained his glasses, but walking away, he realized it was pouring down rain. His path led down the street where he took shelter in a conveniently located bar. Hours of drinking liquor turned his pain into bitterness. When the man behind the bar told Reuben he had had enough, he asked him if he could telephone a taxi for him. Reuben's answer was "yes." The taxi took him home to

262

Rebekah.

It was dark, well after suppertime, but Rebekah had left the table set with a few things on it and Reuben's plate with a coffee cup and his two saucers. When Reuben walked into the house, Rebekah asked him if he wanted to eat. He answered her by taking the edge of the table cloth and yanking it. The dishes, food and all went flying all over the kitchen. Reuben let out a few curse words, went to his bedroom and slammed the door shut.

CHAPTER TWENTY-ONE

$\mathcal{R}$ebekah stood still for a moment, then she quietly cleaned up the mess. When she was finished she slowly opened the bedroom door to check on Reuben. He was lying in bed with his clothes still on. She went over to the bed and asked, "ole man, are you all right?"

He looked up at her and said, "The boy was only seventeen years old."

Rebekah reached to the foot of the bed and pulled a quilt up over her husband. Then she quietly walked out of the room, pulling the door closed. She believed Reuben was referring to their son, Marion. Even though Marion was sixteen when he died, she thought Reuben was just mistaken about the age. She knew Reuben had always blamed himself in some way for Marion's death. Rebekah felt compassion for her husband on this night. She had no idea that his grief was for the loss of his grandson in Tallapoosa, Georgia.

The next day, Reuben acted normal, just as though nothing had happened. He destroyed the letter that was in his pocket. The next week, he wrote a name and a phone number on a piece of paper and sent it to his daughter, Annie Mae. Written on the paper was Rebekah Kincaide's name with their current telephone number. When Annie Mae received the paper with the information on it, she folded it and put it in the little box Joseph had kept the ring in. She then put the box in a safe place.

Ten years after Annie Mae died, her daughter, Nellie, found the little box among some of her mother's things. When Annie Mae died in 1983, she had been living with Nellie. When Nellie found the box, she opened it and took out the piece of paper. She saw the name Rebekah Kincaide on it with a phone number that was scratched out and another number written under it.

The change of the phone number had occurred when Reuben moved to live with his daughter. He had not given Annie Mae his daughter's name, just her phone number. Out of curiosity, Nellie went to the phone and dialed the number. A lady answered the ring and Nellie asked her if she could speak to Rebekah Kincaide. The answer was, "No, Rebekah Kincaide is no longer living."

Nellie hung the phone up, having no idea who she was talking to, so she just threw the slip of paper away. The woman Nellie had spoken to was Reuben Oliver Kincaide's daughter. The year was 1993 and Rebekah Kincaide had been dead since 1976. The daughter was perplexed by the phone call. She did ask the caller where she got the name and phone number and Nellie said that she found it in a box. Other than that, no information was exchanged.

Both parties of this phone call would have been totally shocked if they had known that the one named Nellie was talking to her aunt and the aunt, Reuben's daughter, was talking to the little red-headed girl she had seen Reuben with many years ago. This daughter was fourteen years old when she lived in Birmingham, Alabama, with her daddy. She had seen Reuben in a restaurant with a dark-haired lady and a little red-headed girl. Then Nellie had been just a little girl with her mother, today she was the caller without knowledge of the true connection. Reuben had died four years before this phone call was made. He was not there to explain anything about the phone call. He had also died without her having asked him about the lady and little red-headed girl she saw him with in Birmingham.

The call had come too late for Reuben to be confronted with a connection to his past. Reuben harbored the knowledge of his grandson's death. It was added to the secrets he had hidden from Rebekah about his past.

By 1970, Reuben was eighty-two years old and he spent his days hoeing in his orange grove. From Rebekah, he still demanded his three meals a day, and they had to be at exact times. His wife continued to nurture him in every way she could. The date of Reuben and Rebekah's fiftieth wedding anniversary was approaching and their nine children planned a celebration. Their marriage had taken place in December 1920. They had stood together in the back of a feed store in Moulton, Alabama.

265

Now it was 1970 and they lived in Orlando, Florida.

The celebration had to be delayed a few weeks past the anniversary date because they waited until the youngest son returned home from his second duty in Vietnam. All the children gathered coming from different places around the globe. The youngest daughter, Martha Lou, brought her son and her husband from Rhode Island where her husband was stationed with the navy. Frank was a naval officer and he always called Reuben, "Mr. Kincaide." When he knew he would be coming to the anniversary celebration, he decided to buy a gift for "Mr. Kincaide."

On previous visits, he had noticed that Reuben carried an old rusty knife in his pants pocket, so Frank decided he would give him a new knife. He bought a small black pocket knife called "old pal."

Shortly after Frank, Richard and Martha Lou arrived at Reuben's home, Frank, Richard and Reuben went for a walk out through the orange grove. That's when Frank took out the new knife and handed it to Reuben. Frank said, "Here, Mr. Kincaide, I brought you something."

Reuben took the knife and turned it over and over in his hand. He opened the blade and closed it a couple of times before he said, "It's a fine knife. I thank you for it." Then Reuben reached into his pants pocket and pulled out the rusty old knife. He handed it to his grandson, Richard. He said to Richard, "Here boy, you keep this one. It's no good to me anymore."

Richard took the knife. Looking at it he thought the knife was old and not any good for anyone anymore, but his granddaddy was giving it to him and that made it special. He dropped the old knife into his pocket. He would keep it always.

Reuben had first seen the old knife when Jessie tried to stab him with it, but instead Jessie got stabbed himself. Then, by strange coincidence, Reuben's grandson in Tallapoosa found the knife and Reuben had swapped his ring for the knife from his grandson. Now that grandson was dead and Reuben gave the knife to his youngest grandson to keep.

The fiftieth wedding anniversary celebration was grand. Rebekah was wearing a lovely dress that a daughter-in-law made by hand. The dress was a soft cream color with gold trim and Rebekah wore a beautiful white orchard flower. Reuben had on a nice suit, tie, new shoes and a new grey hat.

266

Upon entering the ballroom reserved for the occasion, everyone's eyes were drawn to a beautiful three-tiered cake. The cake was baked and decorated by another daughter-in-law. It was decorated with wedding bells, golden numerals (50), and on top were four tiny gold doves. Then there was a tier divider of white swans with fluffy white net tail feathers, and the bottom layers were decorated with gold angels. It was truly a work of art and love.

In attendance were Reuben and Rebekah's nine living children, twenty-one grandchildren, three great-grandchildren and a few other relatives. Also several close friends of the family came. As Reuben and Rebekah cut the cake together, they looked happy and healthy. Reuben had shared fifty years of his life with this woman. He was now eighty-two years old and Rebekah was sixty-eight. At that time, they did not know, but Rebekah would live only six more years. Reuben would live longer.

For the anniversary occasion, their daughter, Martha Lou, wrote a message called "One Marriage." Reuben kept the paper all of his life and once in a while he would take it out and read it. Reuben was reassured of the love and devotion of his children as he read:

ONE MARRIAGE

It's been a time of joy, happiness, sadness and much frustration, but the years have passed and the togetherness of one woman and one man has stood strong; and, against the magnificent pressure of life itself, the two have accomplished a fruitful life.

The earth continues from beginning to end for God had created it. Fifty years ago, God created a marriage and from this marriage came children and from these children came children — such is the plan of life and each child will tread the earth from birth till death — along the way the child touches many and behind him leaves a remembrance.

Our thought continues to turn back to the marriage of one woman and one man that made all life possible.

We the children shall forever hold our memories of days shared with a mother and a father who together gave us dreams and who together provided the comforts of life — the needs during sickness, the clothes to cover our bodies, the arms to hold us during times of happiness and times of sadness.

From this mother and father much has been given to a family, to a world. The time from 1920-1970 has been marked with a marriage that shall not be forgotten and has been a time for friends to cherish each encounter with fondness.

In this time when the people cry for peace among all children and life seems so complicated, if each one could just take a moment to make a count of their individual life blessings, and so be forced to share with their brothers and sisters.

We the children are thankful today for a mother and father who have given us life, a home, and a glow of inward humbleness before God and a way of simple life among all mankind.

May the burdens we have put on them be taken away with a remembrance of times of joy and happiness. May this day and each day forward be a time of rejoicing and knowing that in your fifty years of marriage you have produced a fulfillment of life for your children. You have drained from life itself the necessities for these your children.

We your children share with you today our life and all that surrounds us. Many memories, many gifts and the greatest of these is love.

One Child,

Your daughter,
Martha Lou.

Reuben knew that at all cost, Rebekah, and his children by her, must never know about the past life that had produced another wife, two mistresses, three children and four grandchildren. He could not risk losing the obedient devotion of Rebekah and their children. He would continue to live with his secrets.

Martha Lou's husband had received orders to be stationed with the NATO forces on the island of Sicily. Martha Lou, Frank, and son, Richard would be leaving the United States to live in Sicily. Reuben hated to see her leave and before he said goodbye to her he said, "I have something I want to give you." He went into his bedroom and brought out his pocket watch. He held it up to Martha Lou's ear and asked, "Is it still running?"

She said as she listened carefully, "Yes, Daddy, it is still ticking! I can't believe it still runs."

"Well," Reuben said, "I want you to keep it."

Tears came to her eyes. She took the watch and held it with both hands, somehow capturing all the memories of being that little girl sitting on her daddy's knee. She gave her dad a kiss on the cheek and said, "Thank you, Daddy, I will keep it forever."

Reuben and Rebekah were concerned about Martha Lou, Frank, and Richard so far away in Sicily, but it would be another daughter whose life would be struck with tragedy. This daughter had a son who served a tour of duty in the Vietnam War. As soon as he returned to the United States, he was discharged from the military. He chose not to stay in service. He was able to obtain a good job, but he was plagued with nightmares and flashbacks of the war.

His mother said he would often go to the back door of the kitchen and tell her that "they were out there in the woods."

When she asked him who they were, he told her, "You can't see them, Mama, you can never see them. They are always there."

This boy's mother knew her son had experienced some terrible things in Vietnam. She prayed that time would heal the wounds of his mind, but a mother's love and prayers could not save her child. One night as she lay sleeping in her bed, her son borrowed a gun from his brother saying that he was going hunting the next day. No one will ever know what was in his mind, but after his brother went to bed, he tied two chairs together back to back, put a pillow in one, then rigged the shot gun with a string to the sofa. When the shot rang out, piercing the silence of the night, the Vietnam War had claimed another causality.

His name would not be placed on the memorial wall in Washington, D.C., but he was not alone; there were many American soldiers whose name cannot be found on a list or on a wall — many who suffered and died because of the war. The grief of mothers and families all over the country remains unmeasured.

Reuben rushed to the bedside of his dying grandson. He was strong and supportive of his daughter in her time of need. After the funeral, Reuben walked away with a pain in his heart that transcended the burial of this grandson. He no longer turned to his God and asked why. He reached down inside himself and brought out the strength and character of that little farm boy who once stood proud in school, and he faced the world head on.

It was a time of great social and political crisis in the United States. The country was in frustration over the Vietnam War when Richard Nixon was elected to the office of the presidency in 1972. President Nixon drew the confidence of the people when he withdrew American forces from Vietnam, but a cloud shrouded him when a political scandal forced him to resign his office. He was the only president of the United States to ever resign. Gerald R. Ford was appointed to be the country's thirth-eighth president. He inherited serious economical problems as well as the political scandal concerning the Republican Party. He ran for re-election in 1976 but lost to a Democratic Party nominee, Jimmy Carter.

Reuben was a strong believer in the Republican Party, but he was proud that a farm boy from Plains, Georgia, was the president of the United States. Reuben jokingly said, "Guess he had lived to see the day they would let anybody live in the White House." Reuben was eighty-nine years old when Jimmy Carter took office. Even though Reuben was proud to see a fellow Georgian become president, he was happy that he also lived long enough to see the Republican Party move back into the White House in the 1980s.

Dying had never been an option for Reuben. When he was in his eighties, he bought a one-foot-tall lime tree and planted it in the back yard. Rebekah said to him, "ole man, I don't know why you want to plant such a little tree, you will never live to see it grow up."

Reuben said nothing to his wife, but in his mind he knew he would not only see the tree grow, but he would see it bear fruit. Reuben often said, the only sad thing about growing older is having the ones you love plucked from your life one by one.

In 1974, Reuben had received a letter from his daughter, Annie Mae, who lived with her daughter Nellie in Tallapoosa. Annie Mae moved into the house with Nellie when her husband passed away in 1971. She didn't write to Reuben often these days, but on this one occasion, she felt the need to let him know something she had heard about. A member of her mother's family who lived in Albany, Georgia, told her that just recently a Victoria Sherwood was admitted to the nursing home in Albany. She knew this because she worked there and she remembered that Victoria Sherwood was from Tallapoosa.

She also knew that at one time this lady, Victoria, had been married to Reuben Oliver Kincaide. Since it was no secret with the family in Albany that Annie Mae was Reuben's daughter, born out of wedlock, then this member of the family thought Annie Mae would be interested to know that Reuben's ex-wife was in the nursing home. She also told Annie Mae that

270

she had heard Victoria say all she wanted was to see Reuben one last time before she died.

Reluctantly, Annie Mae wrote and told Reuben about Victoria's request to see him. From the day he read the letter, Reuben began making plans for a trip to Albany.

Since Reuben had moved to Orlando in 1950, several of his children had moved their families there. One of these children to do so was his oldest daughter by Rebekah. It was this daughter that he would ask to take him to Albany, Georgia. Reuben had been married to Rebekah over fifty years and he had become an expert at deception. He told Rebekah that he was going to Georgia to look at property. He knew she would not want to go because she was not interested in moving away form Orlando.

Reuben asked his daughter to drive him to Georgia without any explanation as to why he wanted to go there. He told her he would pay all the expenses. The daughter made no hesitation in saying yes to her dad's request. All of her life she had obeyed her dad and tried to please him; this time was no different. She was happy to take him on a trip.

When they arrived in the city of Albany, Reuben told her how to get to a hardware store. She found the store and parked her car directly in front. Reuben got out of the car, closed the door and walked into the hardware store. He was confident that she would not follow him. Once inside the store, he walked straight through the store and out the back door. This door led to the street behind the store. Reuben crossed the street and walked a short distance to the nursing home. He asked the girl at the front desk if he could visit with Victoria Sherwood.

The girl looked at Reuben. He was an impressive looking man dressed in a suit and tie, wearing a dress hat, so she could see no harm in letting him visit the lady. She escorted him down the hall through glass doors in the back to a small garden area. It was just past lunchtime in the middle of the day. It was springtime in Georgia so the air was pleasantly warm in the garden.

Seated by a small, white wrought-iron table at the end of a short, brick pathway was a lady. She had her head bent down engaged in reading a book. She was wearing a blue robe. The robe was made of a flowing material like chiffon with folds that hid any design. Draped across her lap was a delicate pale-blue coverlet that hung down over the wheels of the chair. As the girl approached with Reuben, she said, "Ms. Sherwood, you have a visitor."

Victoria raised her eyes. It had been twenty-four years since she last saw this man. She gently closed her book, and with a voice so soft you could barely hear, said, "Reuben, is that you?"

Reuben stood before her with his hat held by both hands. He looked into beautiful blue eyes. He saw the face of the woman he had loved all of his life. In his mind and through the mist on his glasses, he gazed at a young girl with soft white skin and long dark curls. To him she never aged because his love for her had remained the same.

The girl, seeing that the two people obviously knew each other, asked Reuben if he would like a chair. His reply was, "No, thank you, I can't stay long." When the girl walked away, Reuben stepped closer to Victoria and said, "Yes, Victoria, it is me."

Victoria held out her hand, "I hoped you would come, Reuben," she said, "here take my hand."

Reuben laid his hat down on the little table and took her hand in his. "You are still the most beautiful girl in the world. Victoria, my sweet, sweet, Victoria." He kissed her hand and held it gently.

Victoria took her other hand and traced the lines on his face as he bent close to her. There were no tears in her eyes, only adoration on her face. It was as though they had just seen each other yesterday. They rejoiced in the sight and feel of each other. There was no time for blame, shame, explanation, forgiveness or tears. It was too late to dwell on the past. Victoria wanted only to savor the moments she could be with the one love of her life.

Reuben granted her no whys, wherefores or reasons. He talked only of the present. He was relieved that she tired quickly, giving him reason for such a short visit.

When he said to her, "I think I better go," she made no resistance.

He lowered his head close to her and she put her frail little hand around his neck, then said, "I love you for coming to me. I'll love you forever."

Reuben took her hand away and kissed her lightly on the cheek saying, "I love you too, Victoria."

Reuben did not say goodbye. He reached over to pick up his hat from the little table next to Victoria. There, placed on top of the table in a small glass bowl filled with water, was a white gardenia. It floated freely atop the water. The aroma from the flower that filled the air was familiar to

Reuben. As he turned to walk away, his memory was of a porch on a house with tall white columns, where a table draped in cloth sat with a dish filled with white floating petals. The vision was of a house in Tallapoosa, Georgia, where he first saw Victoria.

Today he would walk away and leave her there.

Returning to the car, Reuben gave no explanation as to where he had been. His daughter asked no questions, although she did wonder just why he was in that hardware store so long and he didn't buy one thing. She had waited patiently and said nothing to her dad when he opened the car door, got in and said, "Let's go home."

Raindrops fell on the windshield of the car. Reuben's daughter said as she turned the windshield wipers on, "Looks like we are going to have some rain."

Reuben's reply was, "That figures."

Two years later, Reuben needed strength and courage more than at any other time of his life. He would endure the death of his wife, Rebekah.

Rebekah had been sick for some time, but she never worried about herself. She had devoted her life to her children and her husband. She spent her lifetime doing the best she could for her ten children. Her biggest heartache had been when she lost her first born, Marion. She knew there was a blood problem with her children. Once when her youngest daughter was very sick she told the doctor, "My children don't have pure blood in them. Her blood is not good."

Whatever Reuben had told her about the bloodline in his family, Rebekah never repeated. She never laid blame on anyone. She approached every hardship of her life regally and with an expression of love.

The one thing that Rebekah derived great joy from was her needlework. For months, even years, Rebekah poured her soul into creating quilts for her children. She tried to teach all her daughters how to make quilts. It was to her two oldest daughters that this labor of love would not be lost. Before she died she asked them to complete the quilts that she had started piecing together. She explained to them the pieces that were to go into each quilt and told them which child to give the finished quilt to.

Like most women of the time, these daughters did not have the luxury of time and concentration these quilt pieces required, but once they began to fulfill their mother's wish, they found that time had another value, lost to the modern world. Today, because of these two daughters' completion of their mother's miraculous work of handmade quilting, each of Rebekah's children possesses a quilt made from the threads that run through time.

After Reuben realized that Rebekah was not well, he told her to stay in bed in the mornings as late as she needed; he would take care of his own breakfast. He always got up early, sometimes around five o'clock in the morning. He would make his coffee, then get out the cereal and milk. He always placed two bowls on the table, one at Rebekah's place. When he was finished with his cereal (always Kellogg's Corn Flakes) he would put his dirty dish in the sink, leaving Rebekah's bowl on the table with a spoon beside it.

There came a day when Rebekah had to go to the hospital. The news was not good. She had cancer and was expected to live only three months. The children all gathered about her in the hospital. Rebekah summoned all her grace and energy to spend her last hours with her children.

At one point, one of her daughters made sure that Reuben would have some time alone with his wife. She had reason to believe that Reuben had some confessions to make to her mother. In the absence of his children Reuben stood by the hospital bed and looked at his wife. She lay frail and weak on a pillow of white. She was the purest person he had ever known. He had taken her when she was only eighteen and she had been with him for fifty-six years. Reuben was fourteen years older than Rebekah and he never dreamed he would lose her.

The first time he saw her he lied to her about his age. He told her he was seven years younger than he really was. His guess was that if he had not lied to her from the start, she would never have become his wife. He had met her at church and he knew the type of family she came from. Her religious beliefs were strong and Reuben was certain that if Rebekah had known about his marriage to Victoria, his affair with Mary and Tasha and his children he had left behind, she would never have succumbed to his desires.

Reuben began his marriage with Rebekah by plucking out seven years of his past life, and he spent the rest of their married life telling lies and keeping secrets. His deceptive life with her was for the purpose of never telling her the truth about seven years of his life. Rebekah lay in her bed and just looked at Reuben. There was nothing for her to say. She had given her whole life to this man. She would take with her many of Reuben's secrets, but she knew in her heart there was a lot about Reuben she would never find out.

On this day all that seemed to matter was what they had shared together. Rebekah's only request from her husband was that he watch over the children as long as he could. She said to him, "They need you now, Reuben. Don't leave them."

Reuben's reply to his wife was, "Don't worry ole woman, I'll take care of everything." Without touching her, Reuben turned and left the room.

A few days later, Rebekah died, surrounded by her children. On this earth, she left nine children. Both she and the children knew what it was like to be loved deeply and tenderly.

Rebekah was taken back to be buried next to her son in the Caddo Cemetery in northern Alabama. When the service was over, Reuben stood at the edge of the grave and dropped a single red rose from his hand. He had not forgotten their promise to each other about the rose when their son, Marion, died. Together, Reuben and the children left Rebekah in the fields of her ancestors. They would carry with them her graceful ways, her charm and they would strive to emulate her quality of being who she was. She would remain an icon of their lives.

When Reuben returned home to Orlando from the funeral in Decatur, Alabama, he went into a state of depression. The children were all worried about him. He had chewed tobacco most of his life and when the children noticed he was not chewing it anymore, they asked him about it. His reply was, "They told me not to chew my tobacco anymore."

The children understood this to mean he was having visions. Their doctor's advice was to treat him normally. Don't make an issue of things and he would, they hoped, come out of it. Depression is normal after the loss of a mate.

Reuben remained living alone in his home in Orlando. One daughter lived nearby and she came most every day to attend to his needs. All the other children came in and out so that their dad would not be lonely. After a few months, the depression left Reuben and he emerged a kinder, more gentle man.

The first time Reuben's youngest daughter, Martha Lou, returned to visit her dad after her mother's death, she told him about something that happened to her. "Daddy," she said, "when Mother died and I was riding in the car on the way to her funeral, I was looking out the car window at the sky. There I caught a glimpse of a long white skirt and I was not startled

275

when I saw the beautiful lady with the face I remembered. Do you recall me telling you about her when I was a little girl?"

Reuben, looking at his daughter said, "Yes, I remember."

"Well," Martha Lou continued, "When I saw her this time she wasn't carrying a basket of flowers, but in her arms was a long white robe. The view was kinda misty at first, but then I saw Mother standing there. The beautiful lady placed the robe around Mother's shoulders and then several angels gathered around them. I saw them only for a few seconds; then it was like the clouds lifted all of them into the blue sky, until I couldn't see them anymore. Daddy, do you think it was the same lady I saw before? Why do you think I saw her again?"

Reuben's reply was, "I don't know why you would see such a thing. I don't know anything about stuff like that."

Martha Lou could see that her dad didn't understand what had happened to her so she didn't tell him that before the lady disappeared into the clouds, she looked back at her and in Martha Lou's heart she heard the beautiful lady say, "Someday, you will be me."

Every year in the month of May, Reuben began to make his pilgrimage to the Caddo Cemetery for Decoration Day. There he and some of the children would place flowers on Rebekah's and Marion's grave. Family and friends would gather in remembrance of their loved ones.

It was the second year after Rebekah's death that Reuben asked his daughters to take him to Tallapoosa, Georgia. They could stop there on the way to the Caddo Cemetery in Alabama. Reuben master minded the visit to Tallapoosa with his two daughters. He told them he had been born and raised there but had not been back there in many years. He said his purpose in going there was to find his parents' graves. He even had them make flower arrangements to place on the graves.

When they arrived in Tallapoosa, Reuben pretended that he wasn't sure just where the Kincaide family cemetery was, so they would need to ride around and look for it. He directed them just outside of town to a cemetery off the main road. There was a little church on one side of the road and the cemetery was across the road. Reuben told them to park over by the little church. He got out of the car and immediately said to them, "No, this is not it."

But, he proceeded to walk across the road and down through the cemetery over a little hill where the girls could no longer see him. The two women looked at each other wondering where he was going if this was not the right cemetery. Neither one of them followed him. They waited by the car until he returned. When he came back to the car, he got in and said to them, "Let's go, and stop down there at that house and I will ask someone if they know where the Kincaide family cemetery is."

When they got to the house he was talking about, Reuben got out, once again leaving them in the car, walked up to the house and talked to some people there. Of course the daughters had no way of knowing what he said to the people at the house, but when he got back into the car, he directed them straight to the Kincaide family cemetery on the opposite side of Tallapoosa.

Reuben's two daughters who were with him that day had absolutely no way of knowing at that time, that the grave he stood before once he disappeared from their view, was the one he had visited twenty years earlier. It was the one where he had met a little nine year old boy, named Joseph. It was Mary's grave. Reuben knew exactly where he was and whose grave was there at Mt. Zion Cemetery. He was also sure that his daughters would not question his actions.

Several years after Reuben's death, these two daughters and Reuben's youngest daughter, Martha Lou, would find themselves parked at a little church across the road from the Mt. Zion Cemetery. In their quest to find the truth, the discoveries had led them there. Searching for names on the tombstones, they found Mary's. Now they knew that on that day in 1978, their father had visited the grave of his mistress.

Before the girls drove away from the little church, they recalled to Martha Lou their time spent with their dad there. One sister was sitting in the back seat and she was furious to think her dad had deceived them, the other sister cried. Martha Lou was amused at their reactions to knowing the purpose of their dad's visit to this cemetery. She could make light of the situation because she was not played for a fool.

Reuben had a real knack for telling his children part truths and only what he wanted them to know.

When he arrived at the Kincaide family cemetery with his two daughters, he got out of the car, and walked down the pathway among the stones of his ancestors straight to his papa's grave. He knelt before the hand carved old Georgia stone and said to his daughters, "This is it, this is my papa's grave."

277

For a moment he looked around, then he told them that the grave next to his papa's was not his mother's grave. He said that grave was there when they buried Papa. He also told them that his brother, Frank, had carved the F. M. Kincaide, D. 1913 on the old stone. Reuben's daughters could see that the cemetery was old and not well cared for. Reuben made no explanation as to what happened to all the family members. In fact, he didn't want to stay at the cemetery but just a few minutes. Perhaps someone who knew him might show up and he couldn't chance that. He did tell the girls that he wanted to buy a nice headstone for Papa's grave and replace the old one.

That was the extent of their visit to Tallapoosa. Later that year Reuben did return and after sixty-five years, made good on a promise to his papa. He had a marble stone erected to mark his grave. The old stone he gave to one of the daughters, and today it is kept by his youngest daughter, Martha Lou.

CHAPTER TWENTY-TWO

$\mathcal{F}$or several years, the daughters and sons of Reuben and Rebekah took their dad on his Decoration Day trip which, each year, included stopping by Tallapoosa to visit Papa's grave. The Tallapoosa visit was always brief — in and out of town as quickly as possible. To these children, Reuben made no acknowledgment that he had living relatives there, certainly he did not tell them about a daughter named Annie Mae who lived in Tallapoosa with her daughter, Nellie. Nor did he mention Molly, the girl who was married to his nephew Dan and had lived with his brother, Frank. Reuben said he did not know where his mother was buried. He never made any attempt to go to his brother Frank's graveside. When it came to visiting his mother's and brother, Frank's grave, Reuben could not take the chance of Molly seeing him there because she lived very close to that site. Reuben had told Rebekah and their children so many lies about all these people and he had no intention of being confronted by anyone in Tallapoosa that could tell them the truth. When any of the children took him to Tallapoosa, they always accepted anything he told them and never asked any questions.

Four years before Rebekah died, one of the daughters was passing through Tallapoosa when she was on a trip with her husband. Reuben was not with them, so they decided to stop and ask if anyone knew of any Kincaides who lived there. They were told about an elderly man and his daughters, and given directions to their house. The man turned out to be a cousin of Reuben's and he told Reuben's daughter and her husband that yes he knew Reuben.

Along with that he told them Reuben was married and had a child when he left Tallapoosa many years ago. He said the wife had moved away, but a daughter of his worked in downtown Tallapoosa in a dime store. Reuben's daughter and her husband were shocked at hearing this and they wanted to make sure it was true, so they went to the courthouse and got a copy of the marriage certificate and also a paper showing the divorce and that there was a child, named Vanessa.

The daughter was torn apart after finding out this much of her dad's life that he had lied about. Rebekah was still living when her daughter found this out and no way was the daughter ever going to tell her mother about what she had learned. She knew it would hurt her mother, so she would keep the secret also.

After Rebekah died, one of her sons went to Tallapoosa, curious about his dad's life there. Reuben was still living, but the son would not ask him for information. He obtained from his sister the name of the cousin she had talked to on her visit to Tallapoosa. When Reuben's son went to Tallapoosa, found the cousin and talked with him, the cousin told him that Reuben's daughter now lived in Atlanta. He gave him her name and phone number.

Reuben's son called Vanessa on the telephone and told her who he was. He told her that her dad was alive and lived in Orlando, Florida. Vanessa hung up on him after saying he was lying, that her daddy was dead. Vanessa's husband, Jessie, was right with her and he assured her that it was just a crank call. When Vanessa began to question her husband, Jessie went to extremes to protect her from the truth.

He had a tombstone erected at a grave in a remote place in Alabama and took Vanessa there to see it. He repeated the story her grandparents had told her that her daddy died in 1917 with the flu and was buried in Alabama.

At this time, Vanessa had moved her mother, Victoria, from the nursing home in Albany up to a hospital in Atlanta. Her mother's health was failing fast.

For some reason Vanessa wanted to hear the truth from her mother's lips. She asked her, "Mother, is my daddy still living? Does he live in Orlando, Florida?"

Victoria turned her face and looked out the window of her hospital room. She searched the dark clouds for a patch of blue sky. After a few moments, she looked at her daughter and said, "When I see your daddy in heaven, I will tell him all about you. You know, sweetheart, I loved your father all of my life."

When Victoria looked at the face of her sixty-eight-year-old daughter, she saw a little child, the baby girl whose daddy had deserted her in 1915, sixty-seven years ago. It was 1982. It was too late for Victoria to tell her daughter the truth. Vanessa and Jessie buried Victoria in Atlanta.

Two years later, Jessie would also die without ever telling Vanessa, Reuben's daughter, what he had so expertly kept secret from her. For Vanessa it would not end there. The voice of the man on the telephone saying her father was alive would haunt her and five years later she would seek the truth.

Reuben's son, the one who made the phone call to Vanessa, never tried to contact her again as long as Reuben was living. He never told his dad that he knew anything about Vanessa. He in no way confronted Reuben with what he knew. He maintained that if Vanessa wanted to find her dad, she knew where to find him.

After Reuben's visit to Victoria when she was in the nursing home in Albany, he never returned to her. When Reuben recovered from his depression of losing Rebekah, he longed to rush to Victoria. She was the only love he had left. He had outlived Tasha, Mary and Rebekah. The first girl he had truly loved was still alive. He was finally free again. They could be together. But, it was too late. Time had rendered Victoria incapable of being with Reuben.

It was Reuben's daughter, Annie Mae, that made the phone call to Reuben saying that in the morning edition of the Tallapoosa newspaper there was an article about the death of Victoria Sherwood. She had been a socialite of Tallapoosa. She came from a well-known family, therefore the people of Tallapoosa were interested to learn about her death at age eighty-seven.

Reuben hung up the telephone and walked over to the window. He was standing there looking out the window and jingling the change in his pocket when his daughter, Martha Lou, opened the outside kitchen door. Martha Lou, in her cheerful voice, called out, "Good morning, Daddy, you doing all right?"

Without turning around, Reuben said, "It's all over now."

Having no idea what her dad was talking about, Martha Lou asked her

281

dad if he was ready to go to the grocery store. That was why she had come that day, to take him to the store and to fix his lunch. When Reuben turned to face his daughter, she could see he was upset. She said, "Daddy, are you okay? You look like you don't feel well."

"No, nothing's right. I'm selling the house. I'm moving out," was Reuben's reply.

"Why? What's wrong? This is a sudden decision, isn't it?" Martha Lou questioned. She was shocked at her dad for saying these things.

He had remained in the same house after Rebekah died. All the children visited him and they were all so pleased that he was doing so well. He had kept "home" intact for them for six years.

Reuben went into his room and got his hat. Walking back out through the kitchen, he said, "Let's go to the store."

His daughter drove him to the store and he went inside with her. He always had a grocery list, which usually had the same items on it: corn flakes, milk, bread, coffee, two large packages of lunch meat, pet milk, butter, tomatoes and bananas. Martha Lou took the list and began to gather the items on it and put them into the grocery cart.

When he got in front of the counter that had wine on the shelves he stopped the cart and looked at his daughter. "You want to get some wine?" he asked.

"I don't care," she said, "whatever you want, Dad."

Reuben reached to the shelf and took a bottle of Mogan David wine and put it in the cart. When they got back to the house, Reuben poured his daughter and himself a large glass of wine. They drank wine while Martha Lou fixed one of his favorite lunches: salmon patties, sliced tomatoes, bread and a grease gravy made by heating grease that was kept from frying bacon and pouring a tiny bit of coffee into the hot grease.

Reuben poured the grease gravy over his tomatoes and bread. The fact that Reuben ate this grease gravy amazed Martha Lou because she was health conscious. But, her dad was ninety-four years old, so she didn't bother trying to tell him that grease wasn't good for him.

By the time lunch was over, the wine bottle was empty. Reuben sat at the table with tears in his eyes, trying to explain to his young daughter that he got terribly lonely living in this house since her mother died. He wasn't able to keep the place up anymore and he couldn't sit inside and watch someone else do it. He said he would see if he could move into the house with another daughter who lived in Orlando. She had a big house and told him before that he could live with her. He said also that the neighbor next door wanted to buy his place so he would sell it to him.

Martha Lou cried, telling her dad, "Daddy, then we won't have a home anymore. Where would we have our Christmas tree? Is it the end of our getting our Christmas sacks?"

Reuben assured his daughter that they could have a family Christmas tree in the house where he would be living and he said, "As long as I can depend on you to help me, we will have the Christmas sacks."

The hour grew late and Martha Lou had to go home to her husband and son. She had drunk several cups of her daddy's strong coffee so she wouldn't feel the effect of the wine. She hugged her daddy goodbye. Driving away, she looked back and saw him standing at the door. Maybe he was right, he must get lonely there by himself so much of the time.

What this daughter didn't know was that when Reuben told her "It was all over now," he wasn't really talking about selling the homestead. The four women he had loved so dearly were all dead. He was ninety-four years old and he had lost them all.

Later that year, Reuben sold the home place and moved into the home of his daughter, who lived in Pine Hills near Orlando. He kept his promise to Martha Lou about having the family Christmas tree, and she kept her promise that she would help him fix the Christmas sacks.

Till this day, even though Reuben is no longer there to help with the sacks, Martha Lou fixes them every year and places them under the Christmas tree. Nine sacks, for each one of Reuben and Rebekah's living children. Each one has their name on it and each sack holds that special magic that these children grew up on. It's the magic of bonding, two parents' miracle of love. When Martha Lou prepares these sacks, she is not alone. They are there.

It was 1982 when Reuben sold his home and moved. He closed out his post office box in Orlando and he made a phone call to his daughter, Annie Mae, in Tallapoosa. He told her he was moving to live in the house with one of his children in Orlando. He gave Annie Mae a new telephone number where she could call him. He did not tell her the name of the daughter he would be living with.

Annie Mae got the little box out that held the slip of paper on which she had written Rebekah Kincaide's name and a phone number. She marked the phone number out and wrote down the new phone number her dad had just given her. She left the name Rebekah Kincaide on the slip of paper, changing only the phone number. She then folded the paper, put it back into the little box and returned it to its safe place.

Annie Mae had lived with her daughter, Nellie, since her husband's death. She often talked to Nellie about Reuben, but she always referred to him as Uncle Reuben. She had not told Nellie or her son, Billy, that Reuben was their grandfather. The phone call Reuben made to Annie Mae telling her about his move and giving her his new telephone number would be the last time he talked to Annie Mae.

Shortly after that call Annie Mae became extremely ill and her daughter, Nellie, had to take her to a hospital in Atlanta. Annie Mae stayed in the hospital there until her death a few months later. She was never able to tell Nellie about the little box in her dresser drawer, the little box that held the slip of paper with the phone number where she could call Reuben. She was also unable to tell Nellie that living in Atlanta was a lady who was a relative of theirs.

Annie Mae always knew about Vanessa. She knew that Vanessa was her half-sister. These two little girls had grown up in Tallapoosa. They had attended the same school, but their lives were different in every other way: Vanessa raised by indulgent grandparents, believing her daddy was dead, and Annie Mae, born to an unwed mother, raised with a step-father, but knowing her daddy was alive and that his name was Reuben Oliver Kincaide.

Annie Mae was a kind person, a good person, who knew that her mother, Mary, loved her father, Reuben, and she also knew that Reuben loved Mary. Annie Mae would never hurt either her mother or father by telling Vanessa that they were half-sisters. Also Annie Mae knew about Jessie, Vanessa's husband, and she was afraid of him. When Annie Mae went into the hospital in Atlanta, Jessie was still living, so even if Annie Mae had wanted to contact Vanessa before she died, there was the threat of Jessie.

Therefore, Annie Mae died without Vanessa knowing they were half-sisters and Annie Mae also died knowing she had half-brothers and sisters living in Orlando, Florida, but they would never know her.

After Reuben had not heard from Annie Mae in several months, he made a phone call. He always called collect so the call could not be traced since his daughter he was living with always paid the phone bills. Also, he made his calls when his daughter and her husband were away from the house, usually on Sunday mornings when they were at church.

When the call went through and the operator asked for Annie Mae, a woman's voice told the operator that Annie Mae was deceased. Reuben could hear the voice of Nellie, his granddaughter, on the line, but Nellie had no idea that it was her grandfather who was calling.

When Reuben's daughter and her husband returned from church, Reuben came out of his room holding a map of Georgia in his hand. He told them he wanted to go to Georgia. He said he wanted to return to Tallapoosa and find his mother's grave. The daughter and her husband took Reuben to Tallapoosa. They searched every cemetery he directed them to and Reuben just went from cemetery to cemetery never asking anyone in Tallapoosa for information or directions.

Reuben guarded his deception. He was not searching for his mother's grave. He was searching for his daughter, Annie Mae's grave. He was also going to cemeteries where relatives of his wife, Victoria, were buried. He did not know that Victoria was buried in Atlanta.

After three days of searching, Reuben sat in his daughter's car, held his head in his hands and cried like a child. The daughter he was with had no way of knowing what these tears meant. He only told her that he wanted to find his mother's grave so he could put a tombstone up like he had done for Papa's grave.

The tears were proof of grief in his heart. Reuben was now ninety-five years old. Over sixty-eight years ago he had jumped aboard the six o'clock evening train leaving Tallapoosa. He had spent a lifetime of covering up the seven years of his life before he left this town. The ties that bound him to this place had forbidden him to stay away. With the death of his daughter, Annie Mae, the strings had finally been cut. Only the memories would be left to deal with.

Reuben was certain that none of his children by Rebekah knew about his past life in Tallapoosa. He was also certain that his daughter by Victoria did not know that he was alive. When he visited Victoria for the last time, he had promised her he would never under any circumstances reveal himself to their daughter, Vanessa.

Because of Reuben's control over his children, he was secure with his certainties. What Reuben did not know was that the daughter who was with him during the search of the cemeteries was at that time in touch with a cousin who lived in Tallapoosa. This daughter had knowledge of part of the truth about her daddy's life in Tallapoosa, but when she was there with Reuben she did not know about Reuben's daughter, Annie Mae. The daughter that was known about was Vanessa, the one who lived in Atlanta. Reuben's son also knew about Vanessa, but neither the daughter or son ever told Reuben what they knew.

It was not until after Reuben's death that this daughter, plus three others, would find Annie Mae's grave.

After a year of research work, four of Reuben's daughters stood before Annie Mae's grave, linking their arms around each other. At long last they had found their sister.

It was late afternoon and the sun was going down. The cemetery was serene and in the distance a train whistle was blowing as it rolled through Tallapoosa. It was the six o'clock train, headed for Atlanta. Since September 1915, the lonely sound of the passing train had pierced the sight of the setting sun. As Reuben's daughters spoke softly while standing in this lonely place, they asked each other the question, why? Why had they never known their sister Annie Mae? It had been seventy-nine years since she was born. Why had Reuben kept them apart? These daughters could only guess at the answer as they pieced together the puzzle of their father's life.

Reuben kept his secrets intact and he was still experiencing life in the 1980s. At this time, he was surrounded by his children and grandchildren living in Orlando, Florida. He took part in everything he possibly could in order to make his children happy. In so many ways, he was trying to be both mother and father to them. He knew Rebekah would want him to be good to the children. When he was ninety-five years old, he gave the nine children a copy of a tape he made for them. On this tape, he recited the poems he had learned as a child in school in Tallapoosa. He used no notes, only his memory as he recited: "The Drunkard's Boy," "Sheridan's Ride," and "Dewey's Stand in Manilla Bay."

Reuben encouraged all the children to get a good education. He went to his grandson, Richard's high school and gave a lecture on World War I. Everyone was amazed at his mental abilities at age ninety-five. Even at this age, he maintained a strong interest in the politics of America. He was a supporter of Ronald Reagan when he took office in 1981 as president of the United States.

Reuben believed President Reagan reconciled the nation's continuing anxieties about the future. Reagan would do this by reaffirming traditional faiths in the country's special virtues and capacities.

Reuben had lived since 1888. He had experienced the many changes of the United States' economic growth, international power, and social divisions. Through all the good times and the bad times, Reuben remained proud to be an American citizen. He often said he went from the sound of the first automobile motor to the "sonic boom."

When the space shuttles were launched from Cape Canaveral, Florida, Reuben would go out into the yard in Orlando and search the skies to see the spacecraft accelerate into the heavens. It was January 28, 1986, when Reuben watched the booster rockets careen away from the space shuttle Challenger. He stood transfixed in horror seeing the massive orange fireball, the two trails of smoke across the cloudless sky and the thousands of pieces of debris falling through the air. The spacecraft had exploded! Seventy-three seconds after liftoff, something went wrong. All seven astronauts aboard were killed. It was the worst catastrophe in the history of American space exploration.

Reuben knew that this tragedy could close down the country's space shuttle program indefinitely. But, the space program was not defeated. On September 29, 1988, Reuben's youngest daughter, Martha Lou, walked into his room and turned on the television. She said, "Daddy, let's watch the space shuttle go up."

Reuben was tense as he watched the television screen. He joined the rest of America as they watched the shuttle Discovery's launch flawlessly into orbit. Reuben said to his daughter, "Well, they are back in business."

He had lived to see the age of discovery begin anew. It was 1988. Reuben had lived over one-hundred years.

Reuben's children who lived in and near Orlando, Florida, gathered to plan a one-hundredth birthday celebration for their dad. Everyone agreed it should be held at the Orlando Naval Training Center. Their dad had always honored the military and he was very proud that many of his children had served and were at that time serving their country. Due to the fact that his son-in-law, Frank, was a retired naval officer, it was possible for the grand celebration to take place at the officer's club on the military base.

Invitations would go out to family and friends all over the United States and several foreign countries. Local and state officials and even the president of the United States was invited to attend. The children, realizing this should not be a surprise event for their dad, elected the youngest girl, Martha Lou, to tell him about the celebration plans.

When Martha Lou approached her dad with the information, he became very agitated. She said to him, "Why, Daddy, what's wrong?"

He shouted at her, "I want no part of it!"

They had been seated at a table, but Reuben jumped up, began to pace the floor, jingling the change in his pockets.

Martha Lou was not going to let it go at that. She and her brothers and sisters had put too much preparation into the planning not to follow through. She said to Reuben, "Daddy, we all got together and have decided to give you this party. If you are worried about the cost, don't be, because we are taking care of everything. Everyone is helping out. We are all sharing. I don't understand why you won't let us do this for you. Tell me what I can do to make it okay with you."

Reuben sat back down at the table. He looked into his daughter's eyes and said, "I can't have a lot of publicity about me. There are things in my past no one must ever know."

Martha Lou had no way of knowing what her dad meant by this statement. She assured him, "I promise you, Dad, there will be no reporters to bother you. There will be nothing in the newspaper. It will be a private affair for your family and friends."

"You give me your promise," Reuben said.

Martha Lou reached over and took her dad's hand. As they shook hands, she said, "It's a deal."

On the day of the celebration everything was perfect. All the children had a role to play. Reuben was escorted into the building by two grandsons wearing their United States Air Force uniforms. He was wearing a tailor-made suit, a new hat, new shoes and he walked tall and proud. He was still quick in wit and attentive in thought. He was physically fit despite having a one-hundred-year-old body.

Different ones paid tribute to him in different ways. His youngest granddaughter moderated a cake-lighting ceremony, which took everyone from tears to a joyous singing of "Happy Birthday." One of Reuben's granddaughters composed a song. Her angelic voice filled the ballroom and tears filled Reuben's eyes as he heard the words.

Reuben's sons paid tribute with presentations, readings and comments of gratitude. Family and friends brought gifts to honor this man who was born April 11, 1888. He stood by the table which was elaborately decorated with three separate cakes. They signified one-hundred years. Reuben Oliver Kincaide was living the 36,498 day of his life.

As he looked out into the room of faces, he could see nine of his children, twenty-seven grandchildren and thirty great-grandchildren. Reuben had asked one of his grandsons, who was a member of the Florida Department of Law Enforcement, to guard the doors and make sure no strangers got into the building. The grandson fulfilled his granddaddy's request wondering, but never asked why.

At the day's end there had been over three hundred people there, but all had been invited guests. There were no strangers in attendance, and the ironic thing was this man whose life they came to celebrate, this man named Reuben Oliver Kincaide, was indeed a stranger. Reuben still had a hidden past.

Out there was a daughter, seventy-four years old; a granddaughter, fifty-seven years old and other grandchildren. There were graves of lost loves, records of wrongdoing and family forgotten. When Reuben closed his eyes at night these were the faces he would see.

Reuben's one-hundredth birthday party was held in April and in May he took his pilgrimage to Caddo Cemetery in northern Alabama. There he stood before Rebekah's grave and watched his children as they decorated both her and his son, Marion's, grave with beautiful flower arrangements. As soon as the decorating was finished and a few photos taken, Reuben was ready to leave. On the way back to Orlando, he visited Papa's grave at the family cemetery in Tallapoosa. His demeanor was the same. Place a bouquet of flowers on the grave, take a photo as he stood there jingling the change in his pockets and ride out of Tallapoosa without speaking to anyone.

Only once had he risked confrontation with someone who knew him in Tallapoosa. That was one year when his daughter, Martha Lou, and her husband were with him at the Kincaide cemetery, and Martha Lou asked him if he knew where his mother was buried, because he had told her that the grave next to Papa was not his mother's. When Martha Lou asked him this, he waved his hand around and said, "Oh, she is buried somewhere around here, but I can't find her grave."

At that same time, Martha Lou's husband asked Reuben, "Mr. Kincaide, did you live near this family cemetery when you were young?"

Reuben said, "Yes, I lived here on the farm at one time. Do you want me to show you the old home place?"

Martha Lou's ears perked up; she couldn't believe her dad was going to show them where he lived when he was young. He had always been so secretive about that.

Without hesitation, they got in the car and drove down the winding dirt road from the cemetery to the farm. Reuben had them park the car across the road from an old barn. He got out of the car and pointed across the open fields. "There," he said, "all in the valley we grew our crops, we fished the river on the back side and hunted the woods beyond the open fields." Then he pointed up the hill to a large white house. There was a driveway that led to the house, but he made no effort to go up it. He said, "See that big house up there on the hill? That was my grandparent's house. I used to play around that big porch."

Martha Lou just knew that at this point her dad was going to tell her the true story about his family and his life growing up in Tallapoosa, but instead, Reuben just stopped talking and turned away from the house on the hill.

It was evident that the old house had been restored with a new roof and white siding, but the stone-stacked chimney revealed its age. Martha Lou could tell that there was someone living in the house. If Reuben knew who lived there he did not say.

There was a newer house built across the road from the old barn. Before her dad could stop her, Martha Lou walked into the yard of the house and spoke to some people sitting on the porch. She said, "We are Kincaides. My dad, Reuben, used to live on this farm. Did any of you know Reuben?"

The ladies began to explain that they didn't know anyone who ever lived in that big house on the hill, and didn't know the people who lived there now, but one lady said, "Down there at the barn is a man who might know Reuben." She then called out to the man. Martha Lou looked toward the barn and saw an elderly man walking up to her, answering the call of his name.

Martha Lou walked to meet the old man. She reached out her hand to shake hands as she said, "My name is Martha Lou Kincaide. My father's name is Reuben. Did you know Reuben?"

The old man did not shake her hand. He said loud and clear, "Yep, I know Reuben."

Martha Lou turned to face her dad, but to her surprise, Reuben was sitting in the car out on the road. He called out in a mad, agitated voice, "Let's go!"

Martha Lou said, "Why, Daddy?" She couldn't believe her dad's actions. Why did he not want to speak to this old man? What was his hurry to leave? But instead of questioning her dad, Martha Lou said to her husband, "I guess we better leave, Daddy is ready to go."

They left the old man standing in the yard having said nothing more. As they pulled away, Martha Lou looked out the car window and thought to herself, someday I am coming back here and talk to that old man. Martha Lou never returned to Tallapoosa with her dad after that and the old man died before she could talk to him again.

Reuben had come close to recognition and confrontation so after that he limited his visits in Tallapoosa just to the cemetery. On his last visit at one-hundred years old, it was no different.

In June, after Reuben turned one-hundred, he fell in his room and hurt his side. His health had been good up until then and he was a stubborn man about going to the doctor. He sat in his rocker in his room day after day, refusing to go to the doctor. Finally Martha Lou threatened to not come back to see him if he wouldn't let her take him to the doctor, and the daughter he was staying with was distraught over what to do. They knew their dad was in pain from the fall and he began to have other physical problems.

Reuben couldn't accept the need for medical attention. He told his daughters, "Your mother went to the hospital and she never came back."

The morning came when pain took over and fear faced reality. Reuben told his daughters they could take him to the hospital. His stay in the hospital lasted eight days. Reuben had an excellent mind, but his one-hundred-year-old body was failing fast. The decision was made that he should go to a nursing home where he would have the best care money could buy.

Reuben had a stigma about nursing homes. He had heard horror stories about people who were put in nursing homes. He was very leery of going to one, but his daughters made sure he had the very best. After he was at Rosemont for a few days, he became aware of the excellent care he was receiving. He had a private room. The staff's expertise was always evident. His medical care, personal and private needs were taken care of with devotion and professional service.

As Reuben settled in to stay in the nursing home, he was visited every day by family and friends. His children showered him with attention and care. Doctors and medical people from all over the country came to the Rosemont Nursing Home to view this one-hundred-year-oldman. They all marveled at how good his mind and memory were. They couldn't believe the condition of his skin, eyes and erect body stature. Some said this man must have lived his one-hundred years in a vacuum to be in such good shape. Had they only known the story of this man's life, they would have thought it a miracle that he had lived at all!

This man was a "secret" carrier. His life, although healthy, was never clean and open, never free of burden. Reuben had cursed his God, believing he had lived the life of four men. His life had been separated by four women, Victoria, Mary, Tasha, and Rebekah. Reuben had loved all these women. His feelings became secrets because he could not risk the loss of any of them. Each life he carried in separate pockets of his mind, but ultimately he was left to live alone.

His room in the nursing home had the scent of gardenias. One of his daughters had placed a potpourri mixture near the big green chair that he sat in most of the day. She had no way of knowing that the gardenia smell would assist Reuben in his reflection of his past life with a woman named Victoria. There were no photos in Reuben's room at the nursing home. He did not want them there. He did, however, ask for his hat to be left in his room.

CHAPTER TWENTY-THREE

*R*euben went to the nursing home in the fall and, surprisingly, was well enough in December to go to his daughter's house where his room was still kept exactly the way it had been the day he went to the hospital. He went back on Christmas Day to spend the day with his children.

His children gathered in front of the family tree. The old Santa Claus ornament Reuben had bought sixty-three years ago, hung on the Christmas tree. The "sacks" had been prepared and lined the skirt of the tree with presents all around. Reuben designated his youngest son to pass out the gifts and the sacks. After watching all the children receive their gifts, Reuben went to his room where he opened his.

When Reuben left late in the afternoon to return to the nursing home, everyone hugged and kissed him goodbye. It was the last Christmas he would share with his children.

A few days after Christmas, Reuben's youngest grandson came to visit him in the nursing home. Richard was wearing his United States Air Force uniform. He had been home on leave and he came to tell his grandfather goodbye before he had to go back to his military post.

Reuben talked to his grandson about politics. He said how glad he was that he had lived to see the days that would end the Cold War. He said for four decades, this power struggle between the Soviet Union and the United States had been a threat. He gave President Reagan credit for bringing an end to the Cold War.

Reuben hated to see Ronald Reagan leave the office of president, but he assured his grandson that the man who was recently elected into office,

George Bush, would take up Reagan's mantle and do a good job.

That day Richard and Reuben discussed everything from rising cost of living in the United States to drugs and homelessness. They also got around to talking about Richard's love life. Reuben said to his grandson, "Be sure you pick out a good one!" Later Richard would wonder just how many good ones his grandfather was talking about.

Before Richard left, Reuben asked him if he still had the old rusty knife he gave him. Richard answered, "Yes, Granddaddy, I do; do you want it back?"

Reuben said, "No, son; you keep it." Then he told Richard he wanted him to have his shotgun. He said that maybe someday he could go hunting with it. "Up in northern Alabama," he said, "there is a forest, a wonderful place for game. I guess they still let you hunt there. I used to spend a lot of time in that forest with your grandmother."

When Richard could see that his grandfather was tiring, he shook his hand and told him goodbye. Reuben looked at his grandson standing there in his military uniform. "I'm very proud of you," he said.

The new year 1989 arrived. On the days Reuben was up to it, his daughters would take him out of the nursing home for the day. He always wanted to go to his daughter's house where he had planted some grapevines in her back yard. He would tell the girls all about how to grow grapes. He never told them about the years he had spent in Tallapoosa when his family grew so many grapes on the farm. Perhaps it was the wine making that kept him from telling the whole story. He knew that several members of his family became alcoholics and he knew that Rebekah had taught their children never to drink liquor in any form.

Reuben had planted a banana tree in his daughter's back yard when he was one-hundred years old and it thrilled him to watch it grow. Reuben loved to plant things. It seemed to be like a race with him to see if the plant would live because he thought that would mean so would he.

Even though Reuben was in a nursing home, he had no intention of his life being over. As long as his mind was good, he was sure he could overcome any physical problem. His children continued to visit him in the nursing home. One day in February he began to tell them the story of an investigator. He said, "There was an investigator here to see me. He sat here by my bed for a long time."

The day he told his daughter, Martha Lou, about the investigator he also told her something else. The words he spoke to her at that time would seem like a strange thing for him to say to her. At the time, Martha Lou just passed it off as an endearing saying. The day would come when these words would hurt her deeply. The words her daddy spoke were, "I never had but one wife and that was your mother."

Later when Martha Lou remembered these words, the sadness came not because of the untruth of the words, but the fact that her daddy had looked her straight in the eyes and lied to her.

When Reuben told his daughter Martha Lou this lie, perhaps he thought she had sent the investigator to his room to ask him all kinds of questions about his past life. He was almost one-hundred one years old, but that did not keep him from lying to the investigator. He told him no truths and the next day he repeated his lie to his daughter.

What Reuben did not know was that someone was looking for him and they sent an investigator to Orlando to see if, in fact, this man in the nursing home was Reuben Oliver Kincaide, born in 1888 in Tallapoosa, Georgia. Was this the man who had married Victoria Sherwood and had a daughter named Vanessa? Was this the man who left his wife and child in 1915, and was this the same man whose death had been confirmed by grandparents and a husband of his daughter?

Could it be true that he did not die of the flu in 1917 and that he was indeed alive and living in Orlando, Florida?

The person who needed to know the answers to these questions was Vanessa, Reuben and Victoria's daughter.

Vanessa had been told all her life that she was not related to any of the Kincaides who lived in or near Tallapoosa. She was told that her grandparents on the Kincaide side had gone back to New England after her father died. She had no interest in anything she was told about the Kincaides in Tallapoosa.

It was not until five years had passed since a strange man's voice on the telephone haunted her, did she seek the truth.

Only after her mother and her husband's death did she wonder about this person on the telephone and a man in Florida. When the investigator visited Reuben, he did not know if his daughter, Vanessa, was living or dead. He had not seen her since the day he deserted her. He had promised a dying woman that he would never interfere in Vanessa's life. He had kept that promise. His daughter was now seventy-five years old and living in

Atlanta, Georgia.

Spring arrived in Florida and Reuben was feeling content. He looked forward to his daughter, Martha Lou, coming to be with him at lunchtime. He always enjoyed her visits. They would talk about current events and she would tell him jokes to make him laugh.

Reuben was seated in his comfortable chair when the door to his room opened and the figure of a woman entered the room. At first he wasn't startled but when he looked up at her, he thought he was seeing a ghost. The woman immediately took charge. She laid her keys on his bedside tray, and paced the length of the room to look out the window. When she turned around, she began her verbal attack on him. Her questioning was relentless. In her rage she provided the answers to her own questions. Her tone grew louder with each accusation.

Reuben was stunned. He couldn't get out of his chair. He tried to talk but his voice was weak. When she paused in her assault, he tried to explain, but she gave him no say. He was trapped with no way out.

Whatever was happening at this point, the fact was this woman was tormenting this one-hundred-year-old man. His old body was broken, he was weakened in spirit and now this person was destroying his mind. Reuben had lived his life on the edge of criminal activities, on the run, weaving a web of deceit. He had kept secrets. Some people thought that Reuben had a mind of steel and a heart made of solid rock. But, on this day, he sat before his executioner, fearful and in need of compassion. The curtain was torn, the darkness revealed. He was vulnerable and this woman was taking advantage of him.

From down the hall of the nursing home, they could hear her shouting. They rushed to Reuben's room. Sensing a danger, the woman picked up her keys and ran from the room. She ran out the door, past the nurses, down the hallway to the outside. In the parking lot a car was waiting. On her way out, she sped past a lapis blue Mercedes that was bringing another visitor to the man she had just destroyed.

This visitor now entering the nursing home was Reuben's daughter, Martha Lou. By the time she got to her dad's room, the nurses had returned to their station. They had checked on Reuben and to them he seemed okay. But, from the moment Martha Lou walked into the room, she could tell there was something wrong.

Her dad was sitting in his chair leaning forward. He had his hands folded with his fingertips together. He kept pressing the fingertips together, back and forth. He didn't look up when Martha Lou approached to kiss him on the cheek. She said, "Good morning, Daddy, are you all right?"

Reuben didn't answer his daughter with a yes or no. He began to stutter, "She was here, she, she said, some awful mean things to me." He began to sob.

Martha Lou put her arms around his shoulders and said, "It's all right, Daddy. I'm here. We will fix whatever is wrong."

She then straightened him up in his chair, then pulled a chair for herself up close to him. At that time, she thought that probably one of her older sisters had been there and he just didn't like something she said to him. She was sure he would calm down in a few minutes.

But Reuben continued to try to explain to her what had happened. She understood him to say, "I tried to do the right thing. I did the best I could."

He continued to weep and stutter. Martha Lou tried her best to assure him that "she" didn't mean what she said. "Everything's okay. Daddy, please just relax, everything will be fine," she pleaded with him.

Then Reuben waved his hand violently and said as loud as he could, "She picked up her keys and stormed out of here!"

He scared Martha Lou when he did this. She knew then that something was definitely wrong with her dad. She ran down the hall to the nurses station. "Come, quickly, there is something wrong with my dad."

The nurse said, "Well, I don't think so, I just checked him earlier and he seemed fine."

"I'm telling you there is something wrong. My dad never acts this way and I have never in my life heard him stutter like he is doing now," she explained to them as they were on the way to Reuben's room.

Together they settled Reuben down. His lunch came and they encouraged him to eat. He ate most of his lunch, but gave little response to anything else. Martha Lou did not question him about what happened earlier. She and the nurse thought that maybe it was just a passing thing.

Martha Lou sat with him until around three o'clock when the nurse came in, and they put him in bed for a rest period. Reuben fell asleep and Martha Lou slipped out of the room and left the nursing home. When she arrived home, she wept in her husband's arms. "I'm concerned about Dad," she said. "Something is terribly wrong."

From that day on, Reuben was never the same. He stopped talking in complete sentences. He said only a few words here and there. He muttered fragments of a mangled mind. He was never able to tell anyone who the woman was who visited him on that fatal day. Who was the woman with the tyrannical voice? Was it Vanessa, his daughter by Victoria? Did she find her father after seventy-four years? Was it Nellie, his granddaughter by Annie Mae? Had she found out that Reuben was not her uncle, that he was her grandfather? Or, was it possible that another daughter made him face his sins?

Perhaps this she-devil came to Reuben as the result of her knowledge of his wrongdoing. Could it have been a little girl who almost died from a hit- and-run accident, a gangster betrayed or someone avenging an unjust hanging? How many years does it take for someone to seek revenge?

One month later, Reuben was one-hundred one years old. The doctor deemed he had suffered a stroke. It was April 11, 1989. Reuben had turned inward; his thoughts were no longer of the outside world. As America debated the relevance of its economic miracles and its model for the world, Reuben used all the strength he could muster to be with his children.

They gathered for his birthday celebration in the dining room of the nursing home. Reuben was wearing a white shirt and tie, dress pants, shined shoes, and on his wrist he wore a watch. As they sang "Happy Birthday" while bringing out the cake, Reuben sat erect in his wheelchair. He had a big smile on his face when he read out loud the message printed on the cake. "101, Happy Birthday, Dad."

The latest edition to his family was a five-month-old great-grandson named Andrew. They placed Andrew on his lap and Reuben put his arms around the child. Andrew played with the watch on his great-grandfather's wrist. Balloons were brought in to everyone's delight and Reuben enjoyed eating a piece of the cake. When he grew weary, he tilted his head back slightly and raised his arm to look at his watch. One of his daughters, noticing her dad's familiar action, asked, "Are you ready to go back to your room, Dad?"

He replied, "It's time."

The day ended. Reuben's children returned to their rapidly changing world. Looking back over the past one-hundred one years of history that Reuben had experienced perhaps the best summation would be: After hardships of wars and economic depression, there had been stability of governments and numerous inventions to better the life of mankind. Most importantly there was a sense of gradual gain for everyone. In the United States of America, the people maintained their dreams.

Reuben Oliver Kincaide had lived on this earth from 1888 until 1989. For Reuben his pursuit of dreams was over. On May 30, 1989, Martha Lou drove her lapis-blue Mercedes into the parking lot of the nursing home. She sat for a few minutes collecting her thoughts and composure before another visit with her dad. The day was a wonderful spring-like day. There was a sweet gentle breeze that so often surrounds one with the warm Florida sunshine. The nursing home was an excellent facility and they had taken good care of Reuben. Everyone had grown to love him just as all his children did.

As Martha Lou walked in the door to his private room, she could see her dad lying in his bed next to the big window. He was lying on his right side holding the bed rail with his left hand. She walked over to the side of the bed he was facing and gave him a cheery greeting, kissing him on the forehead. His eyes lit up when he saw her and he smiled a big smile. He had not spoken in several weeks.

When he first suffered the stroke he would say a few words now and then, but later he said nothing to anyone.

Reuben's hand began to rub the rail of the bed as his daughter pulled up a chair so she could sit close to him. She began chatting away about the events of the day, but he quickly became agitated and was trying his best to tell her something. She stood up and removed his hand from the railing. Holding his hand she leaned close to his face. He seemed to be saying the name "Vic." Martha Lou did not recognize the name and she was so amazed that her dad was saying something.

"Yes, Daddy, yes, I understand what you are saying. Tell me what you want me to know. Please, Daddy, you can do it, try hard." Martha Lou was indeed trying to understand what he was trying to say but she really had no idea what "Vic" meant. She thought it sounded like a man's name. Perhaps an old friend of her dad's.

Reuben's effort to talk lasted only a few moments, then he looked up at his daughter with a pleasant smile on his face. He relaxed and they shared a few minutes of silence before the nurse brought his lunch in. The nurse offered to help feed him lunch as she prepared him in a sitting position and fixed his tray. Martha Lou told her she would take care of him. Helping him with his eating was the only thing she could do for her dad now and she came everyday at lunchtime.

He ate very slowly and seemed to have difficulty swallowing. She didn't force him to eat, but did try to get him to take liquids. When he was satisfied with enough lunch, she removed the tray and settled him down in bed again.

Shortly, he became restless and began thrashing around with what little energy he had. Martha Lou ran for the nurse and several came into the room. They worked over him, applying an oxygen apparatus to make his breathing easier. Once he was settled they assured Martha Lou that he was okay, then they left the room.

Martha Lou looked at her dad lying there. This little fellow who once stood strong and erect, jingling the change in his pockets, checking the time on his watch and wearing his hat, now was so helpless, so out of character for his dynamic personality. He had always amazed everyone with his wit and vitality. Then, when at the age of one hundred he continued to have an alert mind and didn't even walk with a cane, his children began to believe what he had always told them, "I am going to live forever!"

But on this day, this one daughter realized that her dad was not going to live forever. The aging process had taken over. She stood there before him with tears streaming down her face. Reuben looked up at her longingly as though to say, "Can't you do something help me?"

Martha Lou leaned onto the bed, gathered her arms completely around him and laid his head on her breast. She stroked his silver-gray hair and began to talk to him in a low but strong voice, "Dad, you have had a long life. I'm sure you did the best you could to make it a good one. You once told me that your only regret was that you could never make enough. There is no need for you to worry about that now, because all your children are fine. You gave us life, Dad, and you will always be a part of us. So, it is okay, Dad; just let go."

Martha Lou did not know if her Dad needed permission to die, but she had given herself permission to let him go.

Reuben closed his eyes and drifted off into sleep. His daughter lowered his head to the pillow, covered his frail body with a warm blanket, and as he rested she sat in a chair for a long while.

Looking out the window, she could tell rain clouds were gathering.

She knew her dad would not want her driving in a rain storm so she kissed him on the cheek and slipped quietly out of the room. On her way out of the nursing home, she informed the nurse at the desk that she was leaving.

That was the last time she would share with her dad. An hour after she got home, she received word that he had died.

Martha Lou hung up the telephone and walked over to the window of her kitchen. She touched the window pane with the palm of her hands. She could feel the beating of the rain. Reuben Oliver Kincaide had crossed fields and mountains, oceans, rivers and streams. There had been little sunshine in his life and today, after 36,914 days of living, he made his final crossing in the rain.

News of Reuben's death was printed in three newspapers: one in Orlando, Florida, another in Decatur, Alabama, and one in Tallapoosa, Georgia. They all read the same: 101 YEAR OLD FORMER RESIDENT DIES. Reuben Oliver Kincaide, son of Francis Marion and Mary Ann Kincaide of Tallapoosa, Georgia died May 30, 1989 in Orlando, Florida.

"Mr. Kincaide was born April 11, 1988 in Tallapoosa, GA, served in the Army during World War I in 1918 and after returning went to North Alabama where he met and married Rebekah McCormick. He moved to Orlando, Florida in 1950. He was a painter until he retired at the age of ninety-one."

"He was in excellent health until he was one-hundred years old. His wife, Rebekah, died thirteen years prior to his death and he lived alone for six years. Then he moved in with one of his daughters for six years. Due to failing health, he had been in a nursing home for nine months. After such a long and healthy life, he has left three sons, six daughters, twenty-five grandchildren, thirty-one great-grandchildren and a host of friends and relatives. Services were held in Orlando, Florida and interment at Caddo Cemetery in northern Alabama."

The nine children Reuben had by Rebekah attended the interment. These children's relationship with their dad had been a pattern of affection, respect, devotion, tolerance, admiration, and Reuben's dictatorial behavior. He had taught them to be responsible for themselves and their world. Reuben believed if these children had known the truths of his life, they would never have understood. Innocent or guilty of wrongdoing, he was never capable of facing their judgment.

Therefore Reuben died with secrets locked in his heart. When the light in his eyes went out and his mind drew dark and still, only his soul possessed his life's secrets. The youngest son stepped forward and dropped a single red rose into the grave. The grave was covered with the earth of their mother, Rebekah's ancestors. All nine children gathered round and stood by their father's grave. In silence they wondered, who was this man from Georgia? They had buried a stranger.

In years to come, some of these children would seek the truth. Martha Lou wrote the story.

The words on Reuben Oliver Kincaide's tombstone read: "Our Dad, Pride, Courage, Patriotism."

A summation of this man's deep feelings as portrayed to others by his actions. He walked the face of the earth for over one-hundred years. Today his body and soul have left the earth. His spirit, however, is still · here.

If you go wondering through the Southland these days, you might happen upon a place called Tallapoosa. Stop and look around. See the kudzu growing on the banks of the railroad track, listen to the wind in the trees that line the river and savor the smell of the blossom of spring when the town is draped with the dogwood in bloom. When you leave, look over your shoulder. Reuben Oliver Kincaide's memories are still there.

Should you travel to Decatur, Alabama; Sanford, Florida; Jeffersonville, Indiana; Louisville, Kentucky; or Orlando, Florida, you will find him there.

If you read about or visit the Argonne Forest in Europe or the Bankhead National Forest in northern Alabama, you will feel the agony of a foot soldier and believe in his dreams of tomorrow.

If, by chance, you see a man jingling change in his pocket, or should you meet a child named Martha Lou, look into her eyes; you will find Reuben there. Together you may wish to search the heavens to find the rainbow beyond his crossing in the rain.

THINGS TO REMEMBER

REUBEN'S HAT — Several of his hats remain in the family today.

POCKET WATCH — Reuben's daughter, Martha Lou, keeps his pocket watch on her desk in her writing room.

TRUNK — Rebekah's truck disappeared after she left it with family in Alabama.

CALENDAR — The calendar that had a picture of WWI soldiers on it was most likely burned by Reuben before he died.

THE KNIFE — Reuben's youngest grandson still has the old rusty knife.

THE RING — The ring that Reuben gave Rebekah when they got married was given to one of their daughters.

ALL PHOTOGRAPHS — The photos mentioned in the book had been copied and many family members have copies.

QUILTS — All Rebekah's children have a quilt pieced together by their mother. Daughters continue to quilt.

SANTA CLAUS ORNAMENT — Reuben and Rebekah's oldest daughter keeps this likeness of Santa Claus.

THE SACKS — Since Reuben's death, the children gather each Christmas and the sacks are prepared by Martha Lou.

HOUSE ON AMELIA STREET — The house Reuben owned in Orlando, Florida, has been torn down. The Sports Arena now stands at the site.

OLD CYPRESS TREE — The old cypress tree that Reuben shared his secrets with still stands on the St. John's River shore in Sanford, Florida.

THE BIG STREET CLOCK — The clock that Reuben saw when he went to Sanford, Florida, still stands on First Street.

BANKHEAD NATIONAL FOREST — This is a popular place to visit in northern Alabama.

COTTON — Cotton fields can still be seen in Alabama — only a few of Rebekah's family members are farmers today.

KUDZU — Still grows wild in Georgia

WALT DISNEY — Disney World is the number-one entertainment attraction in the world the house Reuben lived in near Disney World, Orlando, Florida, still stands.

JOHN DILLINGER — In 1994 a re-enactment of the killling of John Dillinger was held in front of Chicago's Biograph Theater. It is not documented that Reuben was ever involved in gangster activity during the 1930s.

RECORDS — No criminal records have been found. Military service has not been documented. Son born in Sanford, Florida, and died in WWII has not been verified.

DECORATION DAY — The second Sunday of each May, this day is commemorated at the Caddo Cemetery in Northern Alabama. Reuben and Rebekah's children make beautiful flower arrangements to cover the graves.

JINGLING OF CHANGE — The habit that Reuben had of jingling the change in his pockets is carried on by his youngest grandson, Richard.

In the deep South on hot summer days, the sun will draw up the moisture from the ground. The moisture will fill the clouds until they burst. Rain will fall to earth, giving it new life.

Reuben was born in April, the month of seasonal showers. He would spend his life Crossing In The Rain.

FROM THE AUTHOR

I did not write this story to prove the facts of Reuben's life. It is only my perception of what happened.

To anyone searching to find the truth of someone's life I suggest you compile documents of fact and then make your own decision about the truth.